Parental Damage
by
Jack Marriot
ISBN: 978-1-9165001-8-1

Published by

i2i Publishing
Manchester. UK
www.i2ipublishing.co.uk

Dedication

To Sal, my rock, my friend, my wife and lover, for all your faith and support, many thanks.

Parental Damage

Chapter 1

The Fighter

The punches came thick and fast. Thud, thud my head rocked back and forth with each jolt, a cascade of bright lights dancing around my head. The noise from the crowd drowned out by my own thoughts, 'Got to stay up, don't go down'. Through the muffled noise I became aware of a strange sound, a voice loud and methodical. "One a two a three a four" I was being counted out, ding ding. I knew that sound and it had never sounded sweeter.

"What are you playing at?" said Dave as I sat down on the stool. I didn't answer, he wouldn't understand, how could he? We were different people and my answer would only confuse him even more. "Get out there and fight, you know you can out box this guy, don't mix it up, box Jack, box!" urged Dave.

A second later the time keeper's voice bellowed "Seconds out round three," ding, ding, the bell rang. I rose quickly to my feet as Dave pulled the stool through the ropes and screamed, "Box, Jack box".

This was the round I was waiting for. The poor mug was breathing out of his arse. He was confident, you could see that, why wouldn't he be? He'd just knocked the shit out of me for two rounds. Bang, bang, his jab hit me square in the nose. I could taste the blood as I snorted deeply, forcing it down the back of my throat. I brushed my thumb across my nose, arched my back holding my hands up high. I shrugged off any pain I felt and edged forward.

"If you feel pain it means yer alive; when you don't feel pain your dead, remember that". My father's words raced through my thoughts; inadvertently a smile crept from the corner of my mouth. It was the look on the other guy's face that gave him away. I'd seen it before and knew it well. The right hook he threw was never going to land. It was thrown in desperation, a desperation born of fear. I rolled low to my left, the punch going over my head and in one fluid movement appeared high on his right side. The left hook I caught him with was a peach and the moment it landed I knew it was lights out. He span a half turn his head driving his body round in what seemed like slow motion as he crashed to the canvass, his gum shield tumbling out of his mouth across the ring. The ref knew it was over and didn't even start the count. The doctors were dashing in and out of the ring and in the confusion, I just stood there watching the blood from my nose drip onto the canvass.

I felt an arm around my neck pulling me. "I knew you could do it, but next time don't give me a bleeding-heart attack you little shit". Dave ruffled my hair and I smiled.

The changing room was busy, there were other boxers warming up on the pads, their trainers barking instructions. "Left, left right, quicker let's see some speed, roll the punch over the top, that's more like it, stay focused".

"Hi Jack, good fight mate" said Bobby Harrison who was seated on a wooden bench. I nodded and sat down beside him.

"You fighting soon?" I asked.

"No the bastards have moved me to the end as my opponents not showed up yet. It's fucking typical. I warmed up and everything, not to mention, I've got a date later, guess she'll have to wait, I'm worth it." he said throwing me a grin.

I liked Bobby he was always joking and never seemed to suffer from nerves. I liked that; I had no doubt he did get nervous, but he hid it well.

Bobby stood up, "I'm off for a smoke, catch you later".

I didn't answer I just smiled as his lanky frame and shocking yellow hair disappeared out of sight. I reached inside my sports bag and pulled out a can of coke. I hadn't realised how thirsty I was and swallowed it in one continuous gulp. After finishing, I let out an almighty belch and ceremoniously threw the can across the room into the waste bin by the door.

"Looks like you needed that kid," said a lad across on the other bench.

I'd never seen him before, but he had one of those faces that seemed familiar. "Yeah thirsty work this fighting," I grinned.

"Hungry?" he said as he reached into his bag between his legs and threw me a packet of crisps. I tore open the packet and rammed the contents into my mouth; I'd not eaten since lunch. A stinging sensation made me remember the tear along the inside of my mouth as the salt found its way in. I winced and screwed up my face. The sounds of laughter echoed around the room as the stranger and I became a step closer to becoming friends.

"I'm Martin Benton," he said standing up. He was quite a stocky lad with cropped hair and as he offered his hand, I noticed a perfect set of white teeth.

"Jack Marriot," I said as we shook hands. We chatted for a while, talk of past fights and victories. We were lost in our own little world as we laughed at each other's stories.

"Martin up next," a voice said from the other side of the door.

"Gotta go mate see ya again," said Martin as he jumped up and strode out of the changing room, the door banging into the wall as he pulled it open harder than he needed too. I smiled and thought to myself, yeah that's the adrenalin kicking in! I wasted no time in getting changed and within minutes was out of the door and running towards the bus stop eager to get home.

The night air was biting cold and I knew the bus would be ages, it always was. I threw my bag on the floor and lent heavily against the bus shelter window. It was late, I didn't know how late, I'd given up on watches. I had a habit of breaking them and as a consequence was never on time for anything. I was lost in my own thoughts when a sudden noise made me turn quickly. A drunk had wandered into the bus shelter and was proceeding to piss up one of the windows. The pissing didn't bother me, it was the fact it was running across the floor and all over my bag.

"Oy you, silly old bastard watch what you're doing," I snapped.

The drunk span round his dick still in his hand. "Fuck off you little bastard, you want a clout!" He cursed as he began to move closer to me putting himself away as he did so.

"Range Jack, remember range," I heard my trainers voice in my head. I shot out a jab hitting him full on the nose; the force sent him crashing into the window, a look of total bewilderment on his face. I was about to follow on with a left hook when I became aware of how frail he looked, he was already a beaten man, his eyes darting around looking for a means of escape. "Go on Fuck off, you silly old bastard," I shouted as I kicked him up the arse as he made his exit.

The bus was warm, and the top deck was unoccupied. I sat at the back, put my feet up and drifted off to sleep. The jolt of the bus stopping made me wake with a start. 'Oh shit,' I thought 'I've missed my stop'. A glance out of the window confirmed my fears. I jumped up grabbing my bag and leapt down the stairs. "Hold up mate I've missed my stop let me off," I screeched as I stood at the buses exit doors. "Fell asleep did ya?" smiled the driver as he pulled over and I exited on to the pavement. The bus pulled away and I looked up at the night sky, "Oh God why me?" I said aloud. The run home was about two miles, a distance I covered in about twelve minutes, running was hampered by the wet bag I held out away from my clothing; the smell of urine wafting around the night air. I turned the key in the lock and gingerly opened the door, the lights were all off everyone had gone to bed. I crept up the stairs and quietly closed the bedroom door behind me. The sheets smelled crisp and fresh and after a few minutes the blankets began to heat my frozen frame. I laid back and thought about the night's events, six fights six wins, I grinned to myself before drifting off to sleep. I was twelve years old.

I could hear Dad whistling downstairs in the kitchen as I walked across the landing to the bathroom. It was Saturday morning, so Dad was happy, no work and an afternoon down the pub with the lads to look forward to. I'd be bloody whistling as well I thought! I ran the tap into the sink splashing the cold water over my face. I raised my head and glanced in the mirror A large swelling had formed underneath both eyes; I prodded them and winced a little. I certainly looked like I'd been in a fight. I picked up my toothbrush and spread a large blob of toothpaste onto the worn-out bristles. As I began assaulting my teeth with great vigour, the tear on the inside of my mouth gave me a sharp reminder of the night before. I opened my mouth and poked at it with my index finger. To think I bloody well won! I smiled to myself. The smell coming from the kitchen met me as I was half way down the stairs, bacon; Dad always cooked bacon on a Saturday.

"Well how did it go son?" he asked without turning round.

"Guess" I said cockily. Dad turned to look at me and never being one to make a fuss hid his surprise at the lump of mashed potato that used to be my face.

"Lost then did you? Or were you involved in a car crash on the way home," he teased. "Lost? I knocked him out, you should have seen it, it was brilliant".

"I did see it son," he said as he walked past me ruffling my hair and then promptly disappeared out of the kitchen, the door closing after him. That was typical of Dad and the nearest to a compliment I was ever likely to get. I never really understood adults' emotions, all guarded and afraid; it was as if to show your feelings was a weakness and to be frowned upon. The bacon sizzling in the pan dragged me back to reality.

" Want a sandwich Rocky?" asked our Steve, he'd been sitting at the table reading the paper and was peeking over the top of it. As far as older brothers were concerned, our

Steve was okay, he was four years older than me and his full-time occupation was chasing women. Dad would tease him and say he spends more time in the bathroom than a woman and because of his curly hair nicknamed him Shirley Temple, a remark that pissed him right off. I would often use this to get him mad when we argued and would run off shouting Shirley Temple at the top of my voice. Steve would never chase me, he tried once and after five hundred yards nearly keeled over, after that he had decided it looked cooler not to run after me. The bacon sandwich tasted like heaven as I devoured it with great gusto.

"Slow down our kid you'll bite yer fingers off in a minute" laughed Steve.

"I'm bloody starving. I haven't eaten since yesterday afternoon," I shot back.

"You'd better have this as well," said Steve as he slid his sandwich over to me. I was not used to Steve showing me any form of kindness and the only time he would give me his food would be after he'd spat in it behind my back. He'd then laugh hysterically as I ate it. I was that hungry I didn't care. I snatched it off the plate and ran out of the kitchen stuffing it into my mouth as I left. I didn't look back, but if I had, I would have seen Steve shaking his head and smiling, not out of malice but out of love.

Monday mornings always came too quickly; Dad would wake me before he left for work at five thirty. "You'll never be a winner if you lie in yer pit all day, up yer get and do yer five miles son and remember I'll be watching you!". I don't think Dad ever really did watch me run those five miles every morning but with a Dad like mine you didn't take any bloody chances. Five miles was easier to cope with than the look of disappointment on his face when you let him down, not to mention the back hander you got if he thought you were taking the piss! Dad wasn't a bad bloke, he just had high standards and wanted the best for us. He had a problem showing love in any form, I guess it went against his macho image. There were the odd times when his guard

10

would slip, usually after a Saturday boozing session with the lads, he would come home pull me close and tell me over and over again how much he loved me. I liked those times and would make sure I was awake when he came home. I don't suppose he ever knew how much they meant to me and Steve, but we loved him anyway.

The roads were always just coming alive when I ran on a morning, but I never really noticed anyway. I would do most of the five miles in a total daydream, I would pretend I was a famous boxer and that people would say, "Hey, isn't that that Jack Marriot? He's gonna be the champ you know.". It was my way of forgetting the ten house bricks Dad had lovingly wrapped in a towel and put in my rucksack. "This will make yer legs strong and give you stamina," he'd say. The only thing it ever gave me was a bad back but hey you live and learn. Breakfast according to Dad was the building block of the day and if Dad said it you did it, so every morning I would fight my way through six slices of toast, one pint of milk with six raw eggs in it, one pint of fresh orange juice and a large bowl of cereal that resembled rabbit droppings. It was little wonder I spent most of my school day in the toilets, the teachers must have thought I had dysentery!

School was one of those things I attended because I had too. I never really fitted in. At first it was because other kids picked on me for the way I dressed. I couldn't afford the fancy clothes they had, and Steve's cast offs were always four years out of fashion. Then it was the fact that they became afraid of me. Dad always said, "Don't be a bully but stand up for what's right". I didn't know what was right but knew I wasn't going to get the shit kicked out of me on a regular basis. I was never really taught how to fight in the street but found it was something I could do better than most. So that was that, you took the piss out of me and I gave you a good hiding, end-result - nobody took the piss. The downside to this is you have loads of friends who hate your guts but never dare tell you. I wasn't a fool and even in

11

the early years could pick out the ones who hung around me because they felt safer being my friend rather than my enemy. I would often lie on my bed and cry to myself, nobody really wanted to know the real me, I was known for what I could do rather than for what I was. I could write poetry and would cry at sad films but that's not the recipe for a winner, so I hid it and hid it well.

"Marriot are you listening to me?" questioned the teacher. I always hated Mr Lyndon he was our English teacher and also taught P.E, he was a big man with a large beer gut to match. His teeth were stained, and his beard often held the remains of his previous meal. It was not the way he looked that I didn't like, it was his bullying manner. I never did like or respond to bullies.

I looked up from the book I was pretending to read, "Yes Sir, I was," I said politely but he wasn't going to let it drop.

"Well what did I just say then?" he challenged.

"Don't know Sir guess I must have missed that bit," I answered submissively. I had just given him the excuse he needed, the smell of stale beer and cigarettes reached my desk before he did.

"What did you say boy?" he demanded, prodding me in the chest with his finger. I was in a position I didn't like, it was what you would call a no-win situation. I decided that the best option was silence, but Mr Lyndon had other ideas. "Well" he said leaning into my face, "are you going to answer me boy?" His voice had by now raised a couple of octaves and his face had a healthy red glow. I really did want to answer but couldn't think of anything to say that wouldn't make matters worse. A grubby hand reached out to grab my collar, instinctively I brushed it away and almost as soon as I'd done it I knew it was a mistake. "What do you think you're doing boy, you want to have a go?" Mr Lyndon raged, "Come with me," he said dragging me from my seat by the hair. I could hear the rest of the class's excited conversation even as the door closed behind us.

I was then ceremoniously frog-marched through the maze

12

of corridors and every now and then I would receive a shove in the back from Mr Lyndon just for good measure. He had by now completely lost the plot and walked directly behind me mumbling to himself, "Kids got no respect, do as they want; parents need a good talking to". It puzzled me no end how somebody who obviously hated children so much chose to work with them, it wasn't until years later I realised why, what's the point in being a bully if you've got nobody to torment? I was no stranger to the Headmasters office and immediately took up my usual spot in front of his desk.

"Well Jack, what have you been up to this time?" said Mr Bond the Head. He didn't want a reply, he already knew what I'd done, and I sensed the build up to a long lecture that would make a wooden leg fall asleep.

"I am so disappointed in you, what on earth has got into you lately? You are constantly in trouble fighting and being disruptive". Mr Bond was a slightly built man with a pointy nose and round glasses; he was always immaculately dressed and reminded me of a quiz master from the telly. I always sensed that he was a caring man and didn't agree with corporal punishment, the look on his face as he caned you was one of utter disgust. I often thought how lucky we were that somebody like Mr Lyndon didn't dish out the punishment as my arse would have been ripped to shreds. "I don't know what I can do with you Jack, you're an intelligent boy but don't want to apply yourself".

'Oh please God I thought just let him cane me; I can't do with his amateur psychology.'

"Mr Lyndon says you tried to strike him, this is a most serious matter. I am afraid I will have to write to your parents and get them to come in and see me". Oh bleeding terrific it's now gone from a simple caning to a beating within an inch of my life from my old man.

"Please don't do that Sir," I grovelled.

"Give me one good reason why I shouldn't?" he said looking over the top of his glasses.

"I promise to try and keep my nose clean, Sir, and to

13

apologise to Mr Lyndon". Oh God what was I saying, apologise to Mr Lyndon, I'd rather remove my own tonsils with a pair of scissors.

Mr Bond looked at me thoughtfully. "I tell you what I am prepared to do," he began. "I am going to give you some time to think about your behaviour. I am going to suspend you from school for the rest of the week, after which I want to see a marked change in your behaviour, now get out of here" he said pointing at the door.

The following morning I did my five-mile run and because Dad had left early for work, I managed to intercept the letter from the school I knew was imminent. Dad would never find out about my suspension. The way I saw it, I was doing us both a favour. I wouldn't get a good hiding and in turn Dad was happy believing I was being well behaved. It seemed logical to me, and besides, I was definitely a fully-fledged member of the self-preservation society, so my pert young arse would keep its covering for a little while longer. Thank God. I used my time off school wisely, always making sure I got home at the usual time even though Dad was never home before us, it paid to be careful. I'd been caught truanting before when he came home early due to a strike and my arse had only just recovered from the thrashing it had received back then. I was in no hurry for a repeat performance. I occupied myself during that suspension in my favourite place, a place that was mine where you were bloody unlikely to bump into a copper or a school truant officer. They were stupid and assumed that all kids who bunked off would head into the city and the large shopping centres, fucking idiots. They obviously thought all kids were as fucking thick as they were.

I loved the canal, the peace and quiet where I'd skim stones across the surface, pester the anglers and hang my feet in the water. I never minded my own company, I guess after mum left us it was easier not to rely on anyone else. I will always remember the day she left, the house had a strange atmosphere and Dad kept hugging me and would go

14

all quiet. I didn't know what was happening, just that things had changed and would never be the same again. I never did ask why mum left, It was kind of understood that we didn't talk about her anymore. After that Dad started drinking, he would come home late at night and fall over the furniture, this was followed by a stream of obscenities directed at himself and then he'd go quiet eventually falling asleep. I never really thought about Dad's feelings, and his drunken antics were a great source of amusement to Steve and myself who never really thought about how unhappy he was. The canal became a kind of sanctuary to me and in times of sadness I would find myself there crying and muttering under my breath like a mad man. The anglers slowly got to know me, they would share their sandwiches and let me reel in the odd fish, it was my place and I never took anyone else there.

The suspension from school came and went and in a lot of ways I was disappointed to have to return. Mr Lyndon had decided I would be his whipping boy and no opportunity to verbally assault me slipped through his grasp. I hated that bastard, but fate was to give me the opportunity for revenge, an opportunity I wouldn't let pass. It was one Monday morning, and all of my class were lined up on the football field in our sports kit. Mr Lyndon was kitted out in his best track suit; he must have had a magic mirror because he really fancied himself and would strut about with his chest puffed out, his stomach sucked in and a self-satisfied expression on his face. to the rest of us he was just a fat smelly old bastard!

"Right fall in line," he barked.

"Here we go again, ten laps of the field while he smokes twenty fags, arsehole," said Adrian one of my classmates. Adrian was a tall lanky streak of piss, but his sense of humour would have me in stitches. We were never really close but would share the odd moment of madness.

"Right then on my whistle ten laps of the field as quick as you can," said Mr Lyndon. There was a unanimous moan from the whole class, but we set off running all the same. My time spent running the streets each morning was paying dividends and ten laps didn't even raise my heart rate. I loved to see the look on Lyndon's face as I ran the legs off the others. It was obvious it got right up his nose. The whistle blew long and loud, we were rather perplexed by this as we had only run four laps. "Come here and form a line. Marriot you don't seem to be getting a lot out of this, so I think we will have a bit of a change", grinned Lyndon as he threw a rugby ball towards me. "Right class we are going to have a little go at the noble game of rugby, form two teams and line up on both sides of the field".

"Now he's gonna give us a right pasting the bastard," whispered Adrian as he fell in beside me. I nodded in agreement as I had a strange feeling that what was about to occur had little to do with rugby and more to do with legalised assault.

"I will now demonstrate the tackle, Marriot come here," ordered Mr Lyndon. I walked into the centre of the field and stood before the now chuckling Mr Lyndon. "Right then, watch and learn, watch and learn." he said eyeing up my tiny frame. I must have looked pathetic. I was twelve years old, weighed eight stone and had legs like bits of string. "Marriot throw me the ball," he smirked. I duly obliged. "That's pathetic," he said returning it to me with all his force. "Now throw it properly". I really didn't want to do this, I knew whatever was about to happen would end up being my fault. I stood there looking at the ground, the ball held loosely in my hands. "Give me the ball" he shouted, once again. I threw it back, but it fell short and landed by his feet. Mr Lyndon bent over scooped up the ball and with an evil look in his eye addressed the rest of the class. "Right then we are going to practice the tackle; a tackle when carried out properly should bring down the biggest opponent. I will demonstrate how it's done". I knew that this was the part where I came in and didn't wait to be volunteered; I walked over to the now beaming Mr Lyndon

16

who was relishing the thought of looking good at my expense.

"Where do you want me Sir?" I groaned.

"Oh very nice of you to offer Marriot, I will run with the ball and I want you to tackle me, come on then," he shouted over his shoulder as he set off running. I knew there was no getting out of it so gritting my teeth I charged full speed towards the prancing Mr Lyndon. The tackle was probably the worst that anybody had ever made, but not being one to miss out on an opportunity to inflict pain, Mr Lyndon threw his entire weight on top of my little frame, his elbow strategically placed in my ribs. The wind shot out of my lungs at a rate of knots and as a very smug Mr Lyndon raised himself to his feet; I rolled over and buried my head in the ground. "That is what can happen if you don't tackle properly," he announced to the rest of the class. "Get up Marriot you girl, you're not hurt," he sneered at me.

"That guys a complete bastard," said Adrian as he walked over and helped me to my feet. The colour had by now returned to my face and my lungs were once again filling with air.

"Fuck off and leave me alone," I shouted at Adrian. It wasn't his fault, but I was angry really angry. Adrian took note of the look on my face and made a hasty retreat.

"Marriot, let's do that again but this time I'll tackle you," said Lyndon as he tossed the ball back towards me. I'd barely got my hands to it before Lyndon ran towards me like a bull elephant. To say I wasn't frightened would be a lie, but my anger had always overcome any fear I'd had and this time I'd had enough. I side stepped the oncoming charge just at the last moment, Lyndon tried to turn to counter it, it was a mistake, the ground was soggy, and he slid awkwardly to the ground his face biting the dirt. The rest of the class giggled uncontrollably at the site of this bearded walrus wallowing in the mud. "Marriot what are you playing at? You're supposed to let me tackle you," he bellowed.

"But Sir" I protested, "I thought you wanted to tackle me

17

properly".

"Oh, you want me to tackle you properly," he scowled as he climbed to his feet. "Get running then boy and I'll show you how it's done". What ensued can only be described as one of the most memorable events of my life. It consisted of ten minutes of gut-wrenching laughter all directed at an increasingly desperate Mr Lyndon. You see the one thing that didn't cross the mind of our bullying sports master was my fitness and speed. It was like a tortoise trying to outrun a gazelle. The ball was tucked closely under my arm and I ran like the wind turning and twisting as the out of breath bully closed in, the more I ran the more frustrated he became and the howls of laughter from my classmates didn't help calm the situation. Unfortunately all good things must come to an end as did this episode.

"Mr Lyndon what on earth is going on here?" demanded a very unhappy Mr Bond. It was not a good day for our Mr Lyndon. The school sports field was overlooked by several classrooms and the excited pupils within these had massed at the windows in fits of laughter at the spectacle that was unfolding before their very eyes. "I, I was just showing the class how to tackle," spluttered a nearly tearful Mr Lyndon. "My office" snapped the Head as he turned on his heels and marched off.

The events of that day made me a very popular pupil for the next week or so. Other kids would walk past and slap me on the back and start laughing. It was good to be liked for whatever reason but like all fame it was soon forgotten. The one person who never forgot that day was Mr Lyndon, I noticed he looked at me differently, it was a kind of controlled loathing with no outlet, he knew he couldn't hurt me anymore and so did I.

It was a Friday night when I first had an idea that things were somehow different. Dad was in the bathroom whistling like a budgie on speed and there was an air of happiness that wafted through the whole house. Steve was even being nice to me. I naturally assumed he was planning something or

18

perhaps Dad's mood was just infectious but anyway it made a refreshing change, so I didn't question it. I was in the living room watching TV when the door flew open and as I looked up, I saw a sight I will never forget, Dad in a brand-new suit, hair neatly brushed and smelling like a tart's handbag.

"Well, what do ya think?" he asked. I didn't answer, just raised my eyebrows and gave him a cheesy grin. "Get out of here" he laughed as he jokingly took a friendly swipe at my head. "You young ones don't know class when you see it," he said as he straightened his tie. It was not often Dad was in such a good mood and it seemed like an ideal opportunity to push my luck.

"Dad, you know I'm boxing at St Patrick's next week?"

"Yes," he replied knowingly.

"I could really do with some new boxing boots, my trainers are a bit worn out!" and as if to strengthen my argument I added, "The other lads all have them".

"Mmm and these new boots will they make you box any better?" he teased.

"Oh Dad go on please," I begged.

"Tell you what son, you win your fight next week and the boots are yours," he smiled.

I leapt from the sofa and hugged him tightly. "Thanks Dad I'll win, you'll see".

"Steady on tiger you'll ruin my suit," he laughed, if only he'd known how much I loved him at that moment, but like him I found it hard to say out loud.

A week was a long time in the life of a twelve-year-old and the run up to the boxing match seemed to take forever. I was desperate for those new boots. I'd found a pair in the Kay's catalogue and would gaze longingly at them at least twice a day, the page became that badly creased it would fall open to it when you picked up the book. I was a cunning bugger even then and would leave it lying around as a subtle reminder to Dad, as usual he pretended not to notice but I caught him looking at them once and smiling to

19

himself. I never said anything, I just closed the door and crept away .The day of the fight arrived, and I'd trained like never before, my early morning runs were much faster that week and when Dad came to my room to wake me at five-thirty, he'd find I'd already gone.

The fight was to be held at St Patrick's boxing club which was in the basement of an old church. I always found this rather confusing, a church was a place of worship, the meek shall inherit the earth and all that, and beneath the altar were hordes of eager youngsters knocking the crap out of each other. The entrance to the gym was at the back of the church down a narrow set of steps that were often littered with the used condoms that clandestine lovers discarded after their intimate encounters. The priest once fell arse over tit on one and even though it was quite comical not one of us uttered a word.

Father Barrie was a nice man, an Irish Catholic in his early sixties. He had a slight limp, a left over from the polio he had suffered as a child but above all Father Barrie was a man not to mess with. I was in a hurry that night and skipped down the steps two at a time. I wasn't nervous about the match, I just wanted those bloody boots. I swung open the door and, in my eagerness, nearly knocked poor Father Barrie for six, he stepped to the side and gave me a stern look.

"Good evening Father," I said in my politest voice. I don't know what it was about priests, but they always made me feel like they knew every little thing about you, a sort of divine psychic. This always made me uncomfortable. Nobody should have that kind of power, I thought.

"Good evening young Jack, and are you boxing this evening?" he said stroking his bald head.

"You bet Father and Dad's going to buy me some new boots if I win," I grinned.

"Well young man you'd better be getting inside you don't want to be keeping David waiting," he said placing his palm in the small of my back as though to improve my forward momentum. Father Barrie always called Dave, David, it was strange and at times you would have to think hard to realise who he meant. Dave was Dave our trainer and a more foul-mouthed atheist there never was. A fact he hid well from Father Barrie.

"You're here then," said Dave as I entered the changing room.

"No I'm a mirage," I quipped.

"Get changed you little shit and less of your lip," he shot back pointing to the lockers. Dave and I had a good relationship. I would give him cheek and he would work me like a dog on the bags during training. I never minded and always sensed beneath the abuse he hurled in my direction there was an unwritten understanding that he was there if I needed him. I unzipped my training bag and pulled out my vest, it was an old one of our Steve's and was at least two sizes too big. Dad said it was okay as it would allow me to move when I was fighting, what made matters worse was I actually believed him.

The changing room was cold and as I removed my shirt my skin took on the appearance of a freshly plucked chicken. I shuddered and quickly climbed into my vest. The rest of my kit was little better than my vest, my shorts were white nylon, the kind you can see your underpants through and once again an old pair of our Steve's.

"Come on Jack," shouted Dave through the open door. "We need to get you warmed up".

I slipped on my white plimsolls and throwing my bag and crumpled clothes into an empty locker headed for the gym. Dave was waiting, he already had the punch pads on and beckoned me over to him.

"Come on Jack we need to warm up before the rest of the lads get here," he snapped impatiently.

I'd been training with Dave since I was ten and had only recently started entering matches; he used to call me Twiglet when he first trained me, this remark was directed at my cotton thread like legs. I never minded, the other lads had

21

nicknames too and Dave only ever gave you a nickname when you were accepted, and it was always well chosen.

"Jab, jab, right hook, slip the punch work Jack work," he barked as I assaulted the pads. This was kept up for fifteen minutes by which time I was covered in sweat and the goose pimples I'd had earlier were a distant memory. "Right good work Jack, get yourself in the changing room and wrap up, don't get cold." He rubbed my head with the pad still on his hand, "You'll be right kid" he said winking at me.

The changing room was filling up with excited kids, talk of past fights, wins and losses were being swapped around.

"Hey Jack, how's tricks?" I looked up to where Bobby Harrison was bent over tying his boots.

"Not bad Bobby, who are you fighting?" I asked.

"Don't know it's a friendly between Market District Club and our lot, who you got" he threw back.

"Gary Spence from Bradford boys," I replied.

"No kidding, he's quite a good lad, he won the North Eastern County juniors last year," he said as he looked me in the face waiting for my reaction, there wasn't one.

"You seen him box?" I asked.

"Yeah last year at Manchester, he was on the same card as me. He's a stylish fighter, looks good but he's never been in with a scrapper, you'll kill him!" he said rather unconvincingly as he rummaged in his bag.

Bobby was two years older than me and was a handy fighter, he'd won the schoolboys the year before. I put a lot of his wins down to his size he was six feet tall with long arms and because he didn't weigh a lot, he fought kids who were at least a foot shorter than him.

Bobby scratched his bleached blonde hair, "Fuck, I've forgotten my gum shield," he announced. He wasn't talking to me he was just thinking out loud. "I'll catch you later Bobby I'm off for a wander, good luck mate, "I offered.

"No problem," he said as he threw a few punches in the air. I smiled at him and closed the door behind me.

The seating area around the ring had started to fill up,

excited parents were talking to their offspring offering last minute advice. It was a strange scene, half of the kids looked terrified and were probably only boxing because they'd been pushed into it by their fathers.

"Mum don't do that," said a young kid as his mum hugged him enthusiastically. He had the full works on, a silk dressing gown, brand new boots and his name was embroidered on the back of his gown. Poor bastard I thought. I'd seen it all before; the new kid with all the gear he would have one fight and never be seen again. We used to say, "All the gear, no idea," and laugh hysterically as some kid in pumps, a vest and holes in the arse of his shorts took him apart in round one.

"Jack are you ready, yer on next?" asked Dave.

"Yep," I nodded, Dave put his fat tattooed arm around my shoulder.

"Box clever Jack you'll be right," he quipped. I walked with Dave's arm still around me back to the dressing room. It was at times like this Dave fussed like a mother hen. I don't think he was bothered about our wellbeing he just wanted us to win. I guess his years in the Merchant Navy had not exactly stood him in good stead for dealing with kids, but he tried. "Oh I nearly forgot I've got something for you," he said as he opened a locker, "Catch". A large white box tumbled through the air and I instinctively dived forward and caught it as it headed for the floor.

"What is it?" I said excitedly.

"Open it and see," he laughed. I tore the lid off eager to get to the contents and there, nestled in tissue paper, was a brand-new pair of boxing boots, my whole face lit up. "They're great," I screeched in a rather strange tone.

"Read the note, you soppy shit," said Dave as he turned his back and began rooting in another locker. I searched through the now discarded tissue that lay on the floor, amongst it lay a simple note, MAKE ME PROUD, DAD.

The gloves felt good on my hands they were a little damp as was usual, sweat never seemed to dry out. I guess the

23

leather held it in.

"They alright?" said Dave as he tied the laces.

"Yeah." I nodded.

"Come on then champ, let's see if those new boots work," he chuckled as he ruffled my hair. The ring was always a lonely place and no matter how many people were around, you felt alone. I must have been a strange sight, a vest that hung on me like an old pair of curtains, white nylon shorts with a hint of my red underpants showing through, and the crowning glory, immaculate white and red striped boxing boots. I didn't care, they felt great, it was like when you had a new pair of shoes and deluded yourself that they made you run faster I felt I could out box anyone.

The bell rang. and I met my rival in the centre of the ring, Gary Spence was every bit as good as Bobby had told me. Bang, bang a double jab hit me in the face, my head spun and for a second, I didn't know my name, let alone where I was. "Jab, Jab and move," urged Dave from my corner.

I could hear muffled noises but, if anyone says they can hear instructions being barked by their trainer in the middle of a round, they're a bloody liar. Bang, bang again I was hit. I moved forward towards the barrage of punches, if I can just get inside, I thought. Snap, snap went his jab this time into my forehead. I continued the chase for what seemed like an eternity and all I got for my trouble was a few more digs. I heard an almighty echo that seemed to vibrate through my entire body. I turned slightly to look for the source, it was then I realised the noise came from inside my own head as a crashing left hook nearly decapitated me. The bell couldn't come quickly enough; it wasn't the beating that bothered me it was the embarrassment.

"How you doing, kid?" Dave's voice penetrated the fog that was swirling round my brain.

"Do you think I won that one?" I asked pleadingly.

"Always the fucking optimist," laughed Dave. "He's a boxer Jack, you can't out box him, but you can out fight him, ignore everything you've been taught and mix it with this

24

kid, his style won't cope with it, do you hear me?" he shouted. I nodded my understanding.

The crowd was anxious to see this other kid win and I could hear the odd snippet of conversation above Dave's ranting. "This won't go another round, the kid in the new boots can't take much more of that!" I looked up trying to see who was talking and as I did so I caught a glimpse of a figure at the back of the room. I recognised his outline more than anything else, it was Dad. I looked away quickly before he saw me. I couldn't look at him like this, he only fathered winners, that's what he told us!

Round two didn't get much better, pure anger and the need to win clouded my thinking and the formidable Gary Spence taught me a few more lessons. "What are you trying to do Jack? I said forget everything you've been taught and fight. I didn't say switch off your bleeding brain," screamed Dave. I didn't answer, there was no point, all I could see was the look on my Dad's face as he hid at the rear of the room. I knew he would never let me live it down. Fucking crap boots I thought, as I glanced at my feet. I knew it was stupid, but I had to blame something. Gary Spence was glowering at me from his corner and the look of self-satisfaction on his face only made me feel worse.

"Seconds out third and final round" called the timekeeper. It was at this point something I can't really explain happened, a feeling of real calm came over me, maybe it was that I didn't care anymore, or I just wanted to get hurt. Gary ran at me, he was eager to continue his systematic beating and one and a half minutes didn't give him long, he didn't want to waste time. I lowered my gloves in order to allow the inevitable punch through; I could see the look of pure glee on his face as he spotted a clear line to the target. The uppercut he threw hit me clean on the chin and sent my head rocketing back, he stepped forward to throw another and caught my right ear as I managed to slip left. It had to be now if I was going to do anything, but he was too fast for me to hit. I led him onto me as he continued

25

punching until I reached the ropes. I put my arms up to protect myself and lowered my head It was then I saw it, a gap between his arms you could drive a bus through. I instinctively turned to my right in order to transfer all my weight to my rear leg and then with all my power drove an uppercut straight into his solar plexus. I heard the air whistle out of his lungs and a strange whining noise follow shortly after. He shot back with the force of the impact and his arms dropped to hold his stomach. I moved quickly onto him my left hand hitting the bridge of his nose which erupted like a hot spring spraying blood all over my new boots.

"Break, break," shouted the ref as he pushed me back. I wanted to finish it, and in my eagerness, moved forward again. "Get back, get back go to your corner" bawled the ref. I moved to my corner, my eyes never leaving my now troubled opponent and waited for the count to begin. It never did, the ref just waved his arms in front of Gary Spence it was over.

"I don't know what I'm gonna do with you" said Dave as he kissed me on the forehead, "well done, well done," he continued. It was then I remembered Dad, I knew he'd be proud of me now, my eyes darted around the room but there was just an empty space where he'd stood.

Chapter 2

The Lover

It was a Saturday morning when things became a little clearer as to the recent change in Dad's behaviour. "Jack come down here son," Dad bellowed up the stairs.

"Coming," I replied, taking the steps three at a time.

Dad was seated at the table. "Come in and sit down," he instructed, as I appeared in the kitchen doorway. "I need to talk to you and Steve about something." I took my place at the table opposite Steve who promptly kicked me in the shin under the table and smirked into his hand.

"Bastard" I shouted at him and kicked him back, I never was good at containing my anger and Steve grinned even more as Dad shouted, "For Christ's sake can't you two grow up for one minute? I have something to tell you both."

We both fell silent and turned to look at Dad. He wasn't angry, far from it, his demeanour was something we'd never seen before, all kind of embarrassed and uncomfortable, it reminded me of the dog when he was a puppy and you'd caught him pissing on the carpet.

"You know your Dad's been on his own for some time he began," his eyes darting between Steve and me. If he was looking for a reaction, he had no chance. Steve contained his emotions as well as Dad and at that point I didn't have a clue as to what was coming next. I stared back blankly waiting for his next sentence. He pushed his chair back and began pacing in front of the kitchen fire, " I've met a woman, a woman I'd like you to meet, she's coming round today."

That was it, what was all the fuss about I thought, "Can I go now?" I said leaping from my seat.

"Hold on a minute don't you want to ask me anything, I mean aren't you bothered?" Dad asked a little bemused by my lack of interest. Bothered what does he mean? I was young and never really guessed the implications of what he was saying to us.

"New, I shrugged," pulling a face.

"What about you?" he threw in Steve's direction.

"Do what you like." snapped Steve. I was rather confused by his reply and the look on his face told me Steve was not a happy bunny.

"She gonna take over from mum?" he continued. "Oh son you know I've been on my own for a long time, don't you want me to be happy?" pleaded Dad.

"Yeah but we're all right aren't we?" Steve protested. The following hour was spent with Dad trying to persuade Steve that things would not change, it was an argument that Steve was determined to win but deep down knew he couldn't.

That afternoon we met her for the first time. She was lovely, all woman and a smell of perfume that entered the room before she did. It had been a long time since a woman had been welcomed into the Marriot house and I was enjoying the attention.

"So Jack, your Dad tells me you are a bit of a pugilist" she enquired.

"Eh?" the puzzled expression on my face made her laugh. She had long blonde hair and kind of narrow blue eyes that partly closed as she looked at you.

"I mean a boxer," she chuckled.

"Oh yeah," I said, my face flushing.

"How many fights have you had?" she enquired.

"Seven, won em all" I answered pre-empting her next question. Steve sat opposite in the armchair at the side of Dad, his face was a dead giveaway he really wanted to be elsewhere.

"What about you Steve, you play football don't you?" she asked.

"Yeah," came the reply. It was delivered in such a way that she knew any further conversation would be hard work.

"That's nice" she replied immediately turning back to me. "I can see you obviously like sports," she said nudging me with her shoulder and giving a little girlish giggle. Dad was silent as though a neutral observer, he sat in the armchair by the fire in his best suit, his thinning hair spread over the bald spot on his head and firmly secured with a liberal squirt of Cossack hair spray.

"Steve, put the kettle on son; Marie could probably do with a cuppa," said Dad.

"Oh that would be nice," she smiled in Steve's direction.

A rather beaten Steve raised himself from his seat. "You want one Dad?" he asked.

"Please son," answered Dad in a voice that was a little more gentle than normal. The door closed behind Steve as he left the sitting room.

"He'll come round Marie, he's a bit moody anyway, guess it's his hormones," Dad laughed.

Steve had really outdone himself when he returned some ten minutes later, there were biscuits, cups and saucers I'd never seen before and served on a tray.

"That looks wonderful Steve," announced the by now increasingly confident, Marie, as he placed the tray on the coffee table in the centre of the room.

"Shall I be mum?" she asked as she went to hand out the cups. That was probably the worst thing she could have uttered short of saying, 'Steve you're a little wanker.'

Steve being Steve seized the moment. "Not fucking likely," he spat and promptly stormed out of the room. My head shot up and my eyes immediately fell on Dad's face. I was waiting for the inevitable explosion, but it never came.

"I'll have a word with him," said Dad softly. I couldn't help but notice the sadness in his eyes as he followed our Steve out of the room.

The following weeks consisted of numerous visits from the determined Marie; and although at thirty she was some fourteen years younger than Dad it didn't seem to matter, if anything it gave Dad a kind of second youth. I would find him singing and whistling about the house and spending

29

hours in front of the bathroom mirror. I even watched through the open bathroom door as he forlornly played with his thinning hair trying to arrange each strand for maximum coverage. Marie was tenacious that was for sure; she would bring bottles of Coke and packets of crisps for me and our Steve when she and Dad returned from the pub, one time she even bought our Steve a pair of football boots, which he promptly left on the bus on his way to a match. I think it was probably intentional. I was not one to rock the boat, I liked her, she was kind to me and it was nice to have a woman to fuss over me like the mother I could hardly remember.

Steve and I would discuss her from time to time, "What do you think our kid?" Steve would ask.

"She's great," I would answer without any real thought.

"She's a right bitch, can't you see that?" he would rant. "She's only being nice to worm her way in and then you'll see what she's like," he'd spit.

I never understood what he meant, I was a kid and if you were nice to me, I liked you. I didn't know that adults could be manipulative, a lesson I would learn sooner rather than later.

The following weeks we saw more and more of Marie, she'd turn up unannounced and let herself in with the key Dad had given her. The bathroom had become an alien environment, it was filled with strange potions and cosmetics, drying knickers and hosiery hung from the shower rails and the bath was always full of hair. I hated coming home and finding them cuddling on the sofa like a pair of teenagers. Dad seemed indifferent to whatever I did and for the first time in my life I was jealous. The boxing club and the canal became my favourite haunts and I would while away the time either walking along the canal or knocking crap out of the punch bags. Dave had even remarked on my enthusiasm for training and had threatened to give me a key to the gym as I always arrived before anyone else.

After a period of about three months, Marie became a permanent fixture. She was just there, and we accepted it. Steve had even made the effort and I swear on one occasion was even nice to her, and me. I still liked her even though Dad was more distant than ever, after all she paid me the attention he didn't.

It was July when they finally got married. Dad and Marie arrived home one Saturday teatime all happy and smiling and as she hung onto his arm, he announced loudly that they'd tied the knot. Steve did his usual grunt of acknowledgement and I beamed like the village idiot. I had no idea how things would change, and I was always affected by other people's moods. The marriage made no real difference at first. Marie was still kind and would always have time to chat to me about my school day and my latest fight. I was happy and even though Dad had started working away from home and I missed him, I felt secure knowing Marie was there if I needed her.

During the weeks Dad spent away from home Marie would do her best to spoil me, little gifts of new clothes and extra pocket money made her my favourite person. We would spend the evenings chatting and it felt good to know somebody had a real interest in what I did. Dad would ring home each evening and warn me to be good for Marie, but it wasn't necessary, I wasn't a bad kid, not at that point anyway. Our Steve never bothered to speak to Dad when he phoned, it was his way of silently protesting against Marie's inclusion in the family.

The relationship between Steve and Marie eventually levelled out. It was an understanding born of the realisation that they would never be friends. Steve would avoid any form of conversation with Marie and in return she stopped trying, the odd time words were exchanged they were generally monosyllabic and followed by an awkward silence. I always looked forward to Dad's return when he'd been working away, he had always been the object of any great feelings I'd had from love to hatred and when he

31

wasn't around, I felt a part of me was missing.

"Your Dads coming home tonight," smiled Marie as I entered the kitchen one morning before school; she was standing at the sink wearing a pair of yellow washing up gloves and a dressing gown.

"What time?" I squealed excitedly.

"Oh he should be here when you get back from school, he's getting a train and it's due in late afternoon," she replied. Dad had been away for over six weeks it was the longest he'd been away since Marie and he had married and the expression on her face told me she'd missed him as much as I had.

"Can I come home early?" I pleaded.

"Don't be daft you can't just come home from school, what would yer Dad say? Besides its Friday, you'll have the whole weekend to see him," she reasoned. I reluctantly agreed and still full of excitement I headed off to school eager to get it over with.

That day was one of the longest I ever spent at school, each second seemed like a minute and each minute like an hour.

"Marriot are you with us? I can see you're here in body but not in mind," teased Miss Pritchard. I loved history classes, Miss Pritchard was a vision of beauty, long blonde hair and big breasts She always wore short skirts and her permanently tanned legs became the object of many a child's desire as they struggled through puberty. It was not unusual to see the boys at the front dropping books and pencils on the floor in an attempt to get a look at her knickers. I was by now fast approaching my thirteenth birthday and although not quite sure why I too had started to look at Miss Pritchard's legs, they were just so long and smooth and in my active imagination I would reach out and stroke them. It was kind of like the impulse to stroke a dog's head, you just wanted to.

"Sorry Miss" I grinned stupidly.

"Come on Jack wake up," she said giving me a knowing

look. I blushed a kind of deep crimson colour and buried my head in the book on my desk.

The yard was busy at break time and the other kids were involved in various games, some kicked around a football and shouted loudly at each other, "Man on, Man on" they would cry as somebody tried to make a tackle. I never liked football and would always be found at the rear of the science block where I gathered with the usual group of smokers.

"Hi Jack, played any rugby lately?" laughed Adrian, he was leant against the wall with two other kids, passing a cigarette between them.

"Give us a cig Ady," I asked.

"Sure," he said removing a crumpled ten pack from his jacket pocket. Ady gave me a light and as I drew deep the smoke entering my lungs made me want to cough.

"What you doing at dinner?" I asked holding in the awful taste deep in my throat.

"I was thinking of going down the chippy, want to come?" he offered.

"Yeah why not? it's crap here at lunch," I replied. "You coming too?" I asked Nigel Platt who was standing beside Adrian. Nigel was waif like in appearance with thin spindle like arms and legs on a short body, his hair had a mind of its own, several hairs always refused to lie down giving the appearance of a lump of watercress growing out of the middle of his head. His clothes although always clean looked untidy; he had a way of holding himself that would have made him look untidy in a Saville Row suit.

"Can I?" he beamed not quite believing he'd been included.

"Sure, I just asked you didn't I?" I said sharply, his face flushed, and he dropped his head towards the floor. "Okay see you at the gate at twelve thirty?"

He replied, "Sure" I smiled back at him.

Dinner time arrived very much like the rest of the day, very slowly. "Right then let's get some chips," I ordered as I strode ahead, Adrian and Nigel quickening their pace in order to keep up.

"You got any money Nige?" enquired Adrian.

"Naw, spent it on Monday," came the reply. "Not very hungry anyway," he continued as if to cover up his embarrassment at being skint.

"It's okay Nige, I've got some, I'll get yer some nosh," I grinned shoving him with my shoulder. I knew what it was like not to have anything and only recently thanks to Marie I had found myself with a substantial raise in my pocket money. The chip butties were piping hot and although we'd smothered it with vinegar it did little to lower the temperature.

"Bloody hell that's hot," said Nige spitting a lump of partly chewed chips onto the pavement.

"See what thanks you get for buying someone lunch," I teased grinning at Adrian.

"Yeah, there's twenty pence worth on the deck," he laughed.

"Sorry Jack I, I mean thanks for the chips," said Nige nervously. I could sense that Nigel was not used to kindness and found it hard to be accepted. It was a feeling I had known and at that moment felt a bond form between us. Nige never knew it but from that moment on he would never be bullied by anyone again, I'd make sure of that.

"Shut up and eat yer sarnie," I laughed chucking a chip in his direction, and for the first time I saw Nige smile. The dinner hour passed quickly and as we walked up the road back towards school we must have looked like we'd been friends for years.

Nige was riding piggy back on Adrian and shouting, "Faster" at the top of his voice. They looked an odd sight Adrian tall and skinny with this waif like urchin hanging like a rucksack on his back. I can't remember a time when I'd laughed so much and by the time it ended, I'd almost forgotten Dad was due home that evening.

To say I was eager to get home that night could not do justice to the way I felt. I didn't even wait for the bus with the other kids, I simply slung my bag over my shoulder and ran full speed the entire two miles home.

"I'm home, I'm home," I shouted through the letterbox after trying the door and finding it double locked. After several minutes of shouting without response I walked round to the front of the house and pulled myself up on the window sill by the finger tips pressing my nose close to the living room window, the light was on and Dads shoes were strewn across the floor. I peered closer; my breath misting the glass, the television was on. 'That's strange, wonder where they are,' I thought out loud. "Hey anybody in? I hollered up at the bedroom window, it's me I'm home.". I took a couple of steps back and looked up at the bedroom window. I saw the curtains twitch and Marie peer out through the gap. I went to wave at her, but the curtains immediately fell closed.

"What's the matter?" said Marie as she opened the door, a look of annoyance on her face.

"I can't get in" I protested.

"Me and yer Dad want some time to ourselves," she snapped; "Now go and play with some of yer friends."

I'd never seen Marie like this and thought it best not to argue

"Okay what time shall I come home?" I enquired in my politest voice.

"Do what you want," she barked slamming the door shut. I stood for several seconds looking at the front door shrugged my shoulders and set off down the street, just to add to the situation the skies opened and the heaviest rainfall since Noah gathered animals two by two descended upon me.

The canal banks were a sea of mud and as I walked along the well-trodden path my shoes quickly became one large clump of sodden earth. "Bollocks" I shouted out loud as I tried to flick the soil away that clung like a limpet by now, up to my ankles. I used a kind of swinging movement like kicking an imaginary football. I found this worked well and occasionally a large lump of mud would release its death grip and fly like a missile up into the air and land in the water with a splash. I managed to walk another couple of hundred yards before stopping to shake off the soil once again. I had always been a victim of circumstance and if I didn't have bad luck, I would have had no luck at all. I guess I'd been tempting fate, but I was nearly thirteen years old and had a tendency not to think things through. I raised my left leg and took an almighty swing in a further attempt to clear the additional weight from my shoes; an explosion erupted as a large clod of mud extracted itself from my foot and hit the centre of the canal. I grinned from ear to ear, that's got it I thought as my foot now felt somewhat lighter, it was the wet feeling as I placed my foot back on the muddy path that alerted me to my predicament, "Oh shit, why me?" I said out loud as I looked at my now shoeless foot. I bent down untied the remaining shoe and threw it over my shoulder into the water, turned and did a half salute and ran off down the towpath to the bridge where I sat and sheltered from the rain. I must have been a sight to behold, by now barefoot dangling my feet into the water in the pouring rain and cursing loudly only to stop briefly to laugh hysterically to myself.

The walk home seemed longer than usual, the rain had still not relented, and my bare feet were now a pale grey colour. The footpaths were like a minefield and I had to perform a skipping motion as I dodged bits of broken glass and large pebbles. I would occasionally stop at a large puddle and wash the mud from between my toes, this eventually turned into a game, and I would seek out the largest puddles I could find and dance like a lunatic kicking the water across the road at passing cars. The street lights were now on and withdrawn into my own little world, time had escaped me. I knew it was late but didn't care. A car horn sounded loudly as it drove past, "Fuck off" I screamed turning to stick two fingers up at them as their lights disappeared into the night spraying a large cloud of mist

36

from the back tyres. I heard the sound of a car engine and spun around in its general direction, to my horror it was a police car pulling up to the side of me.

"Out late son," said the copper as he climbed out of the passenger door. This seemed like a stupid question and because of that I didn't bother to reply. "Where you going at this time son?" he continued.

"Home," I offered rather nonchalantly. "Don't you think you should get a move on, your parents will be getting worried, and where are your shoes?" he added pointing to my bare feet.

"I lost them in the canal, they were covered in mud and I was washing them".

"Okay, okay spare me your life story" said the copper interrupting me "Get in the car."

Chapter 3

The Sibling

Breakfast time the following morning was a rather grim event, Dad kept looking up at me from his newspaper, a knowing look on his face. I had brought the police to the house and he wasn't impressed with that. The only reason I'd escaped a good hiding the night before was the two burly policemen that stood between us. Dad wasn't a bully, just a strict disciplinarian and I was well aware, I'd escaped any physical repercussions by the skin of my teeth. For this reason I would look away sheepishly when Dad looked in my direction.

"Hey, our kid, what time did you get home last night?" blurted Steve, a smirk covering his whole face as he cut into a slice of well-cooked bacon on his plate. Bastard, I thought, he was just trying to set Dad off again. I looked up and swiftly kicked him in the shin under the table.

"Oy you little git, what yer kicking me for?" he said louder than was necessary.

"That's enough, you two," snapped Dad without looking up. He didn't have to; Steve and I knew that tone of voice and it was usually a few seconds away from a good slap round the head.

"I'm going out anyway," grunted Steve as he pushed his plate away, stood up and flounced out of the kitchen nearly knocking Marie flying as they met halfway through the kitchen doorway.

"Hey where's the fire?" called Marie as Steve headed upstairs.

"Hey Alan, aren't you going to say something?" she shot in Dads direction, "He's always doing that, it's like I am bloody invisible."

" I'll talk to him later. Do we have to start the day off with an argument, for God's sake I've only been home a bloody day!" he said as he glared over the top of the paper. Marie knew she wasn't going to get too far with Dad. She had quickly learnt to read the signs and knew he was best left alone when he was like this.

"Okay darling, whatever you think's best" she smiled sweetly.

That afternoon was very long and very boring; Dad had confined me to barracks and for good measure had me doing the sodding housework. "Move your arse you flea bag," I scowled as I shoved the hoover into the dogs back legs. Buster was a long- haired German shepherd and a more idle dog you would never meet. He looked up with a kind of 'if I must look on his face' and slowly and methodically shifted all of two feet in the direction I'd shoved him.

I shook my head, "You daft old sod, out of the room," I said pointing towards the door.

"Don't you be nasty to the dog, he's done nothing to you, it's your own fault you have to stay in," said Marie as she stood in the doorway, "Your Dad will be home soon, and you know what he'll do if you haven't finished the jobs he's given you," she continued.

I don't know quite what came over me. I guess I was just a typical adolescent. "Why don't you just fuck off and leave me alone," I snarled as I turned to face her. Marie was totally taken by surprise and the colour drained instantly from her face.

"How dare you, you wait until your father gets home," she snapped as she turned on her heels and disappeared out of the door.

"Do what you fucking want, you're not my mother," I screamed after her. It was not that I was feeling brave at this point rather that I knew I was in big trouble and I may as well be hung for a sheep as a lamb. The rest of the afternoon was a complete nightmare; I constantly watched the clock and would look out of the window praying Dad was not coming up the road. I really hoped he was in a good mood and as a friend of mine once said, it never did anyone any harm to hope!

Voices in the kitchen alerted me to Dad's presence. I waited for the inevitable, "Jack get your arse in here now," but after several minutes I had still not been summoned. I made my way from the living room into the hall and stood by the kitchen door that was slightly ajar.

"He can't get away with talking to me like that Alan," Marie protested.

"He's just a lad. I will talk to him love, but I don't want to come down heavy every time I walk through the door. He's nearly a teenager and all the changes around here haven't been easy for him," he replied.

"So that's it, you're just going to let him get away with it, it's obvious that you think more of him than me, or are you going to deny it?" said Marie a rather girlish tone in her voice.

"What are you going on about, you want me to beat my son to show you how much I love you, are you for real?" the sarcasm in Dads voice was not wasted on Marie and once again she knew she was not going to win this argument.

"I tell you what get him in here, and I'll have a word with the little bugger," continued Dad.

"Jack come here, your father wants a word with you," Marie shouted up the stairs. I was lucky I'd overheard and just at that moment crept upstairs to avoid being caught listening at the kitchen door. The kitchen door opened with all the drama of a midnight horror movie it even creaked for effect, something I'm sure it never usually did.

"Come in son don't just stand there," beckoned Dad. I gingerly stepped into the lion's den. I never looked up; never stare a mad dog in the eyes my Granddad once told me. "What's all this with you and Marie, swearing at a woman, honestly son what's got into you?" coaxed Dad.

I had no idea what my reply should be so just shrugged my shoulders, besides Dad was talking enough for both of us. This was not unusual when he'd had a few beers. "So let that be an end of it," said Dad getting out of his seat and wrapping his arms around me. It was only at this point I realised I had been thinking of something totally different and had not heard most of what he'd said, being a kid could sure be brilliant!

The rest of the weekend was a little weird, Marie had obviously not forgiven me the tirade of abuse I had levied upon her and at odd times I would catch her giving me a rather odd look, it was a kind of disappointed glare coupled with a, 'I know something you don't expression'. Dad was great, he spent hours in the cellar with me practising my uppercuts and six punch combinations. He laughed really loudly and hugged me tight after knocking me over with a right cross.

"Come on son it was only a love tap," he grinned as he cupped my now bleeding face in his huge hands. God, I loved times like this, me and Dad, no outsiders and the bruises and odd fat lip kind of made it more real. Sunday soon came and as usual I got up went for a run, the people going about their business were a blur as I grunted and snarled my way through the five-mile trek. I stopped at the garden gate and bent over catching my breath, beads of sweat fell from the end of my nose and onto the stone flags.

"Tired son?" I looked up to see Dad standing in the doorway a cup of tea in his hand.

"Naw, not really just a bit hot," I replied, straightening myself up and throwing a few punches into the air.

"Well don't stand about like that get in the shower or you'll get cold," he said ruffling my hair as I squeezed passed him into the house.

Sunday afternoons, Dad went to the pub with Marie and as usual I went to the gym to spend some quality time with Dave.

"Now then you little turd, nowt better to do than come and annoy me on this, Gods day of rest," joked Dave as I entered the gym. "Get changed then times a wasting," he said turning away to talk to another lad.

The changing rooms smelt as delectable as ever, a cross

41

between cat piss and a wrestler's jock strap, it always had the same affect; it gave me a bloody headache if I stayed in there too long. The gym was busy, I was not the only child with nothing better to do on a Sunday. "Hit the bloody thing Jack it's not a kamikaze punch bag it won't throw itself at you". Sometimes Dave's sense of humour was lost on all but himself and I looked at him blankly as he laughed loudly his large belly moving in unison with his laughter. The showers were their usual soothing temperature that day, just above freezing, this had two effects, you didn't waste time in there doing unnecessary things like washing and secondly you spent two hours afterwards waiting for your testicles to reappear from inside your stomach.

"That is fucking freezing," spluttered Kenny his spotty face peering through his towel as he stepped out of the cubicle.

"Not many," I grinned. Kenny was a complete loser, I never disliked him, but he was never going to go anywhere as a boxer. He was fifteen years old and had had more fights than most of the guys in the gym; unfortunately he'd lost almost all of them.

"You fighting next week, Jack?" he enquired.

"Yeah at Halifax Star, I'm fighting Micky Finch from London," I replied nonchalantly.

"Fuck me he's good you know" said Kenny, a hint of awe in his voice. I was not in the least bit concerned as to what Kenny thought after all he would have had trouble fighting off a cold.

"You boys staying all day? Some of us want to get off home you know," said Dave as he leant around the door.

"Coming boss" we replied in sync.

The bus ride home was uneventful and at this time I had no reason to suspect a life changing event was soon to be thrust upon me. The only person who knew what was coming was Marie and she was just waiting to choose her moment! I turned the door handle and walked into the front room, Dad was lying on the floor in front of the fire, he looked up, "Hi son good training session?" he nodded.

"Yeah not bad," I replied as I threw myself onto the couch beside Marie. "Have you had a shower?" she said sticking her nose in the air as though she'd just smelled a fart. "Yeah I laughed it's my kit bag, my kit needs washing."

"Put it out in the hall I'll stick it in the washer later," she smiled. So there we sat Dad, Marie and me watching an old movie in black and white, nobody really watching. Dad was half asleep, I was thinking about Friday's match and Marie, what she was thinking I didn't know but she had a look of expectation on her face I was not quite sure about. A key turning in the back door made Marie remark, "Steve's home."

"Either that or a burglar has a key to our house," I grinned.

"Hi folks," said Steve as he burst through the lounge door, the smell of alcohol beating him into the room. What happened next would have been quite comical if it wasn't for the fact I thought Dad was going to kill him at any given moment. "Hi pops" grinned Steve as he strode over to the now dozing lion that passed as our father. Steve bent over and ruffled Dad's hair, the carefully positioned strands now resembling a tatty straw hat.

Dad opened his eyes "What you doing, son?" asked a rather bemused Dad.

"Do you know I fucking love you, you old bastard" said Steve, a cheeky grin spreading right across his face.

"What is it with you boys, have you found a swear book this weekend?" said Dad shaking his head in mock indignation. "How much have you had to drink son" he continued

"Not bloody enough," laughed Steve.

"I think you should sit down, and I'll make you a coffee," interrupted Marie.

"Whatever" replied Steve falling into the chair by the fire and resting his hand on Dad's balding head. I sat there not quite knowing what to do but knowing I didn't want to miss a single second of this. I looked at Dad who raised his eyebrows smiled at me and winked.

"Get this down you and whatever you do, don't spill it, it's hot," said Marie as she handed the cup to Steve. Steve sat there drinking his coffee loudly and stroking Dad's head, if only I'd had a camera.

After about ten minutes Marie started shifting awkwardly in her seat, "Er I have got something to tell you all," she said nervously.

"Let me guess you're fucking leaving," interrupted Steve "Let me pack you a bag."

"That's enough Steve," snapped Dad sitting up quickly enough to let Steve know he'd gone too far.

"Okay, okay," said Steve apologetically and fell back into his chair laughing loudly.

"Go on love what's the matter," urged Dad.

"Er I, I'm having a baby," spluttered Marie. It's funny how those four little words can have such a profound effect, Dad went a funny shade of white and a vein in his forehead throbbed uncontrollably. Steve laughed so loudly that I thought he was going to wet himself. Me, I just sat there waiting for everybody's reaction. After what seemed like an eternity

Dad climbed to his feet and walked over to Marie, he bent over pulled her from the sofa by her hands and held her close. "That's fantastic news darling, how long have you known?" he quizzed.

"Oh, I'm three months gone," she replied.

"Three months, three months," Dad repeated as though he was making sure he'd heard her right, either that or he was working out if it was his.

"Yes the baby's due in August" grinned Marie.

So that was that, Marie had dropped her bombshell, Dad was obviously delighted, Steve was indifferent and me I was just plain bloody confused. I didn't know how this would affect me if at all, but the worst thing was nobody really cared what I thought anyway. I suppose Dad and Marie were wrapped up in their happiness and never thought to ask how I felt. Oh sure they said, "You are happy about this aren't you?" in a kind of way that said if I wasn't it was tough shit, so I said nothing, it would have made no difference anyway.

Marie's pregnancy passed quickly, she and Dad would spend their time decorating the imminent arrival's nursery and shopping for baby clothes. I became even more of a loner, Dad had little time for me as Marie would demand all of his attention, sometimes I thought just out of spite. Marie kept me at a distance, it was as though this only concerned her, and Dad and I should have no part of it. I got on with my boxing, kind of threw myself into it eventually fighting my way to the junior schoolboys final and losing badly to a kid I could normally have taken apart in round one. It just didn't matter anymore, nobody gave a shit if I won or lost. It must have been catching because eventually I didn't care either! The baby arrived in August, a little boy, he was gorgeous, and I loved him the moment I saw him, all wrinkled features and smelling of sick. I would sneak into his bedroom and let him grasp my little finger in his hand as he lay there gurgling. Marie changed almost overnight, she snapped at me all the time, would hardly even speak to me and would scream like a psychopath if I went anywhere near her offspring. This confused me I loved the little fella what did she think I was going to do to him?

It was my fourteenth birthday when Marie showed her true colours, Dad was working away, and he had given her a hundred pounds to give me to spend on boxing kit. He phoned and wished me a happy birthday. "I've given some money to Marie for you to spend, get yourself some new boxing boots and a robe. I don't want a son of mine showing me up when he goes to the ABA Championships," he laughed down the phone. I never wanted his money I just wanted to be noticed, I would have gladly boxed in my underpants if he'd have been there to cheer me on, but the money would have to do. I went to Marie and asked if I

45

could have the money Dad had given her for my birthday.

"How much is this kit going to cost," she demanded.

"I don't know, the boots are about fifty quid and a new robe about the same," I replied.

"Well you need some new clothes for school as well, so perhaps I should come into town with you," she smiled. I should have been on my guard by now, but I was fourteen and it was my birthday.

The shopping trip was a complete disaster. Marie didn't allow me to buy any boxing kit and spent fifty pounds on school trousers and jumpers. I never saw the rest but shortly afterwards, my new brother was sporting some very expensive designer baby clothes.

I never liked Dad working away, but since the baby was born, I hated it even more. Marie had begun to despise me. I don't know what I did or when I did it, but it must have been my fault.

I don't think in those days when Dad was away Marie ever left me alone for more than an hour. "You've woken the baby you little bastard, get to your fucking room," she would shout and then hit me around the head as I walked past her. She knew I would never hit a woman; we weren't raised that way and what started with a slap to the back of my head progressed into severe beatings.

"What are you doing in Paul's room?" demanded Marie poking me in the chest.

"I was just looking at him," I protested, smack, her hand hit me straight in the face, she threw another one and I lowered my head, this infuriated her even more and she began kicking me and clawing at my face.

"I fucking told you, you don't go in there; you stay away from my son," she was by now ranting. "Get to your room and you're getting no dinner, I don't want to see you until tomorrow," she screamed as she swung me around by the hair and smashed my face into the wall.

I lay on my bed staring at the ceiling, "bitch" I said out loud as the lump on my head began to throb and I started to

46

laugh, better not tell the lads down the gym I've been beaten up by a postnatal lunatic, I thought to myself. A strange scratching noise was coming from the bedroom door and I wondered what it was. I opened the door slowly to find Marie on her hands and knees with a screwdriver in her hands. "Get back in your room, this will make sure you stay there", she scowled waving a padlock in my face.

Things gathered momentum from that point, the beatings were administered with a riding whip, the dogs lead and any other object Marie thought could damage me without the real threat of actually killing me. She used to say, "I am not hurting my hands on you, you're not worth it."

I was still allowed to attend boxing; I think Marie knew Dad would ask a lot of questions if I started missing my training. I had a bit of a problem with one fight in particular. I'd been called for the weigh-in prior to the fight and was a stone lighter than my previous fight, this was purely down to the times Marie would padlock me in my room and not feed me for days on end. She didn't want to kill me. I think it was a power trip, she always gave me water to drink, and I was always grateful, sometimes I'm a real prat! I always looked forward to Dad coming home, I never told him what went on when he wasn't there. I suppose I thought he would think I was making it up, besides Marie was always careful to be really nice to me in his presence.

I still recall the time Dad was home and we were all in the kitchen. I had just won my fight the night before and was really happy. Marie was hugging me and saying how proud she was, and Dad was grinning from ear to ear. I had totally forgotten Marie's dark side and for a moment we were a normal family.

"So what's next Jack," teased Dad, "World title?" he joked as he jabbed me in the chest.

"Oh give over Dad, I'm not that good," I blushed.

"You keep this up son, you are a natural. I've seen you outfight some real good boxers it's only your guts that get you through, don't ever lose that son cos in this world you'll need it!" he said smiling at me with a pride in his eyes I'd never seen before, and sadly would never see again.

Marie was still standing behind me as Dad left the room. I suppose my happiness was more than she could bear. "You don't think you can worm your way round your father, I know what a little bastard you really are," she spat as she shoved me in the back. I spun round a confused look on my face "What have I done?" I pleaded just as she raised her knee hitting me square in the groin and dropping me to the floor, she then kicked me in the back and legs several times for good measure. I was still on the floor when Dad came back into the room. Marie quickly jumped on me and pretended it was a game and she was tickling me, how I hated that bitch.

Chapter 4

Moving on

The following months became gradually worse, if that was possible. Marie was only interested in my brother and used every opportunity to let me know I was just in the way. I decided it was easier all round if I did my best to avoid her; this was relatively easy. I threw myself into my boxing and would hang out after school with Adrian and Nige.

"Hey Jack, you coming to Nige's later?" called Adrian as I walked through the school gates. He was sitting on the wall of a house opposite sucking on an ice lolly.

"Why, what yer doing?" I enquired as I walked over to join him.

"Gonna go down Colditz and shoot my air rifle, what der yer say?" he said a pleading look in his eyes.

"Okay, what time?" I asked.

"Six o clock outside Nige's, I'll meet yer there," he grinned showing a set of red teeth stained by the cheap lolly he'd been sucking.

Colditz was the name the three of us had given to an old derelict mill we used to play in. It stood on the canal bank and we would go to the top floor and throw stones and slates into the murky water.

"Come on, last one to the top does a dare," shouted Nige as he raced along the canal towpath. Nige had come out of his shell over the past months and much to Adrian's and my surprise had a really good sense of humour. I think in weaker people this is a kind of defence mechanism.

"Hold on yer little bastard," I screamed as Adrian and I pushed and grabbed at each other in order to take the lead. The entrance to the mill had been secured with steel panels and wooden boards that were riveted to the outside window frames. This didn't keep us out we had managed to pry back the chipboard at the base of the main door creating a gap large enough to scramble through. It was damp and dark inside, odd beams of light entered via some broken windows on the upper floors and through a couple of skylights that had inadvertently not been boarded up. We raced up the old stone staircase that led to the upper levels dodging the old bits of furniture that had been discarded there whilst trying to avoid breathing too deeply as the stench of stale urine would irritate the back of your throat. Nige had fallen behind and was by now a flight behind us, this was mainly due to the fact I had tripped him up as we got to the first step.

Adrian was just ahead of me and his long lanky legs carried him to the top floor just ahead of me. "Yeah I win," he declared jumping up and down.

"You cheated it's not fair," protested Nige from behind me.

"Never mind Nige," I teased, "The meek shall inherit the earth and all that" I giggled.

"Here look at this," said Adrian excitedly; he was standing by one of the broken windows that overlooked a cement factory across the other side of the canal.

"What?" I said leaning over his shoulder.

"There," he pointed waving his arm out of the window, "Look at that fat bastard," he grinned. I moved closer, in the cement yard. There was a big fat bloke bending over the back of a cement wagon, his arse hanging over the top of his extra-large jeans.

"Give me the air rifle," I demanded.

"No you can't Jack," Adrian pleaded.

"Go on shoot the fat git," said an excited Nige in my left ear.

"Oh fuck it here then, but at least make it a good shot," said Adrian taking the rifle out of the case he had hanging on his shoulder.

I gingerly took the rifle cocked the barrel and inserted a 22 pellet.

"Hurry up Jack before he goes," squealed Nige.

"Steady on Nige you'll wet yer pants," I smiled. The rifle felt good in my hands and I could hear my heart pounding in my ears. I steadied it on the window ledge and slowly pulled the trigger.

The thwack of the pellet leaving the barrel was more than Nige could bear. He grabbed my shoulder almost pushing me out of the window.

"Steady on yer daft git," I barked.

"Fuck me," said Adrian, "Look." The fat bloke was running around the yard holding his arse and jumping up and down. Howls of laughter quickly filled the upper floor of our hideaway; Nige was lying on his back rolling around with tears streaming down his grubby face.

"What a fucking shot," hollered Adrian slapping me hard on the back. I must admit at that moment holding the ABA championship trophy could not have felt as good. It was from this small beginning that my life would gradually spiral out of control.

Marie was in the kitchen when I got home. "Where have you been" she snapped.

"Out," I threw over my shoulder as I walked straight out of the room and headed up the stairs. It was eleven thirty and Dad would have killed me if he'd been home, but he wasn't. Marie and I had at last agreed on something, when Dad was working away the least amount of time we spent in each other's company the better. The bedroom was dark, and I could hear Steve muttering as I slung my clothes on the floor and climbed into bed.

"Bit late 'ain't you, our kid?" he mumbled.

"So what?" I shot back.

"Easy does it squirt; I'm on your side," he said sympathetically.

"What yer been doing or shouldn't I ask?" he quizzed.

"Just out," I replied.

"Still think Marie is nice?" he teased.

"Oh all right so you were right, does that make you

51

fucking happy?" I replied the anger in my voice making it a little shaky.

"Touchy," he continued. I ignored any further conversation and putting my head under the covers soon fell fast asleep. The mornings always came too quickly, and Marie would be on my back again. "Don't do this, don't do that, the stupid cow.

"Jack get down here, I want a word with you," she screamed up the stairs the next morning. I knew it was another excuse to have a go at me and prepared myself for the worst, I wasn't disappointed.

"I thought I told you to put your boxing kit in the washing machine, so why have you just left it stinking in your bag?"

I knew that this was not about my dirty kit but merely a build up to something more sinister.

"I have enough to do looking after the baby without running around after you! You're just a selfish little bastard, no thought for anyone but yourself," she scowled. Her voice had begun to raise a couple of octaves and I knew the signs. Smack she hit me in the face with a clenched fist. I wasn't hurt and could easily have moved out of the way, but this would have just pissed her off even more. Smack she hit me again "You better get it done now or you'll get another one," she screeched.

"I don't fucking think he will," came a voice from behind me. I turned to see Steve standing in the doorway his face contorted with rage and hatred. "Showing yer true colours are you Marie?" he said as he walked towards her.

"It's easy to crack him cause he's only a runt and you know he won't hit yer back. Hit him again and I'll put you through the fucking window!" he shouted into her face now leaning over her. Marie was frightened I had seen that look in kids I'd fought and there was no mistaking it.

"Y, y, y you can't talk to me like that, I, I'll tell yer father," she threatened trying to gain control.

"Tell him fucking what?, that you're a vindictive nasty

52

bitch? I'm sure he will be most interested to hear what you've been doing to Jack behind his back," he snarled. I stood there frozen to the spot. I looked at Steve as he turned towards me.

"You all right mate?" he asked as I wiped the blood away that was running down my nose.

"Yeah I'm okay, I just want to be left alone," I begged, my eyes filling with tears.

"You fucking will be, you will be," he said sticking his finger in Marie's face. I don't think Steve will ever know how my opinion of him changed that day, he became my friend not just my brother and for the first time in my life I really loved him.

Life became a little easier after that. Marie would never raise her hands to me if Steve was around and I would give her as much shit as possible when he was. It was my way of giving her some kind of payback. This was a winning formula but had one major flaw, Marie was no fool and when Steve was out, she would accidentally knock me down the stairs when we passed on the landing, cook food she knew I hated and laugh and say, "Well go without then" when I turned my nose up at it. These games became a ritual and when Dad came home, she would hug me and pretend everything was rosy, and I'd let her. I know Dad knew things weren't right, but he wanted an easy life, it was easier to pretend that nothing was happening.

I still spent lots of my time with Adrian and Nige. Our adventures had taken a different course and we fell into some bad ways.

"Hey, this window's still open," said Nige as he pulled at it. It was a clothing factory near the canal and quite by chance we were passing.

"Let's go in," urged Adrian. I turned to look just in time to see Nige's boots disappearing through the open window.

"Why not," I nodded and one at a time Adrian and I followed Nige inside. "Don't put the light on you dickhead," I whispered as Nige reached for the light switch. "This

53

way," I continued as I pushed open the door of the staff toilet we were now standing in. The factory was just one large work area filled with tables, standing on each were sewing machines and remnants of cloth.

"Hey what do yer think," whispered Nige. He was holding up a woman's dress against his body, "It's no good," he continued, "I will need a new hat and shoes to go with this!" Adrian and I looked at each other and back at Nige and then burst into fits of laughter.

"What else is there?" I enquired.

"Nothing that will fit you, they only go up to size eighteen," giggled Nige.

"Bollocks," I threw back hiding the urge to laugh. I walked over to where Nige was standing and began rummaging through a drawer under one of the tables.

"Da da der da," came a voice across the other side of the room. Nige and I looked up to see Adrian wearing a full wedding dress and veil. His trouser legs rolled up, he looked a real picture all in white sporting a black pair of Doctor Martin boots with bright yellow laces. "Well what do ya reckon, would you take me to be your awful wedded wife?" he giggled.

"Silly bastard! Stop fucking about, let's just have a quick look around and piss off before somebody comes," I ordered.

"Okay mate, only having a laugh, sorry," he replied as he began removing his bridal wear.

The office door at the other end of the shop floor was locked, this only posed a problem for a minute as I kicked the door off its hinge's, and it fell to the floor with a loud crash.

"Fuck me Jack, you trying to wake the dead?" said Nige in a pleading kind of tone.

"Sorry mate got a bit over excited," I replied as I began pulling out the drawers on an old metal cabinet. The cabinet contained personnel files, a half-empty bottle of whiskey and an old cash box made of wood. I took the cash box out and placed it on the desk top I slowly opened the lid and peered inside. I could not believe my eyes, there was more money than I had ever seen in my life, new crisp ten-pound notes and at least twenty of them. I began to count them my heart racing in anticipation.

"Fuck me Jack, how much is there?" asked Nige as he looked into the box.

"Two hundred and twenty quid and a bit of change," I smiled as I finished counting.

"Give us some" he begged.

"Yeah when we get out of here," I replied shoving the cash in my jeans pocket.

"Where's Ady?" I asked as we walked out of the office.

"Ain't seen him," replied Nige.

"Come on," I said, dragging Nige by the collar. "Let's find the silly twat before he does something daft." Nige and I made our way to the other end of the shop floor. "Ady, Ady," I called in a loud whisper but there was no response. "Prick! This is all we need," I exclaimed in Nige's direction. A door to the right of the toilets was slightly ajar and I shoved it open with my foot. It led into a small canteen with a serving hatch at the other end. I could hear a metallic rattling from just beyond the hatch. I put my fingers to my mouth and indicated to Nige to be quiet. We made our way around the tables and chairs like two SAS commandos, our hearts in our mouths. I reached the serving hatch and knelt underneath it. I slowly raised myself up and looked over the top. "Fucking hell Ady you gave me a bloody heart attack, what yer doing?" I asked.

Ady was wearing a pink pinafore with a bra and knickers printed on the front and a hair net, he was stood at the stove clasping a huge cast iron frying pan. "Making a little supper," he smirked pointing toward the worktop where he had laid out the necessary ingredients, bacon, eggs, bread and a large container with about fifty sausages in it.

"You're not bloody right in the head, I exclaimed We're screwing a bloody factory and you want to sit down to supper!"

"I'm hungry, what else is there," said Nige in an excited voice as he pulled open a large fridge door. I knew I was out-voted.

"Go on then full English for me and don't forget the beans." I grinned at Adrian as I took a seat at the table on the other side of the hatch. The scene was set Adrian, Nige and I, sitting in a factory eating a fry-up at ten o'clock at night. "These sausages are frozen in the middle," I teased as I spat out a mouthful onto the tiled floor.

"Well bugger me we've got a food critic," laughed Nige. "Sod off."

I grinned throwing the remaining sausage across the table. This was the unspoken cue for battle to commence and before long a food fight was in full swing.

"You bastard that's not fair," screamed Nige as I hit him full in the face with a fried egg. It stuck to his face like a limpet and Ady and I laughed hysterically.

"Right! You're for it now," he squealed as he ran into the kitchen. I jumped up from the table not wanting to get caught seated when Nige burst back out with whatever he'd got his hands on. Ady wasn't as switched on and just sat laughing loudly at the table, not for long though, a large block of margarine winged its way through the hatch opening and hit him square on the back of the head.

"You bastard, that's it," bawled Ady as he jumped to his feet the margarine falling to the floor. He bent down scooped up a large blob and headed to the kitchen door. Nige was a bright little sod and had anticipated this. He met Ady as he burst through the door and emptied a full tin of chopped tomatoes over his head.

What happened next can only be described as a mini riot, food was thrown in every direction, plates and cutlery went flying as we chased each other throughout the factory laughing like hyenas. Ady had definitely been in the wars and how he explained to his mum the state he was in, I'll never know. Nige wasn't too bad apart from the dry powder

56

fire extinguisher I'd fired all over him, me as usual, I got off Scott free!

The money we'd stolen from the factory soon went. We had Chinese takeaways and bought cigarettes, chocolate and generally had the life of Riley. Ady bought a new jacket that was bloody awful, but he thought it was great. I suppose the fact that it was bought with stolen money made him feel that extra bit special.

"You gonna be buried in that jacket?" I teased as we had a smoke behind the gym at school.

"Your just jealous," he said defensively as he pulled up the collar around his neck.

"Jealous, oh yeah cos I've always wanted an imitation leather jacket," I said sarcastically. Nige stood there trying to decide if it was appropriate to laugh or if the situation was serious. "Come on lets go, it's time for Miss Pritchard's class," I said winking at Nige.

"Oh yeah I wonder if she's wearing those fishnet stockings today," grinned Nige.

The boxing club had taken second place to Ady and Nige and I would often skip training to hang out with them.

"Long time no see" Dave quipped as I entered the gym.

"Up yours," I grunted as I walked away from him and entered the dressing room.

"Hi Jack, how's tricks asked Stuart Benton who was sitting on the end of the bench tying his boots.

"Okay," I said without looking him in the eye. Stuart was everything I despised in someone else. He came from a wealthy family, went to private school and his Dad was some amateur boxing official who no doubt had influence over which opponents his son would fight. This really got to me. Stuart won fights because he fought crap boxers not because he was any good. I remember watching one of his bouts the previous year, and he had quite obviously lost, the other kid was an unknown but better than anyone had expected, he battered Stuart so severely I was surprised the fight wasn't stopped. I was absolutely speechless when they gave the decision to Stuart, and the crowd were none too pleased either. It was because of this, when I sparred with Stuart I would hurt him. I always pretended it was an accident and that I didn't know my own strength. I know that Dave knew what I was doing but would turn a blind eye because, if the truth was known he didn't bloody like him either.

"Jack you get in the ring and spar with Stuart, he's got a fight next week," said Dave. Stuart was two years older than me and for a lad of sixteen was built like a brick shithouse. It never mattered to me, he was too slow, and his footwork had all the grace of an Irish navvy in wellies.

"Move Stuart move don't let him corner you. Jack stop pissing about, put yer guard up," said Dave, raising his eyebrows as he looked at me. I had let my hands drop purely to show Stuart what a crap boxer he was. The other lads at the ringside were smirking behind their gloved hands as I wove and side-stepped each shot Stuart aimed at me. I would roll under his right cross and immediately roll back the other way leaving Stuart looking around trying to find out where the hell I was. It was cruel and humiliating for him, but I was just a kid and it felt good. "Jack get out of the ring if you're not going to box properly," barked Dave as he tired of my show-boating. I didn't argue I just hit Stuart with a straight right as a parting shot and climbed out through the ropes and headed to the changing room. Once there I rifled through my kit bag took out a pack of cigarettes lit one and plonked myself heavily on the bench blowing a stream of smoke into the air.

"They'll kill yer every time kid," smiled Dave as he entered. I was surprised not only by his sudden appearance but at his tone of voice. Dave was always a shouter and being caught with a cigarette in the gym was a hanging offence. "What's the matter Jack?" asked Dave as he sat beside me, I shrugged and took a deep pull on my cigarette. "You have so much talent, there was a time when I couldn't keep you out of here, now your hardly here and when you do come your just fannying around!" he reasoned.

I still didn't reply I couldn't, the tears started to well up in my eyes. I jumped up so quickly it gave Dave a start. "I'm all right," I snapped and ran out the door grabbing my kit bag from the locker as I left. I never looked back, if I had I'd have seen Dave run his hand across his face and look up at the ceiling slowly shaking his head in despair. I made my way to the bus stop threw my bag heavily onto the floor giving it a hard kick then leaning my head against the shelter window I began to cry until I just couldn't stop.

Running away seemed like a good idea at the time, I'd packed my gym bag with some clothes and an old sleeping bag, stolen some money from Marie's purse and shinned down the drainpipe from my bedroom in the middle of the night. Steve was not at home much now, he'd got himself a girlfriend and because of this I would find myself at the mercy of Marie every waking minute. I didn't have a plan. I just left. I spent most nights in Colditz sleeping on the top floor and cursing that bitch. It was bitterly cold at night and I would, more often than not, pace up and down the building until morning. I would then go out and steal a couple of pints of milk off someone's doorstep for my breakfast.

"Hey Jack, you there?" Ady's voice carried up the staircase to the upper floor where I was dozing in my sleeping bag. I'd been awake most of the night. Strange noises would wake me with a start and I would call out, "If there's anyone there, I'll fucking have you!" It was just bravado as for the most part I was shit scared, but anything was better than going home.

"Get much sleep?" Ady enquired as he stood over me as I sat up rubbing my eyes. I pushed the sleeping bag down my legs and crawled out. "What time is it?" I asked.

"Ten past eight, I can't stay I'll be late for registration," replied Ady. "Got yer breakfast though," he smiled as he held up a carrier bag.

I took it from his outstretched hand and began to

rummage through it. "Not more bloody boiled eggs, I haven't been for a crap in four days, still it saves on toilet paper," I laughed.

"Never mind mate, I'll bring you some fish and chips after school if you like," he smiled.

Ady and Nige had been great since I'd run away. They would sometimes sneak out late at night and we would buy a Chinese takeaway and eat it whilst sitting on the roof of our urban hideaway talking and laughing until the early hours. Nige once nicked two bottles of cider from the local off-licence and we got completely plastered. It ended up with us chasing each other across the roof and daring each other to climb down the pitch-black lift shaft. I went first and felt my way down the five floors to the bottom. I was more than a little worried as nobody had actually seen what was at the bottom of it as even in the daylight it was too dark to see.

"Go on then Nige, your turn," said Ady pointing down into the blackness, "We've both done it, go on," he urged.

"Its bloody dark," said Nige in a slightly higher tone than usual "What if I fall?"

"Well guess you won't want the rest of yer Chinese," I giggled pointing to the sweet and sour pork in its foil tray Nige had placed on the floor.

"You chicken or what?" teased Ady. The name calling eventually got to Nige and he reluctantly began to climb down into the darkness until he disappeared. I'd always had a bit of a wacky sense of humour and the bottle of cider I'd consumed had done little to kerb it. I began to giggle hysterically until Ady turned to look at me as I was about to empty the contents of Nige's takeaway down the lift shaft.

"No, no you can't," he whispered. I just grinned a grin that must have told him I was going to do it anyway and we both laughed uncontrollably.

"What you two doing?" a voice echoed up the darkened shaft.

"Oh nothing mate," we said in unison as I tipped the

60

sweet and sour sauce down into the abyss.

"What the fucking hell is that?" came a scream and Ady laughed so much tears rolled down his face. I was in such a state I couldn't laugh and just pointed hysterically down towards Nige and held my other hand over my mouth. The sight of poor Nige when he emerged caused me to laugh so much my stomach hurt for two days. Later that night when they'd both left, I lay in my sleeping bag and laughed out loud every time I thought about it.

During the time I was on the run from home I never gave a thought to what Dad was thinking. I suppose I felt bitter and blamed him to some extent for letting Marie make my life a misery.

I looked forward to the evenings after school when Ady and Nige would turn up and fill me in on the day's events. Nige turned up on one occasion out of breath and gushed excitedly how the police had visited the school and addressed everyone in morning assembly. The police wanted anyone who knew where I was to get in touch with them and left a telephone number on the school notice board. I must admit in a strange kind of way this made me more determined not to go home. I had apparently gained some notoriety, and everyone was talking about me. Ady said some of the other kids were having bets that I'd turn up face down in a canal or some weirdo had whisked me off for nights of perverted pleasure. 'Sod em all,' I thought, 'who really bloody cared anyway. Marie only wanted me home for appearance sake and I'd had enough.'

The six weeks I remained at large wasn't a bowl of roses. I was constantly hungry and although Ady and Nige did their best I was a growing lad and they could never sneak out enough food to fill me up although it was certainly not through the lack of trying. Ady once tried to steal the Sunday joint and a few left-over roast potatoes. His Dad caught him as he went out of the back door and gave him a thorough grilling. Ady had said he was going to give it to the neighbour's dog and his Dad gave him a good hiding for being so bloody stupid. After that Ady played it safe and as a result I got even less to eat.

I decided if I was going to live rough then there were certain things I would need, and food was on the top of the list. It was purely because of hunger, I took to shoplifting. I would go to the supermarket and stuff anything I could get my hands on down my trousers. This worked well for a few weeks, but all good things must come to an end.

"I don't think so sonny," said the store detective as I tried to escape through the door. I'd seen him watching me and knew I'd been sussed so made a beeline for the exit just as he blocked my path. I stopped dead and looked up at him.

"Come on yer little git," he smirked as he grabbed me by the arms. I didn't say anything, there were so many thoughts racing through my mind. 'Oh shit, what would Dad say when I was hauled off by the police? and that bitch how she would relish my downfall.'

The manager's office was just a large room with a desk at one end and a few television monitors along one wall. "Well what have we here?" said the rather arrogant man sat on the edge of the desk. He was about forty years old, balding and wearing a cheap suit.

"Caught this one trying to leave with half the store down the front of his pants," said the store detective as he pushed me further into the office and barred the door with his skinny frame. I knew there was no escape and as the balding guy reached for the phone and said, "Yes Police please." My whole life flashed before my eyes.

The two policemen that arrived to collect me reinforced my belief that things were about to get a whole lot worse.

"Right then you little bugger let's get you home to your parents," said the younger of the two. He was about twenty years old with a spotty complexion and just to cap it off bright ginger hair. He grabbed me by the arm and hauled me out of the seat I was now seated in. I was then frogmarched through the store for all to see.

It was not until we were out of the store that the other

policeman spoke. He was about fifty years old and had a kindly face with eyes that showed a certain amount of compassion. "I think you can loosen your grip Tim," he nodded towards the other copper, "I don't think this young man is public enemy number one, are you?" He winked at me. It was only a matter of time before I became unstuck and as the Police drove the short journey to our house, I would have gladly welcomed death with open arms. I had not been forthcoming with my address but after a few enquiries via their radios the game was up! The door was not answered for an age and at one point I was convinced that nobody was home, a thought that for a brief moment gave me hope in what was my darkest hour!

"You are gonna get it now son, I bet your father won't be too happy when he sees us," grinned the younger of the two coppers. The older one gave him a nudge with his elbow followed by a stern look. He reddened a little and knocked loudly again on the door. The key turned in the lock. I swear it took at least an hour for it to open wide enough to see who was standing there.

"Where the hell have you been? Marie and I have been worried sick," said Dad. He was about to continue but stopped as he seemed to realise I was not alone. "Where did you find him?" he said looking at the two coppers.

The elder one replied, "He was shoplifting in the local supermarket, but don't worry he added as though trying to get me off the hook, they aren't going to press charges."

"Get yer arse indoors. I'll give yer bloody shoplifting. I didn't raise any thieves!" he shouted as I ducked under his arm that was holding the door open and ran into the kitchen. The next half an hour consisted of a barrage of endless questions, the odd "I don't think this is getting us anywhere," thrown in by my new-found friend the older copper, Marie tutting and shaking her head, and me, I said nothing!

"Well we're waiting," said Dad as he stood with his back to the closed kitchen door. "Where the bloody hell have you been all this time? And why the hell did you run off in the first place?"

I didn't want to tell him the truth, he would have never believed me anyway. "Don't know," I said a blank look on my face.

"Do you know what could have happened to you? There are lots of weird people out there," reasoned the older copper by now sitting in a chair opposite me at the kitchen table. "We find kids like you every other day, there not all as lucky as you, some never get to go home, do you understand what I'm saying?" he continued.

I didn't answer just a nod of my head seemed appropriate. "Here I'll show you something," said the younger copper striding towards me across the kitchen. I think he was feeling a little left out and wanted to have his say. He placed both hands around my throat and growled, "Go on try and get up. If I was an attacker you'd be in real trouble!" He was squeezing my throat hard enough for my eyes to start bulging. As he was doing this, he kept shouting, "Go on get out of that!"

I looked at Dad and the look on his face was non-committal. The older copper looked as though he was a little embarrassed, he made a step towards us and then stopped.

"Go on then try," his hands squeezing a little more. I'd had enough of this by now and even at the tender age of fourteen it was obvious even to me that this copper was on some sort of bloody ego trip, and it was at my expense. I tried to remove his hands by grabbing his wrists, he tightened his grip. "Now what? You're in real trouble, aren't you?" he relished. I was pretty close to unconsciousness by now and everything was spinning, it was quite comical really. Dad was by now getting a bit agitated and I could see his anger was now replaced by concern for me, his face told me all I needed to know, and I decided it was time to act. A loud groan rushed from the coppers mouth as my right foot hit him square in the bollocks, "Ahh", he dropped his hands from my throat and held his groin as he sank to his knees. I immediately shot a look towards my father.

I'd done it now I thought and waited for the inevitable hiding that would surely follow. I will never forget the look on Dad's face, it was relief, bemusement and confusion all at the same time. He went to say something but stopped and put his hand to his mouth to hide his obvious mirth at what had just transpired.

"Looks like this young fella can look after himself," said the older copper pulling his partner to his feet. "I guess we will leave you to sort this out yourselves," he continued as he pushed the bent over copper towards the door. "I am sure things will be okay son," he smiled in my direction, and as he closed the door he turned, winked at me smiled and was gone. That was a moment in my life my father would recount with much laughter, and his mates down the pub would egg him on to hear the story again and again. I never knew that he'd found it so funny until years after he'd died and one of his old mates told me how the following day in the pub, he'd gathered a large group of them close and said, "Hey lads you've gotta hear this one."

Chapter 5

The reckoning

Things were very strained after my enforced return home. Dad would often look at me strangely. I would catch him staring at me and he would just shake his head and turn away. Marie was in good form. She couldn't wait to tell anyone who would listen that she had always thought I was a bad lot and now, like an idiot, I had proved her right. I was grounded for over two months as way of punishment. I was never asked why I ran away again and even if anyone began to enquire Marie would nervously change the subject. I wasn't bothered, I didn't think anyone was interested anyway. So it was put down to teenage rebellion, pure badness, mischief or any other phrase somebody plucked out of the air.

Dad had gone off to work on the oil rigs and returned home every three weeks. I know he was concerned about going away. I'd overheard him talking to Marie. " I'm not sure I should go this time love, things are not right. I just feel our Jack needs straightening out before I go away again," I heard him say.

"I will take care of him, what he needs is discipline Marie shot back and besides we need the money. Don't fret love, he'll be alright with me." Dad was convinced and like a dutiful husband set off to earn a crust. I was therefore once more passed into the care of my loving stepmother. This was not a job she shirked, it's strange how some people can get so much pleasure from somebody else's suffering.

School had become my only escape as I was even banned from going boxing. This in itself had told me that Dad was indeed really pissed off as this would be used only as a last resort. Ady and Nige were my saviours they would spend all day just trying to make me laugh, just daft stuff like pulling faces and drawing genitals on pictures they found in school books, immature I know but we were only fourteen.

The nights were the worst. Marie would bolt the bedroom door and I would be left there until morning. I would sometimes sit in silence and if I strained my ears could hear her talking on the phone. It's true what they say you never hear anything good about yourself listening at doors. I was so bored and unhappy during those times, when I was locked in my room, it's strange really, I never was much of a talker but would have given my right arm for a five-minute conversation with anyone, Marie included. The worst thing that had happened whilst I was absent from home was the departure of Steve, he had, believe it or not, got himself a job; he was working in a hotel and had got a live-in position. He probably couldn't wait to get away and I couldn't blame him the lucky sod!

One particular night when I was safely locked in my room I heard a strange noise outside the window a rhythmic tapping, tap, tap, tap, tap, tap, tap. "Oh let me in mate, I'm gonna bloody fall," said Ady as he hung for dear life onto the cast iron drainpipe outside, his head barely visible above the window sill.

"What are ya doing? You daft git I laughed as he hauled himself through the now open window.

"Ya know what they say mate," he grinned, "If the mountain won't come to Mohammed. You fucking coming or what Nige?" he called as he looked down into the street.

"Not so loud," I squealed as I stifled a fit of laughter. The wicked witch will hear you," I said talking about Marie.

"So mate what's the score?" asked Ady as he reclined on my bed thumping the pillow as though to make it less lumpy.

"Same old story , the old cow's downstairs and I'm locked up in my fucking room, great 'ain't it?" I shrugged.

"Yer wanna come down Colditz and hang about? Things 'ain't the same with just me and Ady," said Nige as he rummaged through a pile of magazines under our Steve's old bed. "Bloody hell have you seen the size of those?" he spluttered as he held open a page in an old copy of playboy.

"Where did yer get that? the dirty git, I never knew he had that, give us a butchers," I said grabbing the magazine from his hands.

"I wanna look," screamed Ady trying to snatch it from me. Before we knew it a full-grown tug-o-war had commenced and amongst all the excitement I totally forgot about Marie.

"Get off you prat, yer can look after me," I said, shoving Ady into the wardrobe. He landed with an almighty crash, an old suitcase falling off the top and hitting him squarely on the head as he tried to stay upright.

"What the hell are you doing up there Jack?" came Marie's voice as she began to unbolt the bedroom door.

"Er nothing," I said as she climbed the stairs to the attic.

"Nothing what do you mean nothing? She glared now standing in front of me. It was hard to stop myself grinning as Ady and Nige were pulling faces at me from under Steve's bed where they had hidden seconds earlier.

"Well what were you doing?" she continued.

"I was just getting something off the wardrobe and the suitcase fell off," I said, a smirk gradually creeping from the edge of mouth. Whack, she hit me clean in the face with her right hand and immediately went to follow up with a left. It was instinctive, and I slipped under it popping up to her left side. I hadn't time to relish my slim victory for this sent her into a frenzied attack. She tore at my hair and began kicking me in the legs as she spun me around tearing lumps from my scalp.

"You think yer fucking clever do you, you little bastard. I'll show you," she screamed. I'd never seen her this manic before and began to wish I had just let her hit me with the second shot, but it was too late and as she threw me against the wall my head crashed into it everything went black.

"Fuck me mate, you alright?" said Nige as I began to come round.

"She's fucking nuts mate," added Ady, a look of worry on his face.

"Fuck off and leave me alone," I snarled. "Just go," I said pulling myself to my feet.

After they had both left I went over to the mirror on the dressing table and peered at my war-torn face. I had a scratch from my left eyebrow down to the corner of my lip and my right eye was bloodshot. "One day you bitch," I muttered to myself as I rubbed at the lump now appearing on my forehead. A single tear fell down my cheek. "One day, one day," I repeated.

The following day at school Nige and Ady were a little strange. I guess they just didn't know what to say. At dinner time I went to wave to them as they crossed the school yard and they pretended not to see me. I knew why they felt awkward and just let it go, besides I was a little embarrassed myself. I wasn't best pleased that I'd been beaten up by a woman in front of my mates. I eventually caught up with them after lunch.

"How are you?" asked Nige rather sheepishly as he looked at the ground. Ady just stood there his hands in his pockets rattling some loose change.

"Okay, okay I guess," I mumbled. Ady slapped me in the back "Come on mate we'll be late for History," he smiled as he guided me towards the school block. That was the last time we ever talked about the events of the night before. I think it was better that way, after all fourteen-year-old kids can't make sense of the things that some adults do!

It was not a decision I sat down and made, it was just that I really didn't care anymore. I would steal anything that was not nailed down and if I didn't like the way another kid would look at me, I gave him a good hiding. I didn't really bully anyone, I just didn't try too hard to avoid or talk my way out of situations. I only had two rules, they had to be bigger than me and I didn't kick someone when they were down. Guess I had some principles after all.

Friday afternoon was always my favourite, you could almost taste the weekend it was that close. "Hey Jack, what yer doing after school?" called Ady out of his classroom window as I walked across the school yard at change of lesson.

"Nowt, why" I shouted.

"Meet yer at the gates," he hollered back, I didn't reply I just waved my arm in the air and walked off.

The end of school bell rang, and I made my way through the maze of corridors to the yard. Kids were whooping in excitement at the prospect of the forthcoming weekend and groups of friends had formed to wait for each other at the gates. I sat on the wall and scanned the thronging mass screwing up my eyes as I searched for Ady or Nige.

"You Marriot ?" came a voice from behind. I turned to see a lad I'd never seen before. He was tall, near to six foot with unbrushed dirty blonde hair and a pair of menacing eyes.

"Yeah what if I am," I spat. I was nobody's fool and could smell trouble coming.

"Yer supposed to be a bit of a hard nut 'ain't yer? Me and me mates thought we'd see how hard yer really are!" he snarled pointing towards four other kids. They were dressed in the uniform of Mathew Murray School and as was often the case would turn up on a Friday to look for a fight. My left hand shot out and jabbed the dirty blonde kid straight in the nose. I didn't wait for his reaction, I hit him with another jab as he moved back, blood now pouring from his nose. He stumbled but managed to stay on his feet, the right hand that followed would have felled an elephant but to my surprise he still stayed up. Whack, a blow hit me in the back of the head and sent me sprawling forward into the arms of the dirty blonde kid.

"Look out Jack," I heard Ady's familiar voice as another blow caught me again from behind.

Kids had started to gather and were hollering, "Fight, Fight, Fight," at the top of their voices. The fight had by now turned into a bloodbath. I had been thrown to the floor by the sheer weight of the five lads who were doing their best to kill me. Smack, Smack a fist hit me again and again.

"Yer not that hard are yer?" yelled the dirty blonde as he kept me down with his bulky frame, his mates kicking me in the face and body. Everything was by now a bit of a blur but deep inside I heard my father's voice, "It' only pain, only pain." I don't know how I managed it, but I summoned enough strength to push this kid off me, enough to wriggle out. I was still being repeatedly kicked as I scrambled to my feet and I heard a loud gasp from the spectators surprised I'd got back up. Straight away the dirty blonde came on the attack, he didn't intend to let me recover but I had other ideas. "Footwork Jack, Footwork," I heard Dave's voice. Smack I hit the charging blonde and quickly side stepped hitting him with a right hook behind the ear as he sailed past. I quickly turned still on my toes as one of his mates began to try to get behind me. Whack, I hit him clean in the mouth one of his teeth embedding itself in my hand, he fell backwards onto the floor holding his hands to his face tears rolling down his bloodied cheeks. The rest of his mates were by now a little uncertain of what to do. They were cowards and the thought of getting hurt was not that appealing to them, much easier to attack from the rear. My dirty blonde opponent was a little worse for wear but still on his feet. I had to respect him at this point he was obviously a tough bugger.

"I don't fucking think so," said Ady as he punched one of the other kids in the face who was about to jump on my back. There wasn't time to acknowledge Ady. The blonde kid was already charging back at me flaying his arms wildly. I'd seen this before in the ring it was panic and fear driving him, it was easy to deal with. My hands worked fast a succession of blows drove upwards into his mouth and nose as he repeatedly charged forward his head bowed. He would never have seen the last punch coming, my knees bent, and body half turned. As I sprang upwards all my momentum increasing, the speed and power, crash he fell to the floor not out cold but a moaning jibbering mess.

"I'm gonna kill you, you twat," screamed Ady who was

by now stamping on this other kids head.

I ran over "Ady he's had enough, leave him," I ordered pulling him away by the shoulders. "Go on you lot, fuck off or your next," I snarled at the other two kids who by now looked like startled rabbits. They didn't need a second telling and picking up the kid whose teeth I had knocked out, ran off down the road as quick as their legs could carry them.

"What about him?" asked Ady pointing towards the dirty blonde kid

"Fuck him," I said as I watched him, still on the floor and wiping the blood from his face, "Let's go, it's Friday 'ain't it?" and both Ady and I laughed in unison.

The bus stop was busy and as usual Ady, Nige and I sat on the wall smoking and drinking coke.

"So what was it like?" said Nige pleadingly.

"Nige it's over, let's just forget it and go home," I replied.

"You're just pissed off yer missed it," grinned Ady.

"Ain't just curious," answered Nige rather pathetically.

"Here Jack have yer seen the state of yer face?" quizzed Ady.

"Why am I not my usual handsome self?" I said, letting out a smile that turned into a grimace with the pain. My face was a bit of a mess, a broken tooth, black eye and a gash across my nose from some bastard's boot "All character building, character building," Dad would say!

The bus soon arrived and Ady, Nige and I hurriedly pushed our way up to the top deck. We had our own seats on the bus and the other kids would avoid sitting in them. It wasn't that we ever said anything, it was just the way it was.

"Give us a smoke Ady," I asked, holding out my hand. Ady always had cigs on account of he was a right thieving toe rag and his Dad always left a pack hanging about when he was pissed.

"Ady, he'd say the next morning, you seen my fags?"

"Naw, why yer always asking me?" he'd say innocently as his father hunted high and low rubbing his head in order to clear his hangover.

"There you go mate," said Ady as he passed me a lit cigarette. I took a deep drag the smoke hurt my throat as I drew it into my lungs, but I needed it. I leaned back in my seat put my feet up on the window and closed my eyes.

The following few months were less eventful. I had managed to open up some dialogue with my father and in return had been allowed to continue my boxing. I attended the gym at least three or four times a week but would sometimes give it a miss and hang out with Ady and Nige.

"And where were you on Friday?" demanded Dave as I bent down to open my kit bag one day.

I had my back to him and didn't bother to turn around. "Sick, ya know?" I offered.

"Bollocks," came the reply as I turned in time to catch the back of him as he left the changing room.

"He's got it in for you, the miserable git," said Michael Vessy as he pulled his vest on.

Michael was a crap boxer and not a very decent human being. He had a hygiene problem and brown teeth. He knew I didn't like him and expected to be ignored; he wasn't disappointed. I struggled into my boots threw my bag onto the changing bench and walked into the gym. The punch bag was heavy and hard, the years of constant pounding it had taken from hundreds of would be world champs had moulded it into what was by now a bag of hard cement with a soft patch at head height and in the mid-section where you would practice body shots, this was all well and good as long as you timed your punches correctly and hit the softer parts but if you cocked up you could break a wrist on the harder portion. Whack, whack I hit the bag as it swung back and forth, first a couple of jabs followed by an uppercut to the body. The force of the uppercut would lift the bag in an upward direction and it would fall back down rattling the heavy chain that held it aloft. The noise of that chain gave you a real sense of satisfaction, after all the entire bag weighed at least seven stone and it was an achievement to

73

get the bag to move let alone lift it into the air. The noise of the rattling chain drew the other kid's attention to you and they would stop exercising to stare in awe as you gave the bag a methodical pasting!

Dave never paid any attention. It took a lot more than that to impress him, you would look up and gaze in his direction hoping for some sort of recognition, but it never came. I'd been on the bag for the best part of an hour and as was usual, I then laced up my boxing gloves and took my place at the ringside in order to do some sparring.

"Not tonight Jack, you go and do some exercises," said Dave not even turning to look at me. I knew I was out of favour, sparring was the icing on the cake, the time when Dave noticed you and gave you the benefit of his experience. The fact that I'd been denied this opportunity was purely to let me know how pissed off he was and in return I was too.

The trip home that evening was more than a little lonely. I sat in my usual spot on the top deck of the bus my kit bag thrown between my legs under the seat and my thoughts drifted to Dave and the way he had treated me. Dave's opinion had always been important to me, after all boxing was about the only thing I did well and without it I was good for nothing. I made a conscious decision to work harder and gain his respect. This was to commence the following day with the resurrection of my old training regime.

The alarm rang at five o'clock in the morning. It had been some time since I'd been awake at that time and it took enormous effort to drag my weary frame from under the covers and pull my tracksuit on. I crept down the stairs, the thought of waking Marie did not fill me with dread anymore, merely contempt, after all, I might have to talk to her. The morning air was fresh and still, I stood on the doorstep and sucked it deeply into my lungs, long deep breaths that after a few moments bring your body to life. I had been running about ten minutes when I first became aware of a thumping noise deep in my head. Bloody hell I thought it's my own heartbeat. I had really let things go; my lack of training and the odd packet of cigs had done nothing to assist my cardio vascular system. I ignored it and pushed on. Over the coming weeks my fitness gradually found its way back to its former state and I could manage to hold a conversation after a five-mile run without the assistance of resuscitation equipment. The extra effort I was putting in had not gone unnoticed and the relationship between Dad and me had even got back to normal. This got under Marie's skin and she would constantly try to cause a rift between us. I don't know what had happened, but Dad seemed to take my side more often than hers, I think he knew I was trying and that was enough for him.

My friendship with Ady and Nige grew stronger and we became almost inseparable. Teachers at school had nicknamed us the terrible trio and as you would expect we did our best to live up to our name. I had never really looked forward to school in the past but by now it had just become an extension of the fun and games Ady, Nige and myself had after school.

"What we gonna do tonight?" enquired Nige as he poked me in the back.

I turned in my seat. Mr Lyndon was otherwise occupied. "I don't know, what do you think?" I whispered.

"We can go into town to the pictures or the bowling alley," grinned Nige.

"I haven't got any money, unless you have," I smiled.

"Naw, I'm skint but Ady might have some," he replied.

"Ady," I screeched across the classroom trying to attract his attention. It must have been louder than I thought because everybody turned around in their seats. Mr Lyndon spun round from the blackboard his chalk still in his hand, his mouth half open, he was about to yell something and as his gaze fell upon me he coughed nervously, pretended he'd not heard anything and continued writing on the blackboard. I thought it best at this point not to push my luck and wait to talk to Ady at break time.

The lights of the city centre were like magnets drawing us towards them. We walked up the main street the hustle and bustle of excited voices and music spilling out of open pub doorways and into the night air.

"This is fucking brilliant, what shall we do first?" said Nige pulling at my arm.

I turned to look at him his eyes wide with excitement. "Fuck me Nige, anyone would think you'd never been allowed out before," I laughed.

"Yeah, besides we've only got a tenner between us," said Ady "and it 'ain't gonna go far." he continued.

The bowling alley was situated at the top end of town and by the time we'd reached it we were eager to get inside. I broke into a run, Ady hot on my heels, poor Nige was somewhere around the corner.

"Hang on, he yelled wait for me".

"Three cokes luv," grinned Ady as he thrust a crumpled ten-pound note across the counter of the snack bar. "Where's Nige?" he said, looking towards the stairs that led from outside.

"He'll be here in a minute, you know he can't run for shit," I laughed.

Just then Nige appeared at the foot of the stairs, his face bright red, sweat dripping from his nose and as usual his hair sticking up in all directions. "You could have waited," he forced out in between taking a large lung full of air, "This mine?" he asked as he grabbed a cup of Coke from the table we were now sitting at.

I liked it at the bowling alley, it was not that I enjoyed bowling, I just liked the atmosphere. There were excited kids tugging at their parent's arms and whooping loudly if they managed to knock over a few skittles. Groups of men drinking beer and swearing loudly to themselves when they missed. You could almost taste the anticipation when someone stepped forward swinging the bowling ball high before they finally released their grip. Sitting in the snack bar was usually as near as I got to bowling, it was not that I didn't want to, it was just I never had enough money to play, tonight was no exception.

"So what we gonna do now?" asked Nige as he wiped the coke from his chin with his sleeve.

"Dunno, what do you think Jack?" said Ady. I just shrugged my shoulders and looked away.

"Here look at her in lane ten," giggled Ady.

"Fuck me," exclaimed Nige. "She's gross. Look at the size of her arse!" That was how the remainder of the night was to go, we took it in turns to take the piss out of anyone we could, bald men, old men, young women, fat women, black women, white women you name it, nobody was spared. I don't suppose we were what you could call prejudiced as everybody got the same treatment.

"You gonna sit there all night," grunted the middle-aged woman who was wiping down our table. She was wearing a white hair net and a blue coverall that the snack bar staff had to wear. This was obviously because their jobs were not degrading enough so for good measure they had to look like a twat as well.

"Might do grandma," grinned Ady.

"Don't be so bloody cheeky, I'll be keeping my eye on you", she snapped as she turned on her heels.

"I'll be keeping my eye on you," repeated Nige whilst hunching his back and pulling his eyelid open with his fingers. I looked at Ady then we in turn looked at Nige and burst into fits of laughter.

"Come on you two," I beckoned with a nod of my head as I rose from the table.

"Where we going?" asked Nige.

"I don't know, wherever we end up" I threw back over my shoulder without turning round. The night air had become cold, a layer of frost had formed on the roofs of parked cars and with each breath I released, a cloud of mist floated into the night sky and as if rehearsed, we pulled up the collars of our jackets as we walked down the street.

"Jeez its bloody freezing," moaned Nige.

"Shut up you puff," Ady said his voice, showing signs of annoyance.

"How much we got left?" I asked. Ady rummaged through his pockets and produced a couple of quid. "Well we won't be dining out on that! Come on, times a wasting," I said as I picked up the pace of my stride and the other two hurried to keep up with me. Once again, the terrible trio set off meandering through the city streets, because we had no real purpose, we would stop occasionally to watch couples snogging in doorways. It became a source of great amusement to take the piss out of these courting couples.

"Hey mister, where did you find her Crufts?" we'd shout.

"Cheeky bastards. Go on, fuck off before I give yer a crack," was the usual reply.

"Put her down yer don't know where she's been" we'd continue.

Nige shouted at one couple in his most outraged voice, "Oh I say old chap, I have never seen anything so disgusting, fancy kissing something so ugly in public."

It took several attempts before we got the required response and one bloke chased after us through the town centre. "I'm gonna give you a right hiding, come here!" he snarled. We eventually ended up on the outskirts of town on a bridge near the river. We'd managed to shake off our determined pursuer. We had lost him earlier but would walk back until we saw him again and shout, "Oh giving up already, you wanker" and stick two fingers up at him. The chase would begin all over again and we would laugh hysterically at his pathetic attempts to catch us. The water glistened with the reflection of the street lights upon the surface, the wind swept gently across the river creating shimmering ripples that were slightly mesmerising to watch.

"Gotcha," squealed Ady as he pretended to push Nige off the bridge and into the water.

"Silly git, I could have fallen in," snapped Nige .

"Will you two pack it in," I said in my sternest voice as I spat into the water below.

"I'm bored," groaned Nige.

"You're always bored Nige. We've only been here two minutes; do you want to go home?" I asked.

"Naw, but let's do something," he pleaded.

"Well, if you can tell me what we can do on two quid I'd like to hear it," I shot back.

"Colditz , we could go to Colditz" said Nige excitedly.

Colditz was as uninviting as ever to the ordinary man in the street, but to us it was a giant adventure playground. Dark spooky corners, creaking floors and lift shafts that echoed our laughter as we dropped objects into its gaping black mouth. How could any child not find this a fun place to be?

"Give us a hand," begged Ady as he got his clothing stuck on a rusty nail as he scrambled through a hole we'd made in a door.

"Here," I said as I pulled at his arms and dragged him inside. "Oh fuck, I'm in for it now," he groaned as he looked at the huge tear I'd helped to make in his jumper. Nige giggled nervously.

"Come on you two," I said, ignoring Ady's plight as I disappeared up the stairs. The staircases within Colditz were pitch black at night, there were no windows and you would feel your way around the walls as you climbed each flight. It was not difficult to do, as by now, the position of any obstacles were mapped in our memories. This is why it came as a great surprise when I fell headlong over an object in my path.

"What the?" I grunted as I picked myself up.

"Ady, Nige come here, there's something up here," I shouted down the stairwell. There was a slight echo as my voice reverberated off the walls.

"What?" said Ady right in my ear. He frightened me to death as I had not realised he was by now beside me. I was glad it was so dark as my street cred would have taken a beating if Ady or Nige had seen me jump out of my skin. I could hear my heart pounding in my ears and was convinced they could probably hear it too. "Well what's up?" said Ady in a rather impatient manner.

"There's something here look," I said pointing rather stupidly. I could not see my own hand, it was so dark so Ady could not possibly know where the hell I was pointing!

"Wait, I've got some matches," declared Ady. The rustling noise made it evident he was searching through his pockets. The match slowly began to flicker to life as Ady struck it along the staircase wall.

"What is it?" asked Nige who had by now caught up and was somewhere behind Ady. Ady held the match between his fingers and lent closely towards what appeared to be a bundle of rags lying on the stairwell floor. I stepped forward and prodded at it with my foot.

"Shit" winced Ady as the match burnt his fingers and he dropped it to the floor.

"Quick light another," I ordered. Ady obliged holding the glowing match over my shoulder as he remained behind me. I could feel his heavy breathing on my neck and his free hand holding my arm. I blinked and screwed up my eyes in order to focus through the dim light. I gave the large bundle a sharp prod with my foot, it was hard to the touch and very heavy. I pushed again with more force and moved even closer as it began to roll over.

"FUCK ME!" I squealed as my eyes began to take in what was beneath my feet. I headed straight for the stairs. "Run," I shouted as I pushed Ady in my haste to get away. Ady fell backwards onto Nige and all three of us tumbled headlong down the stairs. I was the first to my feet and didn't wait for the others I just ran and ran downwards into the darkness, I had to escape.

I don't know when I stopped running, it must have been at least five minutes later, and then only because my lungs refused to feed my screaming body any more oxygen. I'd managed to put some distance between Ady, Nige and myself, and when they eventually caught me up I was seated on a wall nearly a mile away, my head in my hands, sweat pouring down my face and sucking in huge amounts of air in an effort to recover my composure.

"What," Ady stopped mid-sentence and drew breath, "What is it?" he said, a worried look in his eyes. Ady had never seen me scared before and this was enough to tell him this was serious.

"A dead bloke," I stammered between breaths.

"Serious?" said Ady.

"Damn fucking right I'm serious. He was dead alright, either that or he was doing a fucking good impression!" I snapped, by now my breath returning to normal.

"What we gonna do?" chipped in Nige who was seated on the wall at the side of me.

"You can do what yer like. I've had enough and I'm going home," I replied. "But we can't just leave him there," said Ady looking at me pleadingly.

"Well what do you want me to do, take him home and put him to bed," I shouted, the hint of sarcasm not lost on Ady and he sheepishly looked at the floor. Why was it I was always expected to come up with the answers? I didn't know what to do, after all it was not as though this was something that happened to me on a weekly basis.

Nige decided to be peacemaker. "Why don't we tell the Police Jack? It'll be alright. They can sort it out, can't they?" he asked in a rather hushed voice.

The thought of turning up at my house with a Police escort was not a thought I relished. I could just imagine the joy Marie would take in telling Dad when he phoned the next day.

"Listen, the both of you, we can't go to the Police, we are not supposed to be in there in the first place, are we?" I tried to reason.

"Well can't we just do it by phone, like they do on the telly. They'll never know it was us, will they?" piped Ady.

"What the fuck difference does it matter if we report it or not, it's not like they'll fucking revive him, he's dead you idiots," I snarled getting more than a little annoyed.

"Well what are we gonna do then?" asked a by now desperate Nige.

"Nothing, we never saw owt, did we?" I said rather menacingly.

"Okay" said Nige and Ady though a little reluctantly. I suppose I bullied them into doing what I wanted, I didn't care. I just couldn't face more disappointed looks from Dad. "One more thing tell nobody, do yer hear?" I finished Once again they both nodded, and we set off in the direction of our homes.

I didn't see Nige or Ady for the rest of the weekend and had no real desire to either. I needed time on my own to think things through. I couldn't get the image of that dead man out of my mind. It wasn't that I'd actually seen him that bothered me, it was the fact I'd touched him, and I felt contaminated. I hated that thought and no amount of soap could wash that feeling away. I spent most of Saturday and Sunday in my room. I would pace back and forth stopping occasionally to look out of my window. I half expected the Police to arrive at any given moment but thankfully they didn't. Marie was happy that I kept out of her way, and when I did venture downstairs I would just make a sandwich and return to my room. I would sit on my bed to eat it and then remember I'd touched that dead bloke and throw it back on the plate in disgust!

I should have had an idea that Monday was going to be a bitch of a day after I left the house and stood in the biggest dog turd imaginable and just to round things off, I missed the bus and had to run all the way to school. My late arrival meant the other kids had already made their way to class and the school yard was deserted. I made my way through the empty corridors and as I passed the various classrooms, I could hear teachers calling out registration, "Simmons" "Here Sir" "Mitchell" "Here Sir" and so on.

I got to my own classroom as registration had just finished. "Marriot, your late," said Mr Barker my form

82

teacher, as I opened the door.

"Sorry Sir, missed the bus," I offered, as I made my way to my seat. Ady grinned at me like the village idiot as I sat down beside him.

"Nice weekend? Do anything interesting? I was DEAD bored," he smirked emphasising the word dead in a manner that was obviously meant to be amusing.

"You knob," I smiled kicking him under the table. Nige just looked up from his desk and grinned like a Cheshire cat at me. I knew these two had been talking and the sudden change in their manner since Friday had me more than a little confused.

Break time was the usual thronging mass of kids hollering and whooping as they ran around the school yard like headless chickens. I had taken up my favourite spot at smoker's corner. "Got one for me?" asked Ady as he approached, his hands buried deep in his trouser pockets, head slightly bowed and a cheesy grin on his face. "Well what do yer know?" he said as he helped himself to a cigarette from the pack I held in my outstretched hand.

At that moment Nige came around the corner, his hair its usual unruly self and his clothes hanging on his body like they'd been put on without seeing an iron. "Nice one mate, you nearly got us there," he laughed as he pushed Ady in the chest with his hand and they both began laughing hysterically.

"What the fuck is up with you two?" I said sharply.

"A dead body, that was a good one," Ady gasped between laughs. Nige was just giggling and hanging on to Ady's shoulder tears of laughter streaking his face.

"You two are priceless, you think I made it all up, what kind of idiot would joke about something like that?" I barked. It really pissed me off that they thought all of this was a flaming joke. I had spent the whole weekend tearing my insides out at the thought of that body, the feel of it as I fell upon its decaying mass and the horror that tore deep at my conscience.

"Well if it is true show us it then," challenged Ady.

"You want to see it, do you?" I said in the heat of the moment, Okay tonight after school and bring a torch."

It was dark by the time we met up outside Colditz. I had wanted to meet earlier but Ady could not get out of the house until after he had eaten his tea. Apparently, it was like some kind of family tradition that they all sat down to eat and discussed the various events of the day.

"You two sure about this?" I croaked, my mouth dry, it was fear although I would not admit it to anyone else.

"Come on then," grinned Ady as he pushed back the old wooden boards on the ground floor entrance. He scrambled through the hole and I watched his feet disappear into the darkness as though swallowed by a giant open mouth.

"You coming or what?" said Ady his head now poked back out through the hole. Nige looked at me and I knew he was waiting for me to go. I didn't want to look like a Nancy, so I stepped forward taking a deep breath as I crawled on my knees through the boards Ady was holding open.

"Give me the torch then Ady," I demanded as I took it from his hand. "Nige, will you stop pulling on my coat. I can't fucking move," I said sharply. Nige didn't speak but loosened his grip, not totally he still needed the reassurance of being close. The torch lit up the mouldy walls of the stone staircase as we began to climb it, our shadows cast elongated figures to the front of us and my heart pounded a rhythmic thud, thud, thud in my ears. The landing where I'd found the body was reached in what seemed like seconds and as we were about to turn the corner I stopped abruptly. Nige bumped heavily into my back and Ady instinctively grabbed at my arm that held the torch.

"Are you two sure about this?" I asked in a rather more effeminate voice than usual.

"Go on" urged Ady as he shoved me forward. I held my breath and turned the corner fanning the light of the torch in front of me, I so did not want it to be true. I wanted it to be a trick of the light a mistake that we would laugh hysterically at and all would be well again. It wasn't, the light lit up the body in all its grisly detail. A middle-aged man, his face contorted in a death like grimace, his eyes open and staring. The smell was overpowering a cross between vomit and rotting meat. I took in the full horror. I didn't move. I was literally frozen to the spot, he hadn't moved since I had rolled him over with my foot and on the floor was a bloody hand print that the light had illuminated. I knew at once it was mine! The vomit that came out of my mouth and nose caught me by surprise and I inhaled sharply. The acidic liquid entered my lungs and I fell to my knees. My mind was racing, and all rational thought was lost; 'got to get out of here, got to get out of here,' I thought. I pulled myself up using the staircase wall and turned half running half falling down the staircase. Ady and Nige were not in front of me and at this time I didn't care I just wanted out. I tore back the wooden boards and threw myself out into the darkness of the night gulping mouthfuls of it's cold refreshing air. I picked myself up my legs moving as fast as they could carry me, and I ran and ran and ran. I didn't see Ady or Nige again that night and as I made my way home, I didn't give them a second thought. All I could see was that horrible image that was burned deeply into my mind. I can still close my eyes to this day and see him, it doesn't fill me with revulsion or the horror that it did then, why would it? I have since seen death on many occasions and merely felt relief, relief that it wasn't me!

I didn't go to school the next day I couldn't face it. I wanted to see Ady and Nige but couldn't face it. I just had a really numb feeling inside. It is hard to explain but it was as though nothing in my life mattered anymore. I had seen death and had grasped the realisation that inevitably whatever we do in life rich or poor, good or bad, that is where it would all end. I wondered the canal banks for most of the day stopping occasionally to smoke a cig and gaze into the muddy water. The rest of the day is a complete blank, my thoughts not rational or focused. I must have been on a kind of auto pilot as I appeared outside my house at precisely the time I would if I had been at school and just returned home. Marie was in the kitchen and barely looked up as I entered the back door, things were no better between us, but she was less confrontational since our Steve had given her the hard word, now she was merely indifferent to anything I did.

Chapter 6

Judgement

The arrival of the Police at the house was a surprise although I should have guessed that sooner or later, they would come calling.

"Mrs Marriot?" said the copper as the front door was opened by Marie. I was in the living room watching telly and could tell by the tone of voice that it was the boys in blue. I jumped out of the easy chair I was seated in and walked over to the window. I peered through the net curtains into the street, "shit" I said under my breath, as my suspicions were confirmed by the Police car parked outside the house.

"Jack," Marie shouted in a voice not as harsh as normal, but then she was good at that pretending to outsiders that she was a loving caring mother.

"You must be young Jack?" smiled one of the coppers as I walked into the kitchen where Marie had now taken them.

"Yep," I nodded in I suppose, quite a cocky manner. I was a teenager what else would they have expected?

"We need to ask you a few questions with regard to a sudden death we are investigating," continued the copper. "We should do this down the station Mrs Marriot," he said turning towards Marie.

"I can't go with him, I have a baby in bed," replied Marie. "You'll just have to take him, and his father can come down when he arrives home from work, is that okay?" she finished, pushing her greasy hair back in what she must have thought was a provocative manner.

"Yes that's fine, nodded the copper but his father must come, we cannot interview a minor without an adult," he continued.

"Oh he'll be straight there don't you worry," Marie said, her stare aimed in my direction.

"Right lets go, young man," said the other copper who up until this point had not uttered a word.

It didn't take a genius to work out what they wanted, after all I'd thought of little else lately. The ride to the Police station was conducted in silence. I was seated in the rear of the Panda car with the two coppers in the front. Occasionally, I would catch the copper who was driving glimpse at me in the rear-view mirror and just as quickly look away when I stared back at him. They were not giving anything away. I guess this was their way of building up the pressure for when they started their interview in order to catch me off guard, I was ready. We arrived at the local station after about fifteen minutes and entered the rear of the police compound via an electric gate that swung open as we approached. The car pulled to a stop by a metal cage that had an intercom fixed upon a pedestrian gate at the side.

"Right, out!" gestured the copper who had been seated in the front passenger seat, as he pulled open the rear door. I looked right into his face looking for a feint flicker of emotion but was met by a blank expression. He was around thirty years old and had a thin moustache and a pock marked complexion. He must have been over six feet tall but was rather fragile and lanky looking.

"Come on lad" Said the other copper as he walked around the car and began pressing the intercom on the gate. A buzzer sounded, and the door swung open. I was the first in followed by the copper who was driving. I knew he was right behind me as I could hear his jacket rustling as his arms moved when he walked. The corridor we entered was painted bright white and the overhead fluorescent lighting made you screw up your eyes. To my left mid-way up the white walls I noticed blood spatter. I looked down and traced its progress from the grey linoleum floor tiles hitting the gloss skirting boards and upwards to where it caught my eye. I wondered how it got there but before I could think too deeply I was ushered through a door at the end of the corridor. There was a large desk straight in front of me, it was about chest height and behind it stood another copper. He was in a white shirt no jacket and the sleeves rolled back to the cuffs and about fifty years old.

"What we got ere then?" he remarked as he looked over the top of the desk his narrow eyes boring into me.

"Jack Marriot, the sudden death Sarge" said one of the coppers from behind me. I was by this time engrossed in my own thought and as crazy as it sounds it was not the body of that old man. I was trying to work out if the copper behind the desk was stood on something or was he really tall? I moved to my right trying to look round the back of the desk, perhaps he was stood on a box?

"Take him to interview room 1, and one of you stay with him, are his parents on their way?" asked the copper behind the desk as I was being led out of the room.

"Yeah Sarge, Dads on the way after work," the tall lanky copper shouted back over his shoulder as the door began to close behind us. I turned long enough to watch the door swing closed and through the narrowing gap I saw behind the desk, it was raised up about two feet and the copper standing behind it didn't look so big anymore. I grinned to myself and stifled a little giggle.

"I'll leave yer here Ken, I'm off for a cuppa, want one?" said the lanky copper to the other as we approached a door marked Interview Room 1.

"No yer alright, I'll find you when I'm done here," answered the other copper. The interview room was less than homely, a shell of a room with a table four chairs no windows and oddly enough cord carpet on the walls. My over-active imagination deduced this was probably to drown out the sounds as you were beaten into a confession.

"Take a seat, you may be here a while," grunted the copper as he pointed to a chair. I took a real good look at him. I'd not really bothered up until now. He was about forty years old, a large black moustache hung precariously under his nose. I thought that a sudden sneeze could blow it right off.

"You want owt kid?" he asked as he put his hand on my shoulder. This was the first time he had shown any kind of consideration and for a milli-second I thought he was going to smile and then it was gone. I didn't answer I just shook my head. "Well if yer change yer mind..." he didn't finish the sentence.

The door behind him opened. "Sorry Ken, I was looking for an empty interview room," said a voice behind me. I turned to look. and in the doorway, stood a young female police officer. She had blonde hair, piercing blue eyes and a golden sun tan. This immediately made me think of her relaxing by the side of a swimming pool in a tiny bikini, sipping sangria. I soon came back to reality as I noticed behind her stood a slim figure head bowed, it was Ady! The door closed as quickly as it opened and Ady never looked up. I don't know if he even saw me, but he looked petrified. I seemed to sit in that room for an age. The silence would only be broken by the scraping of a chair as either myself or the copper moved about in order to stop our arses from going numb.

Dad's arrival was everything I had expected. He swept into the interview room ushered by a copper I'd not seen before and totally ignoring the copper seated with me launched into a verbal onslaught.

"I don't bloody believe this, what the hell have you done now?" he said leaning over me in a menacing fashion. I was about to answer but he didn't give me a chance. "I'm so ashamed of you dragging me down here, I just wonder where you get all this from," he finished, shaking his head.

After Dad was settled down in the seat beside me the copper who had been sat with me cleared his throat and introduced himself. "I'm police constable Mc Kinley and this is my colleague PC Hallam he said, pointing behind him as he looked at my father. "We need to talk to young Jack with regard to a sudden death we are investigating." The colour drained from my father's face and I watched his hand close into a fist under the table, the vein in his temple began to pulsate and I knew he was trying to hold his anger in.

"What you think he killed someone?" Dad said in a rather shocked tone.

"No , no not for one minute, Mr Marriot. It may just be that Jack can help us with some information in order to get a clearer picture," replied Pc Mc Kinley. Dad's fist began to relax under the table and my heart stopped pounding in my ears. It was odd, but I hadn't realised it was beating so loudly until that point. "We are going to conduct an interview if you are happy to do so Mr Marriot, you can request a solicitor be present if you think your son should be represented legally, although I must also inform you your son is not under arrest and at this stage it would appear he has not committed anything to be arrested for," finished Mc Kinley. Dad nodded his head indicating he didn't want a Solicitor and that the interview could commence.

Pc Hallam approached the table and pulled up a chair next to Pc Mc Kinley. He reached into a drawer under the desk and pulled out a file with the words 'witness statements' written upon it in Black marker pen.

"Right young Jack," said Pc Mc Kinley as he leaned over towards me his, face now a foot from my own, his breath smelled of garlic and of the mints he'd tried to cover up the garlic smell with. He then raised his arms in a stretching motion and leant back in his chair as he continued. "We have found the body of a vagrant who sadly died in a disused building down by the canal." He paused he didn't want an answer he was just looking into my eyes for any sign of guilt or emotion. "We are also led to believe that you and your friends found this man some days ago and did not see fit to report it to the police, would you like to tell me why?"

I was more than a little shaken at this and although I wanted to scream at him, "What do you bloody think?" all I could manage was a shrug of my shoulders.

Dad leant over and put his hand on my arm. "Listen son you must tell them everything, be a man and if you've done something wrong, we'll deal with it, but tell the truth," he coaxed. The truth was always one of life's mysteries to me, people always said stupid things like tell the truth and you'll feel better, tell the truth and clear your conscience, the truth will out, Bollocks! Whenever I'd told the truth I got a good hiding or deeper in trouble, it seemed to me you didn't tell the truth you just told people what they wanted to hear and in a fashion they wanted to hear it.

"I was scared," I mumbled, it was worthy of an Oscar, my head bowed, and I swear if I thought I'd needed to, I could have managed a tear.

"But what did you have to be scared about? You hadn't done anything wrong," asked Pc Mc Kinley in a much softer tone. Like candy from a baby I thought to myself.

"I don't know, just was," I answered in a voice somewhat childlike for my years. "You tell us exactly what happened, and Pc Hallam will write it down, in your own time son," he urged.

So that was that I spent the next three hours telling how Ady, Nige and myself had been playing in Colditz and stumbled on the dead bloke. Pc Hallam wrote ferociously on his statement sheets and sometimes when I got carried away, he would have to tell me to stop whilst he caught up. It was odd how in the beginning I had hardly said a word but once I'd got going you couldn't shut me up. I felt important everybody was listening to me, just me and it felt good.

I left the Police station a different way, we came out at the front, Dad pushing me out into the street with his hand in the small of my back. I didn't say anything it seemed best to let Dad start any conversation we were going to have, that way I could gauge what response was needed in order to avoid a clout when we got home.

"Sometimes I bloody despair of you, son," said Dad his hand now placed on the top of my head as we walked, me slightly in front. "There's never a dull moment with you around, come on yer bugger," he finished as he pulled me towards him and ruffled my hair. I knew I'd been forgiven, and Dad reinforced this by stopping at the pub where he bought me Coke and crisps. I remained outside seated on a wooden bench to the rear of the pub. I could see Dad standing at the bar through the top of the frosted window. He was standing talking to another bloke and they were laughing hysterically.

It must have been about a month later when the letter arrived. It was from the coroner's officer and I'd been summoned to attend at an inquest. I didn't know what an inquest was or what a coroner really did but Ady and Nige had got a letter too and it all seemed quite exciting, besides we also got a day off school in order to attend. Ady, Nige and I had discussed what we were going to say at length and in the end it was decided that the truth was probably the best bet, in any event it appeared that nobody really had a concern with what we were doing there and just wanted to hear the nitty gritty. Nige was happy to go along with whatever Ady and I decided, he was still in the doghouse for confessing all to his mum and was trying hard to gain our forgiveness. There wasn't that much to forgive we'd not really got into any bother, the Police were okay and even Dad had been no problem after he knew the facts, but we didn't let Nige off that easy and there was lots of mileage still to be had!

The inquest was a little like attending court all though I couldn't know that at the time. Ady, Nige and I sat in a side room with our respective parents and nervously looked at our feet. It was more than a little weird, nobody spoke a word; all the parents did was smile or nod at each other but never uttered a sound, not unless it was to say, "Adrian stop shuffling", "Jack sit up straight", you know the usual parent child banter. After half an hour or so the glass panelled side door opened and a small bloke in a pinstriped suit with metal rimmed round glasses poked his head in.

"Jack Marriot?" he said in a cheerful but polite manner. Marie pushed me out of my seat. "Here," I declared in a rather loud voice that surprised even me.

93

"This way lad, follow me," he smiled as he led me into the adjoining room. I felt my throat tighten and all my confidence disappear as I surveyed the unfamiliar surroundings. It was a very large open plan room, a man whom I thought was a judge like I'd seen in films, was sitting right at the front and everyone else was facing towards him, he was seated higher than the rest of the room and was looking down like a spectator in a private box at the theatre. Some of the people facing the judge turned to look at me as I walked the length of the room. I didn't look back at them. I just put my head down and wished it was all over. "This way lad," said the man who'd collected me from the waiting room as he ushered me to a small wooden box a little like the one our headmaster stood in at morning assembly. I climbed the two stairs and stood at the top I was now the same height as the judge at the front and gave him a nervous smile as I settled myself, to my surprise he smiled right back.

"Please take a seat young man," he nodded at me. I had not noticed the chair directly behind me until I was told to sit down. I enthusiastically threw myself into it nearly toppling over backwards as I did so. I reached out, my arms flaying around and eventually regained my composure. The sounds of stifled laughter bounced around the room and only the judge clearing his throat whilst looking disapprovingly around the room brought about a sudden silence. I peered over the top of the wooden sides of the cubicle about to offer my apologies, my eyes meeting the judge as we were on the same level, and he winked at me, bloody winked. I didn't imagine it, it was a sly one a bit like when Dad was telling me off in front of Marie for something stupid and when she couldn't see, he'd do it, it was like that, so I winked back, and he smiled, this is so going to be a doddle, I thought to myself.

The man who I thought was the judge introduced himself to me and explained what each person in the court room did, he was called the Coroner and it was a Coroner's inquest.

His job was to find out how people died. I thought how simple his job must be, you could just visualize a scene where a man had been run over by a bus and they had an inquest. It would be highly unlikely he died of anything other than sixteen tons of steel crushing the very life from him, or the body pulled from the canal, in my imagination I drifted off. I was the coroner, "So he was pulled from the bottom of the canal; at this time he was not breathing and had no pulse?" I'd ask. "That's true your honour," they'd reply, "This man drowned!" I'd declare triumphantly, next case please.

"Jack, Jack," the calling of my name brought me back to reality and I looked up as the Coroner spoke. "Now then young Jack he said in a very soft and friendly tone, you and your friends found the body of the deceased is that correct?"

"Er yes Sir," I said quietly.

"And can you tell us exactly what happened? In your own time," he urged as he leant across his desk cocking his head a little and cupping his chin in his hands. The whole story tumbled out, how we had found him and then gone back a second time because the others didn't believe me. Occasionally the Coroner would stop me and ask the odd question, where was the man on the stairs? Did I move him? Why did I not tell anyone? It was pretty painless really. When I wasn't sure what to say, I just said I didn't remember or that I was scared, and this seemed to do the trick.

"Thank you, Jack, you've been very helpful said the coroner, you may go now."

I was stunned it was over so quickly and sat motionless in the chair. "Jack, thank you," repeated the coroner as he motioned with his head that I could go. I jumped to my feet skipped down the two steps and grinned from ear to ear, this time I looked anyone in the eye who glanced in my direction as I left the room.

Chapter 7

Mending bridges

After my appearance at the Coroner's inquest I had decided it was time to behave myself. Dad was getting really pissed off with me and Marie was happy to use whatever ammunition I was stupid enough to give her. I knuckled down to my work at school and kept my nose clean. Ady and Nige thought I'd had a personality transplant and were even brave enough to take the micky out of me on the odd occasion. I restarted my boxing career with a vengeance; it kept me off the streets and channelled any hatred or anger Marie managed to instil into me. It was going to be a new start for me and after what seemed like a lifetime, I had begun to let myself be happy again.

"You gonna hit that bag or make bloody love to it," shouted Dave from inside the ring where he was coaching two of the other lads. I was leaning heavily on the punch bag, both gloved hands wrapped in an embrace around it. I had just completed a marathon session of ten three-minute rounds and battered the very life out of it. Beads of sweat ran down my face and my lungs gulped in large amounts of air but still not quick enough to allow me to stand upright. "Get yourself gloved up Jack and get over ere," continued Dave as he turned away from me. I slowly let go of the bag and walked across the gym past a few other kids who were pounding the bags or doing squat thrusts and speed skipping, getting in the ring for sparring was always the best part of training and I would have happily forgone all the other training and sparred all night.

I loved the ring, the feel of the cold clammy gloves on my hands, the battle of speed, skill and cunning that you played out with the other boxer. I felt alive in the ring. It was hard not to, the sting of cold leather in your face soon told you, you were a living breathing creature. "Move forward Danny, go on don't be frightened" barked Dave from the ropes. "And you take it easy," he threw at me for good measure. Danny was a nice lad about the same age as me, he'd been boxing for about six months and although he had quite a natural talent, he did not like getting hit. This could obviously be a bit of a setback if you wanted to have a career as a boxer. It was not unusual to find this trait in most people when they first put on the gloves and in time, they would gradually learn to deal with it. Whoosh a mighty right hand sailed over my head as I slipped low, whoosh came the left as I came back up. I parried it with my right hand and poked a light but accurate jab into Danny's nose. He stepped back and held his gloved hand to his eyes as they filled with water.

"Keep going Danny, move and box, move and box," encouraged Dave. I could have stepped forward and hit poor Danny with a combination, but this was sparring, and you never did that, besides a bully I was not, and I liked Danny. After sparring I decided to go for a run. I was in the changing rooms lacing up my trainers when Danny walked in.

"Going for a jog?" he asked as I looked up from the floor.

"Yeah, you wanna come?" I replied raising my eyebrows.

"That'd be great give me a sec to put my runners on," he beamed as he reached into his locker. The streets were fairly quiet as we ran. It was about eight-thirty at night, the rain had kept most people indoors and it was by now getting dark. The wet pavement below our feet made a squeaking noise as our rubber soles gripped them, we didn't speak we just ran. I could hear Danny's breathing long and deep a couple of lengths behind me, we'd run a good two miles before we exchanged words.

"You in the schoolboys this year then?" said Danny between breaths.

"Yeah, think so, it's up to Dave, I fucked about a lot with missing training last season and he might not let me, just to prove a point," I replied.

"Can't see that happening," said Danny. "Dave is always going on about you, he says Twiglet's going places, you Jack my words."

"Dave said that," I said, trying not to sound too excited.

"Yeah he thinks you're gonna be his next prospect. I heard him talking to the trainer from Halifax Star at my last fight," gasped Danny by now getting out of breath.

"Just one thing Danny," I grinned in his direction.

"What?" he answered. "Don't ever call me fucking Twiglet again," and we both laughed our happiness spilling into the dark night air.

Danny became one of my regular sparring partners and a friend into the bargain. I had stopped hanging around with Ady and Nige after school as I was now spending every spare moment at the gym. Ady and Nige had run their course we were heading in opposite directions and although we would still share the odd laugh and a cig behind the teachers backs, we all knew things would never be as they were before.

"You're getting as bad as me," I smiled as I walked into the changing rooms to find Danny already there.

"I figure I need the extra training," he laughed. "What's your excuse?"

I didn't answer just flung my bag on the bench and began to get changed.

"Jack you in there?" It was Dave. "What?" I shouted out of the changing room door, he didn't answer. This was one of Dad's tricks; he wouldn't answer because he wanted me to go to him. Why the hell he didn't just shout "Jack come here, I want you," I don't know.

"Yeah Dave," I said as I poked my head around the gym door. "Come here don't be shy," beckoned Dave from the other side of the room. Dave was fiddling with some papers in his hands and as I approached, he didn't look up.

"Here get these signed by yer parents, okay?" he said as he held out two forms without turning round.

"What they for?" I enquired.

"Bloody hell, they teach you nowt at school, read the bloody thing and stop asking me stupid bloody questions will you. Now git out of here, the others will be here soon," he grunted still without turning around. I sat on the changing room bench and quickly scanned the form Dave had given me it read:

Dear parent or guardian,

I am pleased to inform you that Jack has been selected for the National schoolboy's boxing competition. It is a requirement that Jack attends a weigh-in and medical examination at Belle Isle School on the 21st November at 11.30 am. I would appreciate it if you could fill in the attached form giving your permission for him to attend and also to partake in the forthcoming event.

Yours Sincerely
D.Curran Trainer

"Look Danny, he's chosen me to fight in the Schoolboys," I squealed jumping off the bench and running round the changing room.

Danny snatched the form from my hand and read it quickly. "Lucky bugger, well done mate," he smiled trying to hide his own disappointment at not being chosen. I knew he was jealous but didn't stop to think. I was too excited for myself and at that moment nothing could dampen my spirits. Training seemed to last forever that night and kids kept coming up to me either to congratulate me on being chosen or to tell me they had been chosen too. In total out of our gym seven had been put forward for the championships out of eighty kids.

It must have been around ten o clock, when I arrived home the crumpled forms held in my hand in what can only be described as a Vulcan death grip. I dumped my kit bag on the kitchen floor and still wearing my coat burst into the living room. Dad was asleep in front of the fire and Marie was lying on the sofa stroking his hair.

"Shhh," said Marie placing her fingers to her lips and nodding in Dad's direction. I quietly eased myself into the armchair at the opposite end of the room letting out a contented sigh. It was hard to hide my happiness and try as I might I could not prevent a smile escaping my lips.

"What you looking so smug about?" asked Marie in a whisper.

"Nowt, just happy," I whispered back. I was dying to stand up and yell "I'm in the schoolboys - I'm in the Schoolboys," but waking Dad from a nap could be more dangerous than teasing a rattlesnake.

"You got homework to do?" asked Marie again in a hushed tone.

"Yeah," I replied climbing out of my chair and heading to the kitchen. Home work was one of those things that bothered me greatly. If we couldn't learn enough in School time surely, we should give it up and get a job, it made no real sense.

I spent the next few weeks training hard. The anticipation of the Schoolboys kept me busy physically as well as emotionally. I was convinced I could go all the way and wanted that winning trophy more than anything. I wasn't to know I would never fight in that competition and that fate was about to deal me a terrible blow.

It is surely better that we can't tell the future because at least we still have hope!

"Come on son, work, you can do better than that," encouraged Dad as he held up the punch pads. We'd been in the cellar for over an hour and he'd not let me rest once. The sweat was pouring off me and my breathing was heavy.

"Okay, okay, let's see how good you've really got," Dad grinned, "Put on the gloves!" Dad had been a really good fighter in his day and was what Dave would call a dangerous bastard, not really a boxer but a fighting instinct and cunning that could catch even the most accomplished boxer off guard. I slowly backed away as Dad began stalking me a grin on his face from ear to ear.

"What's the matter, yer not scared of your old Dad are yer?" he teased. I shot out two quick jabs both landed one to the nose one to the forehead.

"Ha, Ha," he smiled, caught me that time. I knew my success would be short lived. Dad seemed to thrive on pain and would gladly let me pummel his face for an eternity just waiting for the one moment, the moment when I left myself open. Crack I didn't see it coming. I'd got cocky dancing and weaving jabbing my left hand into his face and smiling. I fell back into the cellar wall a trickle of blood running out of my nose. How did he always manage it, whenever we sparred he would always bloody my nose. It never seemed to matter how many times I hit him, whenever we walked up those cellar steps and into the kitchen he had the complexion of someone who'd just taken an evening constitutional and I always, always had a bloody nose.

"Are you okay son?" he said ruffling my hair with his gloved hand and pulling me close to his chest. As he let me go I could see the blood from my nose had stained his vest.

"Aw look at that Marie's not gonna be happy," I grinned pointing to his chest. Dad reacted by looking down and as he did I put my left hand round the back of his head and hit him full in the nose with my right hand. I would not be the only one leaving the cellar with a bloody nose on that day!

"You little shit," he said with a look of amusement on his face and then began chasing me around the cellar. I would duck and weave and cuff his ears as I moved out of the way laughing hysterically. When Dad got sick of chasing me, he charged head down throwing me to the ground where he jumped on top of me and we both laughed until we cried. This was a good day.

I continued to train hard and it was noticed by everyone. I even started getting good reports from school and was in serious danger of becoming the school swot. When school had ended, I would run all the way home as fast as I could.

I'd decided that if I was to be in peak physical fitness, I would run as much as I could. I'd even increased my morning run to eight miles. Marie pretty much left me alone. She had no real reason to get on my back because I was never in the house. The constant training and running kept me exactly where she wanted me, out of her way.

I very rarely saw our Steve anymore, he avoided the house wherever possible and would meet up with Dad in a local pub in order to see him. Dad told me he was doing well and had moved into a flat with a girl he'd met. I was dead jealous. Why did growing up take so long?

I remember the one day Steve did come to the house. I'd just run home from school and as I turned the corner I noticed a car parked where Dad's usually was. It was an old Cortina a kind of mucky brown and appeared to be held together with rust and epoxy filler. I approached the car and peered into the side window cupping my hands over my eyes to cut out the suns glare. The inside was lined with fur including the ceiling, the steering wheel had a leather cover and the gear knob was in the shape of a boxing glove. I wondered whose it was until our Steve crept up behind me and shouted, "Hey what you doing with me car!"

"Fuck me, our kid, I nearly shit myself, don't fucking do that again," I said as I hugged him. I think he was shocked that I'd actually hugged him. In truth I was too, it was a spontaneous gesture that left us both a little embarrassed.

"You want a ride or what?" Steve said as he gained his composure.

"Yeah please" I replied my voice showing my obvious excitement. I always smile when I think back to that day. I was so proud of my big brother. He had his own car and whilst it may not have been new, I thought it was fantastic.

"See the boxing glove?" Steve said pointing at the gear knob as we sped along. I got that 'cause I knew you'd like it and when anyone asks me about it I tell them our kid's gonna be the next world champ."

I flushed with embarrassment and turned to look out of

the window. Steve had never paid me a compliment until then. I think in his own way he was saying although he didn't see me, he hadn't forgotten about me. All good things come to an end, and Steve eventually dropped me off on the corner. As I climbed out, he lowered his head to look me in the eye. "You take care, life's a bitch but not forever."

Dad was sat in the kitchen, it was Friday and he always finished early when he was working locally. "Did you see Steve and his new car ?" he asked already knowing the answer. I knew Dad had had a drink or two, he always had a look in his eyes that was a little softer than usual.

"Yeah he took me for a spin," I said excitedly.

"Go get the gloves on, we've just got time for a bit of sparring before you go training," he grinned as he stood up. Sparring with Dad when he was sober was bad enough. He gave no quarter that I was only a child, his reasoning was if I could handle him nobody else would get near me. In his drunken state I knew I was in for a rough ride. Dad was not malicious but believed a man should be just that, a MAN. The cellar was always damp and the flaking white emulsion on the walls seemed to hold its musky odour. I laced up one glove and Dad tied the other.

"You ready then?" he smirked as he went to swipe me lovingly. I slipped under it and jabbed him in the nose.

"I was born ready, old man," I laughed as I moved my feet in a display of footwork that would have made Muhammad Ali envious.

"Oh old man, am I? try this for size," he teased as he tried to hit me with an uppercut. It was easy to avoid my reflexes were so sharp I swear I could have caught a bullet. My evasive action spurred Dad on even more and he became determined to catch me. He began by rushing at me wildly throwing uppercuts, crosses and hooks in all different combinations. I was good, and this was probably the first time I actually believed it. Whoosh a right hook sailed over my forehead as I slipped under it, I could hear the air part as it sliced through it. Bang, bang, I shot out my jab hitting Dad

103

twice on the nose in quick succession it began to bleed. Dad was not deterred and kept up his onslaught through gritted teeth.

I don't know quite how it happened but somewhere along the way what began as sparring turned into full scale war. I guess the drink had taken over. The punches kept coming and the more I avoided them using my jab and footwork the more it appeared that Dad wanted to kill me. The punches that missed me were delivered at full power and I knew if I got caught it was lights out for sure. I began to panic and in desperation I fought back as though my life depended on it. This was a mistake, I was my father's son and what was in me was in him ten-fold, a realisation you don't quite comprehend at the tender age of fourteen. I slipped low and thundered a right hook into Dads body. I could hear the breath escape from his lungs and the cellar for a brief moment smelled of the beer he'd consumed earlier. An involuntary grunt echoed around the room as Dad shrugged off the effects of the body blow and continued forward, no matter what I threw he kept coming and I knew that my number was up. I don't even recall the actual punch, just a blackness that enveloped me.

"Son, son you alright?" I opened my eyes and shook my head in order to clear it, everything was spinning, and Dads voice sounded as though he was calling from afar.

"Talk to me son, you okay?" Dad repeated.

"Yeah, I'll live," I replied trying to climb to my feet, my legs wouldn't work properly and began to buckle.

"Whoa there champ, easy does it, easy does it," said Dad as he caught me round the waist and pulled me to him.

The following day I got up and as usual went for my morning run. I liked running on a Saturday morning, the roads seemed even quieter than usual. I also knew that Dad would be waiting at the kitchen table with a cup of tea in hand when I returned.

"Good run?" Dad smiled as I opened the back door into the kitchen.

"Yeah best time ever," I said cockily as I shadow boxed around the kitchen table. "Fancy a few rounds sparring?" I continued. I had quickly forgotten the pasting I'd had the day before and anyway I think we'd both realized that we got more than a little carried away.

"You don't mind if I give it a miss, do you son? Your old man feels a little rough this morning," he finished. I didn't think much of his refusal I put it down to sheepishness after the knockout he gave me the day before. I only wish to this day I'd been right! I noticed a distinct change in Dad over the preceding weeks he no longer offered to spar with me and seemed to have a constant look of determination on his face. I would occasionally catch him grimace when he stood up quickly. When he saw me looking at him, he would force a smile and wink at me, this was enough to convince me I was imagining things and I quickly put it out of my mind.

It was a Monday morning when I came back from my run that I found Dad sitting in the kitchen he was leaning over the table breathing heavily beads of perspiration running down his face. This time I was not fooled by the smile he threw me though gritted teeth.

"You look bloody awful Dad you alright?" I asked, the concern clear in my young voice.

"Oh I'm a little under the weather, I have a bit of an ache in my side," he said as he straightened up putting his hand on his ribs as though to show me.

"Yer getting old," I tried to joke.

"Yeah, guess I'm just a bit past it, and maybe it's taking me a while to get over that punch to the body you gave me the other week," he smiled.

"Perhaps it's a cracked rib and will be okay with a bit of a rest," I offered.

"I'm sure, I'm sure," he repeated as though he was trying to convince me, he hadn't.

I worried all day at school, so much so I was bollocked by every teacher in every lesson I attended. I felt an enormous amount of unease. I don't know entirely what it was that

105

made me feel that way, but I just could not shake it off.

"Wotcha Jack," said Ady as he approached me behind the gym where I was having a smoke.

"Alright," I said in a matter of fact way that indicated conversation was something I didn't want.

Ady never was that bright and continued anyway. "What yer been up to? Not seen yer fer ages."

I shrugged my shoulders and took a drag of my cigarette.

"Want to meet up after school?" he continued.

"Can't mate, got training, my first round of the schoolboys is only four weeks away," I said, still looking at the floor.

"How is the training going? Working yer way up to twenty a day," he laughed pointing at my cigarette. He had a point I hadn't had a smoke in weeks and here I was puffing away for England. I threw the butt on the floor and stood on it triumphantly.

"Gotta go mate, see ya," I called over my shoulder without looking back. The school bell was a more welcome sound on that day than any other I can remember. I ran the few miles home in a sprint, I even beat the kid's home that had got the bus. I gingerly opened the gate into the back yard and as I climbed the six stone steps to the back door, under my breath I said a small prayer "Please God let Dad be alright."

"Where's Dad?" I spluttered before I'd even got through the door. Marie was stood at the sink washing up.

"In bed," came the reply. I threw my bag and coat on the hall floor and bounded the stairs two at a time.

"Don't disturb him," shouted Marie, but it was too late. I burst into the bedroom. Dad was sitting up drinking tea and reading a paper.

"Okay son?" he smiled, "Where's the fire?"

"You okay, what did the doctor say?" I spluttered still out of breath from my run home.

"Oh it's nothing; he thinks it's a cracked rib, he gave me some painkillers and told me to rest," he answered.

106

I broke into a broad grin a wave of relief passing over me. "See I'm just too fast for yer, yer need to be retiring, after all I don't want people thinking I beat up old men," I teased.

The conversation was cut short by Marie. "I told you not to disturb your father, he needs to rest, now get out," she said pointing at the door. I looked at Dad on my way out and he threw me one of his sly winks. Everything was going to be fine and as I made my way downstairs, I stopped to pat Buster who was making his way up.

"It's okay boy, it's okay," I smiled at him as I ruffled the fur on his neck, he nuzzled me with his big wet nose and everything was once again good with the world.

My happiness was very short lived. Although Dad rested for a whole week he didn't seem to be getting any better. I could tell he was in pain although he hid it really well. I also knew Dad could stand more pain than a bunch of Rugby prop forwards and for it to show in his face meant it must have been severe indeed.

It was one Friday when I came home from school, I rushed straight up to Dads bedroom, but the bed was empty. I rushed around the house calling out, but it was silent. My mind raced, and all manner of nightmares began to take shape, where was he? Why had nobody told me they were going anywhere? It was some three hours later when Dad and Marie came home. I was nearly distraught my imagination torturing me to tears. Marie was clutching my baby brother and rushed upstairs to change his nappy.

"Where you been?" I demanded as Dad eased himself into his chair in the living room. He would have had to have been blind not to tell I'd been crying but if he saw it, it was never mentioned.

"I've been to the hospital for some tests son, it's nothing to worry about they just want to find out what's wrong, so I can get better," he said in a quieter voice than normal.

"You are alright, aren't you?" I pleaded as I sat on the floor beside his chair looking up into his face.

"I'll be back sparring in a few weeks you'll see," he said

as he reached out and stroked my head gently. I put my head against his knee and wrapped my arms around his leg and there I stayed a tear falling from my face onto the carpet. I never wanted that moment to end, no words were said but in that moment more love was shared by us both than we'd ever shown each other, I didn't need to say I loved him he knew.

Chapter 8

Misery

A week later Dad was sent a letter from the hospital. I found it on the sideboard in the kitchen and when nobody was around, I gingerly slipped it out of the envelope and began to read it.

Dear Mr Marriot

After your recent examination and biopsy you were informed the results would be forwarded to your General practitioner. We would however like to discuss these in person with yourself and would request you attend the hospital on the 9th of May at 2.30pm where a meeting has been arranged with Mr Purcell the Oncology consultant. If this is not convenient please telephone the department on the number above and we will endeavour to reschedule your appointment.

I placed the letter back in the envelope, my hands were shaking, and I could hear my heart thumping. I knew this was not a good sign, a hospital would not request you to attend unless there was something seriously wrong. I put the letter back neatly and climbed the stairs to my bedroom a numb feeling taking over my whole body. I lay on my bed staring at the ceiling my eyes gradually filling with tears. 'Oh God please, please don't let anything happen to my Dad,' I pleaded. I never mentioned the letter to Dad or Marie and in turn they never mentioned it to me. I know now that Dad was only trying to protect me, but at the time, I could not understand how I was excluded from what was happening. I tortured myself for days and nights up in my bedroom, crying until my head was fit to burst, but like them when I was in their presence, I smiled and pretended everything was fine.

The day of Dad's hospital appointment grew nearer but still nothing had been said to me and as I lay on my bed one night I decided it was time to take matters in my own hands. Moving silently in order not to wake anyone I crept downstairs to find the letter from the hospital. It had been moved from the sideboard, but my frantic searching was rewarded when I found it in Marie's handbag. I strained my ears in case I'd been heard moving around but even Buster had not stirred. I opened the envelope quickly took out the letter and hurriedly copied down the information I would need.

Finally the day arrived. I got up went for my run as was usual, ate breakfast and headed off to school. I had no intention of going to school, but I had to keep up appearances.

The walk into town was a long one but my mind was a jumble of thoughts and this kept me occupied as I walked robotically in the general direction of the hospital. The roads were busy with the usual morning traffic and people going about their business. I was invisible as the rest of the world went by wrapped up in their own thoughts and troubles. I reached inside my school bag and felt around for the pack of cigarettes I knew were inside. I took out the pack extracted a cigarette and lit it, I took a deep drag and looked around for somewhere to sit. The grass verge was soft and a little wet from the early morning dew, I didn't care a wet arse was the least of my worries at the time. I sat for what must have been a couple of hours engrossed in my own thoughts and chain smoking one cigarette after another. I wanted to talk to someone, anyone, to tell them I was scared, that I was hurting and then it came to me Our Steve!

I knew Steve was working at a hotel in the centre of the city but for the life of me I could not remember the name. I stood up, brushing the seat of my pants and began to pace back and forth on the pavement scratching my head as I tried to recall its name. The passing motorists must have thought I'd completely lost the plot mumbling to myself as they sped past and occasionally banging my head with a closed fist. I began walking again not in any real rush just methodically and deliberately in the right direction of town.

I eventually arrived in the city centre to find it was really busy. I'd not been into town during the working day and the amount of activity distracted me for a moment. There were office workers carrying briefcases and dressed up to the nines, buses, lots of buses all holding what appeared to be hundreds of people. I would watch enthralled as a bus ground to a halt and spewed people out onto the pavement, no sooner had their feet touched the pavement than they were off in a thousand different directions. A pigeon landed by my feet and seemed to be looking at me. I bent down to try and coax it nearer, but it flapped angrily and headed skyward.

'The Queens,' that was it, I remembered. My thoughts drifted back to a conversation I overheard on the phone. Marie was standing in the kitchen, the phone glued to her ear, talking to her sister. "Yeah he's moved out gone to work as a chef in a hotel, the Queens I think." That was it I jumped up and down laughing. I'd find our Steve, he'd understand! I then began trawling the city centre for an hour or so in search of the Queens hotel. I'd heard of it but had no idea as to what direction it was in. It would have made sense to ask someone, but I was not thinking straight, and everything was a little confused.

"What time is it mate?" I asked a stranger as he walked by.

"One O'clock" he replied as he continued walking.

Shit I had to find him soon I thought and quickened my walk to a steady run. I must have run the entire length and breadth of the city but to no avail and in the end I was so frustrated I began to cry. The tears ran down my face splashing onto the pavement as I ran now desperately, hoping at any given moment the hotel would come into view.

"You alright?" enquired an elderly lady as I slumped on a wall outside the bus station.

"I need to find the Queens hotel" I whimpered my frustration apparent.

"Oh is that all, look," she said, pointing in front of me. I looked and gradually focused my eyes to where she was pointing. In the distance I could see a flag blowing in the breeze it read QUEENS HOTEL!

The Queens hotel was a very grand affair. I had never stayed in a hotel and momentarily stood frozen to the spot as I approached the front entrance. It had huge marble pillars that seemed to hold up the entire building, there were flags of at least ten different countries flying from several masts that pointed out from the roof at a forty-five-degree angle. I wondered which countries they represented but could only work out four, France, America, Germany and the United Kingdom. The front entrance was at the top of a flight of marble steps and had a large revolving door of stainless steel and smoked glass. Outside stood a man in a concierge's uniform. The uniform was burgundy in colour with gold piping running down the outside of the arms and down both legs, it was completed with a black top hat again with gold piping around the rim, he looked a right ponce!

I pulled myself together and began to climb the steps two at a time. I heard the sound of someone clearing their throat and as I looked up, I could see the concierge moving in front of the revolving doors in order to block my path.

"And where do you think you're going young man?" he said with more than a hint of attitude.

"Inside," I said cockily and ducked under his arm and into the revolving doors, this was a mistake, the bastard put his foot in the door and jammed the bloody thing. There I was trapped in the entrance neither in nor out. The concierge began to try and push the door the other way in order to force me backwards and back out onto the steps. I didn't give in that easy and jammed my foot on the bottom of the glass door thus preventing him rotating the door and myself back into his arms. I would imagine it would have looked quite comical, but I had more pressing issues on my mind.

It was at this point that a middle-aged man began to approach the swing door from inside the hotel foyer, he was on his way out, on seeing this the concierge decided he had better let go as things were getting a touch ridiculous. Woosh the door suddenly released, and I was somersaulted unceremoniously into the reception area where I ended up on my hands and knees.

"Can I help you," came a voice from the other side of the desk. I could not see who it was from my almost prone position on the very expensive red carpet. I slowly climbed upright and in mock indignation brushed down my school uniform. I approached the reception desk and as I came level with it, I saw the face of the person who had spoken, she was a vision of beauty, long blonde locks, piercing blue eyes and a perfect set of white teeth. I was about to speak when I was suddenly hoisted into the air by the back of my jacket, "You're out!" snarled the concierge as he hauled me towards the door. I quickly slid out of my jacket and turned to face him, I instinctively put up my guard and placed my feet in the right position my weight on my back foot.

"Oh look he's going to hit me, fancy yourself as a pugilist?" laughed the concierge as he moved towards me. I knew what a pugilist was, my mind went back to the conversation I'd had with Marie.

"Don't do it, I am a boxer, don't touch me!" I said calmly but firmly. I didn't want to hit him, but I always made myself a promise and that was if you hit me, I would bloody well hit you back.

"Ed, I'll deal with this, leave him and get back outside," said the girl behind the reception. Ed didn't argue I think he was beginning to realize this was not just some snotty nosed kid who he could lead outside by his ear and dump on the pavement.

"Come here, the girl motioned with her hand, smiling as she did so, what's your name?"

"Jack, Jack Marriot," I said grinning stupidly.

The girl broke into a broad smile. "I'm Cathy, your Steve's girlfriend, I thought it was you. Steve never stops saying how you're going to be a world champion someday and now I know why." She let out a girlish little giggle. I liked her immediately and for a split second stood there open-mouthed. Suddenly seeing she was waiting for me to say something, I went to speak but before anything came out, she read my mind.

"You want to see Steve I guess?" she smiled again. "If you go out of the front doors and walk around the back of the hotel, you'll find the kitchen delivery door. Knock on that and when it's opened ask for Steve and they'll fetch him for you, alright?" she finished, again with a warm smile.

"Thanks Miss," I grinned giving her the Marriot wink. I wasn't my father's son for nothing.

"Cathy, you call me Cathy," she called after me as I headed for the revolving doors. I didn't look back and once outside I came face to face with Ed. I straightened my school tie looked him in the face and grinned cockily. Ed just turned away. I had to give him his due he knew when he was beat.

I knocked loudly on the steel door and stepped back whilst I waited for it to be answered. It seemed to take forever before it was pushed open, but I knew I was in the right place as the sign on it read 'Kitchen Deliveries Only!'

"Yes," said the young bloke who now stood in the open doorway. He was about sixteen-years-old with a spotty complexion, he was wearing a white jacket and blue checked trousers.

"Steve Marriot," I said and without another word the young kid closed the door and went back inside. Two minutes later the door opened and there was our Steve. Fuck, it was good to see him.

"What you doing here, our kid?" he asked in a tone that wasn't exactly warm.

"I, I need to talk to you," I said with more than a little pleading in my voice.

114

"I can't just take time off. I'm working can't it wait til after?" he demanded.

"Oh fuck off," I shouted the tears welling up in my eyes again as I began to walk away.

"Where you going now?" he shouted after me I just ignored him and kept walking.

"Okay, okay, give me five minutes and I'll be back," he called after me.

"Right this better be good, what the fuck is it," Steve said shaking his head as walked out of the kitchen door closing it after him. I didn't know where to start but after a ten-minute interrogation by Steve I'd told him everything.

"Why the fuck has no one told me? It's that bitch, she wants us out of Dads life like we never fucking existed. I'll fucking kill her!" he finished by then he was a bright crimson colour and a vein was pulsating erratically in his temple.

"Come on Squirt," he motioned in the direction of his car that was parked outside the rear of the hotel.

"What, what about yer job?" I said without really knowing why.

"Fuck em," he replied as he started the engine and wheel spun backwards out of his parking space.

"Wait here, I'll go and find out where to go," said Steve as he strode towards the reception desk. A wave of relief passed over me as I watched him, he would sort things out and I began to believe that everything was going to be alright.

"This way," Steve called to me across the hospital foyer. He didn't wait, he just walked hurriedly towards the lift without waiting to see if I'd heard him. We took the lift to the fifth floor in silence Steve was deep in thought and it seemed inappropriate to say anything. The lift juddered to a halt and the doors opened onto a white-emulsioned corridor. A sign posted high on the wall read, 'Oncology Department' in big black letters, an arrow pointed the way toward the reception.

"What time is it?" asked Steve as we neared the reception desk where a nurse was bent over looking at a computer screen.

"What yer asking me for? I 'ain't got a watch," I said shrugging my shoulders. Steve cuffed the top of my head gently and looked up at the ceiling rolling his eyes.

"It's twenty-five to three," he declared loudly as he noticed a large clock hanging on the wall.

"What times Dads appointment?" Steve enquired without looking at me, he was too busy scanning the area.

"Two-thirty," I offered enthusiastically.

"Bollocks, I bet he's already with the doctor," he frowned. I was about to say something when Steve grabbed me by the arm and began to drag me in a different direction.

"Where we going now?" I said in a puzzled voice trying to keep up as he pulled at my arm like an attack dog.

"Here!" he announced as we arrived outside a door in the main corridor, a steel plate screwed to the wall seemed to shout out **Mr Purcell Consultant.**

"What do we do now?" I said looking at Steve for an answer.

"Well you can stay here if yer want but I 'ain't come all this way to stand in a fucking corridor," he said, as he put his hand on the door handle and breezed into the room. I followed him like an obedient puppy. Dad was seated on a comfy leather chair directly in front of the doctor only a table separating them. Marie sat to Dad's left and was perched on a cheap plastic chair like we used at school. Both were listening intently as the doctor held the conversation.

The doctor was the first to look up as he stopped speaking mid-sentence. "Er yes, can I help you?" he enquired a rather annoyed tone quite unmistakable in his voice.

"What on earth," declared Marie loudly as she jumped up from her chair like she was rocket propelled.

"You sit down and shut the fuck up," Steve snarled like a rabid dog. She didn't argue, just went a red colour from the neck up and flopped heavily back into her seat, she had the look of a child that had just dropped its ice cream.

"I'm sorry but do you think you could both wait outside?" the doctor offered in a more pleading than instructive manner.

It didn't work. "We're going fucking nowhere, this is our Dad and we have a bloody right to be 'ere," spat Steve.

Throughout all of this I looked at Dad. He had no reaction at all, just a distant look in his eyes. I waited for what seemed an age for him to say something.

Dad eventually spoke in a calm and controlled manner, he didn't bother to look at either of us. "Sorry about this Mr Purcell, these are my sons and I'd like them to stay."

Marie looked like 'she'd lost a tenner and found a bob,' her face screwing up at the corners of her mouth. Steve shot her a look that made her think twice if she had intended to say anything.

"Come in and close the door boys," the doctor nodded a calmer manner now evident.

"Shall I continue, Mr Marriot?" the doctor said shifting uncomfortably in his swivel chair.

"Go on," replied Dad as he looked in my direction. He stretched out his arm and waved his hand slowly to beckon me closer. I duly obliged and stood by Dad's side where he put his hand around my waist. I wasn't ready to hear what was going to be said and Dad must have known I was going to take things badly. I will never forget that, in the very moment when he was going to hear the most terrible news a person could hear, his main concern was me. He was a real man and I will always feel honoured to be called his son.

The word Cancer bounced off the walls like armour piercing bullets, there was nowhere to take cover and my throat began to constrict. I tried to swallow but my mouth refused to co-operate. Steve went a shade of grey white. I looked at him for some reaction, but his stare was frozen on the wall above the doctor's head, a single tear running down his face. I didn't hear all of the words spoken that day. I didn't want to. Years later I try to recall exactly what was

117

said but cannot or will not, the two things I do remember were Dad holding my waist tighter and tighter like he would never let go and me not wanting him to. The second was "Three months, I'm so sorry Mr Marriot!"

We left the hospital in a stunned silence. I followed on from behind, my eyes never leaving my father. Marie was crying and holding Dads hand. Steve was impassive, entombed in his own thoughts as he walked zombie-like, his head turned away from everyone. Dad never spoke what he was thinking at that time. I can only imagine, he never shed a single tear on that day or until the day he died, at least not in my presence.

"You going with them?" Steve whispered to me nodding towards Dad and Marie who were by now several yards in front. I didn't answer just nodded as Steve walked away. I watched him as he got further away his walk getting faster and faster. By the time he was a hundred yards away he was sprinting for all he was worth, and he never looked back.

The ride home was surreal, nobody mentioned what had just taken place, and even Marie had stopped her snivelling and was staring straight ahead as we drove out of the city. Dad reached forward and turned the radio on, it was better than the awkward silence that hung in the air like a hammer waiting to fall. The engine shuddered to a halt as Marie removed the key from the ignition and opened her door. I clambered out of the back seat and slammed the back door closed. I stood on the pavement waiting for Dad to get out, but he just sat there staring across the road into space.

"You coming Dad?" I pleaded as I opened his door.

"You go on son, yer Dad will be in soon" he smiled "Come on," Marie said softly as she put her arm around my shoulder. Your Dad needs a few minutes."

We'd been home for around twenty minutes, I was sitting in the kitchen hugging the dog. Marie was in her bedroom and Dad, he was still sitting in the car. I had never heard the house so quiet, it was like a mark of respect and not even the

118

water boiler over the sink made its usual clanging noise. The back-door handle moved downward, and the door swung open slowly. It was Steve his eyes were red, and his face had blotchy red marks all over it. I knew at once he'd been crying. I had held myself together so far, but he seemed to release all the emotion I'd kept back. I rose quickly from my chair sending it toppling backwards on to the lino floor and rushed into his arms and we both sobbed like babies as he held me tight. We remained in this grief-stricken embrace until the back door once again opened and Dad walked in, he looked at us both and turned away as though he had not seen us, he walked through the kitchen and padded up the stairs and then we heard the bedroom door open and close behind him.

It was over an hour later when Dad came downstairs. Steve and I were seated at the kitchen table drinking coffee.

"Will you boys come into the room I need to talk to you both?" he said not a hint of emotion on his face. Steve and I dutifully rose and followed him into the living room.

Dad had already seated himself in his favourite chair as I walked in behind Steve.

"Sit down," Dad smiled although we could both tell it was a little forced. I sat as close to Dad as I could get leaning from the sofa towards him, so my face was a foot or so from him. I put my hand on his knee affectionately and patted it. Steve sat as far away as he could on the other side of the sofa leaving a four-foot gap between us both.

"I don't really know where to begin, so please bear with me and let me finish," Dad asked in a tender voice. "What we've been told today has been a great shock for all of us," he continued. "Life is sometimes unfair, and we have to deal with things as they come along. I don't want you two to be worried about me, I'm alright, I'm not frightened of dying, it is only a part of life that we must all face at some time." Dad reached out and stroked my face. I caught his hand before he took it away and held it tight with both hands.

Steve was looking at the floor his head bent over, and his

face buried in his hands. A single tear worked its way between his fingers and fell in what seemed like slow motion splashing onto his checked chef's trousers.

Dad cleared his throat. "Steve, he said you're the man now. I'm so proud of you, a good job all grown up and ready for the world. That is all you ever want as a parent, to see your kids grow up safe strong and ready for whatever life brings them. You can handle anything because you're my son and I know you'll take care of everyone when I'm no longer here."

This was all too much for Steve, hearing Dad say 'when I'm not here' was the last straw. Steve jumped up like he'd sat on a drawing pin and stumbled across the room headlong into Dads arms.

"I don't want you to go anywhere Steve pleaded holding back his tears. "I want you to see me married, see your grandchildren, watch them play in the garden with you, don't give in, we can fight this, don't give in." Steve could not continue, he broke down and sobbed uncontrollably. Dad held him in his huge arms and cradled him like a baby, a look of real hurt in his eyes, it was like his very soul had been ripped out. He wasn't bothered about himself, he just could not stand to see his kids tortured like this.

Me, I just sat there numb, it was as though I was watching everything from a distance and although I heard the words that were being said I'd switched off completely.

"Jack, Jack, Dads voice brought me back to reality. Steve was no longer in the room. I didn't remember him leaving, now it was just me and Dad. "You know how much your Dad loves you don't you?" He didn't want an answer, it was one of those questions that was more of a statement than an actual question. I looked up and met Dad's eyes, they were full of concern and he didn't need to say anymore but I suppose he had to.

"You're the light of my life," he continued. "The son who has the ability to carry out the dream I never fulfilled. When the day comes that you hold up a world title belt, I promise

I'll be there watching, cheering you on. You're a fighter Jack don't lose your way, this is a terrible thing to happen to someone as young as you, but your different to other kids your age, your strong and you will come through this and be stronger than you are now." He stopped talking and stood up slowly. My eyes followed him as he began to pace back and forth on the carpet. He walked over to the fireplace and leant heavily against it turning towards me. "Oh son," he said as he ran his hands over his balding head, "I worry more about what will become of you. I know you have a fire in your heart that sometimes you can't control, but you must, don't let life decide where it takes you, grab it by the throat and take from this world what you want. Do you understand?"

Understand, fuck me, Dad had taken to talking in riddles, of course I didn't fucking understand. "Yeah, I understand," I nodded meekly.

The rest of the conversation was based on 'the love each other when I'm gone scenario' that I'm sure Dad pinched from Jesus. I promised faithfully to continue my boxing, work hard at school and be kind to Marie. At that moment I'd have promised Dad anything and what's more meant it!

Chapter 9

Behind Every Cloud

Over the next two weeks the house became kind of a shrine. Relatives I'd never seen would turn up and spend a few uncomfortable hours talking to Dad about times gone by. I would sit silently and loathe each and every one of them. I often caught them looking at me with the kind of pity you would have for a disabled child, not out of concern but kind of because it was the thing to do. I never left Dad's side I wanted to be with him as much as I could. I hated going to school and for the most part I didn't. I would leave as usual hugging Dad tightly and calling "See you later" as I closed the back door and headed down the street. No sooner had I turned the corner than I would head in the opposite direction towards the canal. Boxing became a chore, I hated the time away from Dad, and I knew I could never get this time back and would gladly have given it all up, but it would have broken his heart.

I fought my first Schoolboy's match and beat the kid I fought into a bloody mess within ten seconds. I didn't even box I just beat him and beat him.

"What on earth has got into you? You're going to fucking kill someone," screamed Dave as I sprawled across the bench in the changing room.

"Well, I'm waiting, fucking answer me." I stood up looked him right in the face and spat on the floor.

"Fuck you," I snarled a look of pure hatred in my eyes that Dave had never seen before. I pushed him backwards onto the floor.

"You come here," he called after me, but I had already left the gym. Just the swinging punch bags gave away the route I'd used as an exit. I didn't know at the time but that would be the last time I'd enter Dave's gym and I would never put on the gloves again!

Life at home was oppressive, the house was constantly in silence and I would spend hours sitting alone in the living room whilst Marie sat with Dad who was by now sleeping more often than he was awake. The change in Dad was rapid, he lost weight very quickly it seemed to drop off him overnight. His face was drawn, and he would walk with real care as though every movement left him in agony. I would sneak into see him whenever Marie's back was turned. I would hold his hand as he slept and never took my eyes of his chest as it heaved up and down. It was as though I expected him to stop breathing at the drop of a hat.

Occasionally he would wake from his sleep and manage a few words. "Hi son," he would say in a way that always made me feel he was glad to see me. We talked of things we'd never spoken of before. Dad would tell me of his boxing days and how he remembered me and our Steve 's births and the things we did as toddlers. He always had a way of telling a story that made you feel like you were actually there. "I know I have never been much of a churchgoer," said Dad one day in one of his clearer moments. "But I have never doubted that God is up there watching over us all. I think I've led a fairly decent life, never set out to hurt anyone intentionally and always tried to do the right thing. I think God would forgive me the odd moment of weakness," he laughed as he sat up against his pillows. "What I'm trying to say son is that there is a God up there and everything that happens here is for a reason. We don't always understand what his reasons are but if we have faith, we can deal with anything. I'm not frightened of the moment when my times up. I know where I'm going and that one day, we will all see each other again."

I sat on the bed and nodded my agreement. I had always believed in God, I just had for as long as I could remember. I didn't go to church except at Christmas and Easter but nevertheless I always believed and always would.

The house began to get busier and busier over the

succeeding weeks. Nurses from the Macmillan trust came and would help Dad get out of bed and occasionally downstairs into the living room where he would watch telly nodding off and waking up repeatedly.

More and more relatives came mostly out of morbid curiosity and to gawp at Dad and say stupid things like, "Doctors don't know everything, they could be wrong." Wrong! How the fuck could they be wrong? Dad was a walking skeleton, his face drawn and white, his eyes sunken and he would talk through gritted teeth when the pain became unbearable. Wrong! stupid bastards, I would curse loudly in my bedroom, how I wished they could have been right.

Dave called over to the house after I'd been absent from training for over two weeks. I managed to answer the door as Marie was upstairs sitting with Dad. "Yeah, what yer want?" I asked as I stepped out onto the top step and pulled the door closed behind me. "I was hoping for a word with yer Dad," Dave said nervously. "Is he in?"

"He's in bed, I can't disturb him," I said. The last thing I wanted was Dad finding out I'd not been training, after all I'd promised I would keep it up, besides he didn't need this shit at the moment I thought.

"What's the matter kid? You can talk to me, you know that, I want to help," Dave said gently as he placed a hand on my shoulder.

I pulled away sharply. "Help! You got a fucking cure for cancer then?" I spat viciously.

Dave went a kind of flushed colour and his face dropped. I could tell he was genuinely shocked. "Oh Jack, is it yer Dad?" he coaxed putting his hand back on my shoulder.

I didn't say anything I couldn't, my eyes filled with tears and I cried like a baby. It must have been a real side-show for the neighbours.

Dave was trying to comfort me, and I just wanted to run away but he held onto me until I gave in and he hugged me tight. "It's alright kid, let it out' it's alright," he said as his

124

tattooed arms nearly crushed the very life from me.

This was the last time I would see Dave, but I will always remember him fondly for that one moment. It must have been the hardest thing he ever did showing his soft underbelly to one of his kids, soppy old git.

After that, I carried on pretending I was going boxing, and would hang out on street corners or by the canal until it was time to come home. I nearly got caught out once when Marie went in my kit bag and found I'd not worn any of it. I made an excuse that Dave was off-sick, and training had been cancelled for a week. After that I made sure I brought my kit home dirty and sweaty even if it meant wearing it under my normal clothes and running home from the canal.

My fifteenth birthday was just around the corner and Dad had sent Marie on an errand to get me my present. I never knew this of course but was just glad to have a few hours alone with Dad and our Steve. Steve would visit most days and we would both sit either side of Dad's bed and compete for his attention. When he eventually fell asleep Steve and I would talk in whispers but refused to leave his side for a moment. Marie was still a pain in the arse and would try as hard as she could to keep us away from our father. It was as though she was so jealous, she could not bear us to spend time with him and would hurry back from wherever she'd been then shoo everyone out of Dads room. "Go on out, you know your father needs his rest," she'd say as we were frogmarched out onto the landing.

This day was different. "Hi everyone" she announced as she poked her head around the bedroom door, "I'm back." I held back the impulse to let out a sigh and tried to smile but it was more of a grimace. Steve just did what he usually did and that was to pretend she was invisible. A groan came from Dad as he turned over in his sleep, he did this more and more lately, it must have been really painful as the smallest movement seemed to need working up to before he would steel himself enough to alter his position. The Morphine that was administered by the nurses would help but as Dad's cancer worsened it no longer had the desired effect. The dose had been upped so much that any more would have knocked out an elephant. Dad tried to put on a brave face for everyone else, more often than not he would be caught out by a sudden pain that seemed to lift his body up and throw his head back, and as suddenly as it came it was gone. It was really weird, we'd all go along with the pretence that we hadn't noticed and as Dad gained his composure somebody would say something stupid like, "Lovely day outside, Alan."

"Come down stairs Jack, I have something for you," Marie smiled from the doorway. I shot a look at our Steve who in turn shook his head and shrugged his shoulders. I made my way into the kitchen where Marie was now standing by the table two carrier bags in each hand. "These are for you, your Dad wanted you to have them early this year, cos you've sorted yourself out," she beamed. I smiled and took the bags from her and put them on the table. "I'll open them later I think I heard Dad waking," I lied. I didn't want her thinking she could get round me that easily with her false pleasantries I'd been there before. By pure coincidence Dad had woken and was coughing loudly into a polystyrene cup Steve was holding for him. It was a disgusting sight but one we had all become accustomed to, a thick black and red sputum exited Dads lungs and adhered itself to the edge of the cup slowly sliding to the bottom.

"You alright, Pops?" I smiled caringly as I neared his bed and put my arm around his shoulder, he stopped coughing nodded at Steve to take the cup away and looking into my face grinned and gave me one of his famous winks. My heart was breaking but I never let it show. I leaned forward and kissed his balding head and quickly left the room. I raced into my bedroom and cried myself to sleep. I eventually awoke a couple of hours later. Steve had gone and as I looked through the crack in the door I could see Marie asleep in Dad's arms lying on top of the bed. I quietly went down into the kitchen where an excited Buster jumped up at me tugging my sleeve. He was left out a lot during all of this and would beg for attention when anyone was alone with him. I knelt down allowing him to lick my face, the salt from my tears must have encouraged him and he gave me a proper wash until I giggled and pushed him away. "We'll be alright won't we mate?" I said holding his head in both hands. Buster looked at me and cocked his head to one side as though to make sense of what I was saying. "What's in here then?" I asked mockingly as I held aloft the carrier bags Marie had given me earlier. Buster moved closer and raised his paw. "I don't think it's for you," I patted his head and seemingly to understand, he walked away and slumped heavily on the mat by the back door. He let out a huge yawn and settled down to get comfy. I sat down at the table and excitedly opened the first bag and reached inside. It was the most beautiful boxing gown I had ever seen black and gold silk with my name embroidered in raised gold lettering on the back. I hurriedly emptied the other three bags out onto the floor; a brand-new pair of boxing boots that matched my robe, a pair of silk shorts and finally a pair of Lonsdale leather bag gloves. I slipped the bag gloves onto my hands and began shadow boxing throwing combinations as I moved around the kitchen table. My hands were fast and just a blur of the black leather seemed to hang in the air like cigarette smoke as my fists pumped in and out like a steam piston. I moved faster and faster ducking and throwing ever faster uppercuts and parries. Tears streamed down my face and two fingers of snot started to work their way out of my nose joining together as they met on my upper lip, Jab, jab, duck, hook, cross parry, I continued until totally exhausted I fell to my knees and sobbed uncontrollably.

Dad's condition began to worsen by the day. At night as I lay in my room, I would hear him calling out. You could pick out the odd word but for the most part he would drift off mid-sentence only to resume a minute or so later.

I took him a cup of tea one morning and much to my surprise he was sat bolt upright and greeted me with a

127

loving smile. "Come and sit here son," he said as he patted the bed at the side of him. I did as he asked and perched next to him one leg hanging off the bed onto the floor. "You know son, I love you and Steve so much it breaks my heart to put you both through this. This should be one of the best times of your lives. You should be laughing and enjoying yourselves not having to go through this," he said as he squeezed my hand. I smiled and fought back the tears I knew were probably visible in my eyes.

Dad coughed cleared his throat and reached up until his left hand was holding my jaw, he turned my head until I was looking right into his sunken eyes, they were almost black, and his cheekbones poked at his skin as if trying to burst out. "I love you son, never forget that, I will always be with you, always watching you, so you go out there and grab every opportunity with both hands. I want you to be a man now, because when I'm gone, you'll have to grow up quickly, you know that?" he said shaking my head as if to re-enforce what he was saying.

"Yeah, I'll be alright Dad, don't worry about me," I replied awkwardly. He hadn't finished yet and over the next hour he talked almost non-stop, his hopes and dreams; the times Steve and I had made him laugh, the many scrapes we'd got into. I sat there on his bed and listened intently not taking my eyes from him and nodding occasionally when a reply was called for. It was the first time I'd heard Dad mention my mother and those words will remain with me forever. "Don't go looking for her, she'll bring you nowt but unhappiness."

When Dad had finally got everything off his chest, he picked up his cup of tea from the bedside table and held it towards me. "Make your old man a fresh cup, I guess this one's a little cold." I stood up and kissed him on his head taking the cup from his shaking hand and skipped out of the bedroom without looking back. I smiled to myself as I filled the kettle at the kitchen sink, it had been good to talk like that with Dad and I hoped Marie would make herself absent more often. The back door opened and dragged me back from my thoughts.

"What you grinning to yourself for?" said Steve as he stepped over Buster who was lying in the doorway.

"Nowt" I shrugged.

"How's the old man?" he enquired and without waiting for a reply headed out of the kitchen and began to make his way upstairs.

I was just stirring the steaming cup of hot tea I'd made for Dad when Steve came back into the kitchen and slumped into a chair at the table. "Fucking great, he's asleep and I wanted to tell him something," Steve said as he put his elbows on the table and cupped his face in the palm of his hands.

"I was just talking to him a minute ago, he was wide awake," I offered as though to rub salt into the wounds.

"Well he's fucking asleep now," he snapped as he stood up and walked towards me. "Cheers," he said as he took the cup of tea from my hand and took a large slurp. "Oh fucking hell it's got three sugars in it," he protested as he spat it back in the mug and we both started laughing. Steve and I spent the next hour going up and down the stairs waiting for Dad to wake, he would stir occasionally but not open his eyes.

Steve was pacing up and down like an expectant father. "What is it that's so important it can't wait?" I asked.

"Oh nowt, I want Dad to know first," said Steve dismissively.

Marie came home as Steve was just leaving. "You off" she said as he pushed past her on his way out of the back door.

"Yeah he's sleeping, see ya," he replied and closed the door. "And what about you?" said Marie as she turned her attention towards me.

"What about me?" I asked.

"Well what have you been doing whilst I've been trailing around the shops with your little brother?" I was just about to say I'd been talking to Dad, but she didn't want an answer she was in a strop and began running off at the mouth. "It's

129

obvious you haven't been tidying up, look at the state of this place," she said pointing at a few dishes in the sink. They weren't even my dishes, but I knew it wouldn't matter when she was in one of her moods.

"Get this place cleaned up and then get out of my sight. I don't want you under my feet, do you hear?" she barked at me. I didn't argue and as Marie left the kitchen, I rolled up my sleeves and squirted a larger than necessary amount of washing up liquid into the sink and ran the hot water. The kitchen boiler began clanking as the air in the pipes worked its way out. It was at that moment I heard it, a wail that carried down the stairs and bored its way into my brain. I instinctively knew what it meant and throwing the plate I was holding into the sink I turned and raced upstairs.

Marie was on her way out of the bedroom and met me on the landing her eyes pierced through me. "Why weren't you with him? You should have been watching him, it's your fault," she screamed in my face as she pushed me aside and ran down the stairs. I stood for a moment trying to steel myself not daring to go any further. I could hear my heart pounding and I had lost the ability to swallow my tongue stuck to the roof of my mouth like a piece of old carpet. I took a deep breath and cautiously stepped inside. I approached the bed as my legs turned to jelly each step becoming an effort. What I saw next was everything I'd imagined in the many nightmares I'd had since Dad became ill. The blankets were kicked back, and Dads thin white leg was poking out at a kind of strange angle, he was face down and one arm was stretched out as though he was reaching for something. I was unable to see his face but as I looked at his back, I could see he was not breathing. I don't know to this day why I did it, but it just seemed right at the time. I held back my tears leant over Dad and gently turned him over, he was very light the cancer had seen to that. I then set about making him comfortable. It was not until I'd tucked the bedding back in, closed his half-open eyes and folded his arms neatly across his chest that I allowed myself to break. I remained there lying next to Dad holding his lifeless body until a gentle voice brought me back to reality.

"Come on Jack, you've got to let him go," said Steve as he tried to lift my arm from around Dad's head that I was cradling in my arms.

I turned on him so quickly that he stepped back as though a rattle snake had just struck. "Get off me, go away you bastards," I snarled. I meant it and if one of those people in that room had touched me again, I would have sent someone else to their grave. It was wisely decided by the Doctor, Steve and Marie that they should perhaps give me a little longer. So there I remained holding on and never wanting to let go. I knew I couldn't stay there forever, I just didn't want that moment to end and I knew once it did, I would never see him again, and that was a thought that in my fragile state I just couldn't handle.

After what was probably no longer than an hour, Dad began to go cold. His face, by then, was completely white with a hint of yellow around his eyes. I went to pick up his hand, but it too was stiff and cold, and I knew then it was time to say goodbye. The sound of movement in Dad's room alerted the others that the coast was clear and as I went into my bedroom. I could hear them all climbing the stairs. I sat behind the door pulled my knees to my chest and cried like I'd never cried before.

It was probably an hour later when a gentle knocking briefly disturbed my crying. "Jack its Steve let me in, our kid."

I pulled myself to my feet, wiped my face with my hands and slowly opened the door. Steve had been crying as well; his face was red and his eyes puffy, he was doing his best to be strong but the moment we looked into each other's faces, we could no longer pretend. I threw myself into his arms and together we wept openly sinking to the floor together until the point where we felt embarrassed.

"Fuck me, haven't cried like that since I was five," said Steve as he wiped his face and put on a fake smile.

"Yeah me neither," I lied.

"You know what? our kid," said Steve.

"What?" I asked.

"Things are bad now, but we've got each other and in time it will get easier. I'm not saying we won't always miss Dad, but his loss will get easier to cope with," Steve reasoned.

"You know what else?" I replied, "Not every cloud has a silver lining."

Chapter 10

Rainy Days and Monday's

It always rains at funerals and Dad's was no exception. The crap weather didn't keep anyone away and relatives attended from far and wide. I listened to their pathetic chatter and wished it was them being put in the ground.

"He was so young, makes you wonder, doesn't it, it could be me next!"

"Please God let it be," I thought as I looked at this dried up old bitch hovering about like the spectre of death.

"He was only forty-five, terrible waste," Replied the old woman's friend.

'I don't fucking know any of you, who the fuck are you?' I wanted to scream but my voice remained silent along with my thoughts. Steve stood by my side throughout the whole day and when I needed him, he somehow knew and would lean his shoulder into me as if to say I'm here it's okay. The service went by in a haze, I heard people do readings, songs being sung but all I could do was stare at the coffin and picture my father lying inside.

I fidgeted uncomfortably. I was hot. and the collar of my shirt chaffed my neck. I never was one for shirts and ties and I don't think Dad would have cared if I'd gone in my jeans and trainers, but Marie insisted that I was not going to show her up, so I wore the suit.

The service ended in what seemed like the blink of an eye. The mourners couldn't wait to get out of the church. It was as if they had somewhere else they had to be. Steve helped carry Dad's coffin along with some male relatives I vaguely recognised.

It was still raining as I stepped out into the church yard to be met by huddles of people smoking and laughing. As soon as they saw me they would lower their voices and people with their backs to me would turn and look in my direction.

I walked slowly to the back of the pallbearers and tried not to be noticed, periodically a hand would touch my arm or pat my shoulder as someone walked past. If I looked they would give me a half smile and lower their eyes in sympathy. I stood at the graveside and stared intently into the hole that had already been dug. It was bloody deep I thought to myself as I imagined the amount of digging a man with a shovel would have done in order to achieve such a depth. Marie was taking centre stage and weeping for all she was worth. I caught her eye a couple of times and would stare at her until she looked away uncomfortably. Steve had taken up his place by my side, the coffin had been placed on the earth at the side of the open grave and the priest was doing his ashes to ashes speech. I didn't listen, I was too busy fighting back the tears in my eyes and the lump in my throat. On some invisible command from the priest, the coffin was lifted on to two green canvas straps ready for lowering into the ground. As it hovered over the hole, I tugged at Steve's arm.

"What?" he whispered as he looked down at me a look of concern on his face. "Their putting him in the wrong way round, look." I nodded in the direction of the coffin. Steve turned and stared for a moment before turning back to me, he smiled, the kind of smile that two people share when they know something other people don't. I smiled too. We both knew our Dad and he would have said, "Bloody typical, can't even bury me right, useless bastards," and laughed to himself. To this day when I visit his grave I always stand with my back to his headstone when I talk to him, the good thing is when people place flowers on his grave, they are laying them at his feet. Dad would have pissed himself at that!

A party was held at the house afterwards and everywhere I turned people were talking about Dad and what a wonderful person he was, how he would do anything for anyone and was as honest as the day was long. It made me sick to my stomach. They were a bunch of hypocrites, if they

134

thought that much of Dad why didn't they ever visit. I was fifteen years old and didn't know who any of the bastards stood in the kitchen drinking Dad's whisky were.

"Here squirt get this down yer," said Steve as he gave me what looked like a glass of Coke. I took it and drank it in one.

"What was in that?" I said pulling a face. Steve didn't answer he just grinned and winked at me and for one brief moment I could swear Dad was standing there in Steve's place. The Cokes kept coming and even when Steve was saying I'd had enough, I talked him into getting me another.

"One more, go on," I pleaded.

"You've had half a bottle of vodka, yer gonna be pissed," Steve whispered under his breath.

"Sounds fucking good to me," I shrugged as I leant unsteadily against the wall for support. It felt good the warm feeling in my belly and the numbness that enveloped me, made me feel I could cope with anything. It was inevitable that the alcohol would eventually override my inhibitions and instead of keeping my thoughts to myself they began to spill out.

"You alright," said a middle-aged man I'd never noticed before, as he walked past me.

"What do you think?" I snarled at him and he scurried off like I'd bitten him on the arse.

"Fucking hell, our kid, calm down he didn't mean owt he was just being polite," reasoned Steve. I didn't reply just grinned the kind of stupid grin you do when you think nobody else has noticed your three sheets to the wind.

"Come on let's get you out of here before things get any worse," said Steve as he grabbed my arm.

"Worse? How can they get any fucking worse?" I shouted pulling my arm away as the conversation in the kitchen stopped and every head turned to look in our direction.

"Jack have you been drinking?" demanded Marie as she marched across the kitchen to where Steve and I were standing.

"He's had a couple that's all," said Steve trying to defend me. Marie ignored him and repeated her question but this time with a little more volume. It's never a good idea to confront someone when they've had a drink and I'm sure Marie would by now probably agree with me.

"A drink, have I had a fucking drink? is that what you're asking me?" I slurred as I leant forward into her face.

She tried to get hold of my arms, "Jack will you go and lie down, you're causing a scene," she pleaded.

"A scene, we wouldn't want to cause a fucking scene, would we? Not in front of all these fucking relatives," I shouted, pushing her away and walking across the kitchen. The relatives moved out of my way, it was like Moses and the parting of the sea. I grabbed a bottle of whisky from the table unscrewed the lid and declared loudly, "Let's all have a fucking drink."

I took several large gulps and launched the half empty bottle straight through the kitchen window. God bless Steve, he grabbed me and frogmarched me out of the back door leaving a room full of speechless mourners.

"I'll take care of him, sorry," he said as he closed the door behind us.

It was two days later when I eventually got up the courage to go home and face the music. Steve was great, and not only did he put me up in his flat he paid for the window and went back to the house to smooth things over with Marie. To Marie's credit she never mentioned the funeral incident to me and when I arrived back home simply ignored me. I didn't mind I wanted to be on my own anyway. I passed the days and next few weeks alone in my bedroom hugging one of Dads old coats I'd pinched from his wardrobe. It still held his scent deep in its fabric and if I closed my eyes it was like he was with me.

I didn't bother to go to school. Marie had taken to pretending I didn't exist and so, long as I stayed out of her way, I could do whatever I liked, including bunking off school. Marie no longer bothered to cook or do anything else for me, there was obviously no point in her keeping up the pretence of being a good parent, except that is, to her own offspring. So whenever Marie went out which was a lot, I would run down to the kitchen and make something to eat, sometimes the fridge would be empty and I would have to make do with some toast or a tin of soup from the cupboard but I much preferred food I didn't have to cook as this enabled me to grab it and make a quick retreat to my room.

I didn't see much of our Steve after the funeral. I think the house reminded him too much of Dad, but he would ring up and speak to me from time to time.

"How are you? Is everything okay?" he'd ask and of course I always said I was fine. I liked it when Steve phoned, it made me feel that somebody gave a shit, and everyone needs to know that, whether they admit it or not. I don't quite know what happened, but the calls became less frequent and eventually stopped altogether. If I knew our Steve it was probably some good-looking dolly bird. It was only after the calls from Steve ceased that Marie seemed to step up a gear and her cruel streak reared its ugly head once again. Dad had been dead for around four months and I'd spent the majority of that time like a recluse in self-imposed solitary in the attic.

My weight had plummeted and most of my clothes hung off me. It didn't matter anyway, Marie had stopped doing my washing and I just wore the same clothes until they practically fell off me. I would have a bath on a Friday night. Marie always went out and took my little brother with her, they didn't return until Saturday morning. I had no idea where they went, but in truth I didn't care. The stolen bath always felt like bliss and I would splash about for hours. When I'd finished, I would wash my underwear and a couple of tee shirts in the lukewarm suds. Later I would hang them on the radiator in my bedroom. Friday nights became the only thing I had to look forward to and I would make a real night of it. After my bathing session I would go down to the kitchen and rustle up some food from whatever was lying around. I would then snuggle up on the sofa in the living room with Buster and watch television until the early hours. I was always careful to leave the house as Marie had left it. I would tidy the bathroom and wash up anything I'd used in the kitchen placing it carefully back in the cupboards. It would have been a bad idea to leave any clue that suggested I had been doing anything other than being miserable. I knew how her mind worked!

It was a strange time in my life. It was as though I'd slipped into a black hole, invisible to the outside world and no matter how hard I tried I could not find a way out. It seemed like forever from one Friday to another, but it gave me something to focus on, a glimmer of light in the shit place I was in. It wasn't a life it was just an existence.

Marie's sadistic nature went out of control, she was no longer happy with me just staying out of her way she decided I had to suffer, this turned out to be a big mistake. The first signs of change came one Friday night when as usual I went to get a bath after Marie had vacated the house. I turned on the tap and the water just ran cold. I swished it with my hand and willed it to get hotter, but it didn't. "Bastard, bastard," I cursed. not sure why the bloody thing would not get hot. I decided in the end that a cold bath was better than no bath at all but unlike other baths this one was short and sweet. After I'd dried myself off and hung my clothes over the radiator, I padded down the stairs into the kitchen.

"Right then, what's on the menu this evening," I said, rubbing my hands together as I opened the fridge. "What the...?" I stopped mid-sentence, the fridge was totally bare, it wasn't just empty it was as though it had just been delivered. "Fucking bitch," I ranted slamming the door shut so hard it sprung back open. I kicked it shut leaving a big dent in the middle of it. The food cupboard was my last chance and as I put my hand on the door, I mentally said a

138

little prayer as I slowly pulled it open, it was empty! It was blatantly apparent that there was no food to be had in the kitchen and I knew Marie must have hidden it somewhere in the house. I decided a search was necessary. I was about to start emptying the rest of the cupboards when I spotted it, the biggest padlock money could buy dangling as though taunting me from the cellar door. I have never been one to turn down a challenge and by this point I was that hungry I could have chewed the bloody padlock off. I went at it with every kitchen implement I could lay my hands on but to no avail, take it from me if you're cracking safes you won't get far with a fish slice or a bread knife. I didn't give up easily but after about an hour I'd got that caught up in trying to tear off the padlock I'd actually forgotten I was hungry. I made my way into the living room, Buster followed behind wagging his tail he knew the Friday routine by now. I reached over and pushed the button to turn the television on, you guessed it, it didn't work. It was too much, I cracked. I lifted the television quite easily considering I'd not eaten for two days and with all my remaining strength I threw it across the room sending it crashing into the wall above the sofa as it exploded. Poor Buster shot out of the room as though his tail was on fire, I don't know why anyone calls them dumb animals. The red mist had well and truly taken over and anything that was not nailed down was launched into the air. If it was nailed down, I tore it up and smashed it to pieces. Exhausted I sat amongst the debris and cried myself to sleep.

I was still asleep when Marie arrived home in the morning. I heard her key in the back door and as I opened my eyes and began to focus on the carnage I'd created the night before, I realized exactly what I'd done. "Shit, shit" I swore under my breath as I jumped to my feet and stupidly tried to start clearing things up. I could hear Marie moving about in the kitchen and knew it was only a matter of moments until she made her way into the living room. There was only one course of action head her off at the pass. I had just opened the living room door when she began to shout. "Jack come here, what have you done? Get here now!" I'd forgotten about the huge dent in the fridge door and for a moment was a little confused as to why she was shouting and bawling. The kitchen door was slightly open, and I could see my little brother still strapped into his pushchair by the front door, he looked in my direction turned away and continued to suck his fingers.

I was about to walk into the kitchen as Marie came out and we nearly collided. "What the hell have you been doing you bastard?" she screamed into my face. I could smell cigarettes on her breath and cheap perfume on her clothes. I stood stock still like a rabbit caught in the headlights. I had no pre-planned story, no excuse so I just stood there rooted to the spot, not speaking. "Fucking answer me, you fucking brat," she scowled venomously. Her patience had just about been tested and I thought if I said sorry it might help calm her down.

"Sorry," I whispered under my breath.

"What was that?" she said through gritted teeth, "Fucking sorry, did you say? I'll make you fucking sorry," and with that she grabbed a handful of my hair. It happened that quickly, she totally took me by surprise. In an instant she swung me around throwing me into the kitchen. I tried to stay upright but clattered into the kitchen table and fell headlong over the top of it. She was on me like a hungry lion kicking and clawing at me for all she was worth. I did my best to fend her off by using my arms and trying to crawl under the table. "Come here," she snarled as she pulled me by my leg across the floor.

"Please, please," I begged but it fell on deaf ears. Smack, Smack her hands came down on my face and body, I could taste blood in the back of my throat. She still had hold of my leg and was kicking me in the back and the face.

I just wanted to get away, but she hung on like a limpet. "Fucking ungrateful bastard, I'll fucking teach you," she screamed by now her words were almost indistinguishable.

All I could hear was my own heartbeat.

'Got to get her off, got to get her off,' was all I could think, so with my loose foot I kicked out hitting her in the stomach, she let out a gasp and released her grip momentarily. I was up and on my feet in less than a second and heading for the door. I never made it. Marie charged across the kitchen leapt onto my back and began gouging at my eyes. I reached up to pull her hands free and as I did so I spun round to face her, our eyes met and in that instant the anger I'd bottled up for so long was let loose. I don't remember most of what occurred that day selective memory they call it to give it its proper title. They say its nature's way of shutting out trauma that you can't or won't face up to. Bollocks, I don't remember because I completely lost the plot so excuses aside, I went fucking nuts!

The Police station hadn't changed since I was there with Dad, same colour paint, same smell and same old fucking story. I was in the shit. Again. I was placed in a cell whilst the custody officer tried to find what they call an appropriate adult. This must have been more difficult than they imagined as I seemed to have been in there for hours before the cell door was eventually opened. I looked up to see a middle-aged woman in a floral dress and sandals standing in the doorway, she had curly greying hair and glasses.

"I'm Margaret Turpin and I'm a social worker, can I come and talk to you Jack?" she asked in a rather middle-class voice. I nodded, and she entered the cell and sat beside me. I was slouching on a blue plastic-covered mattress that was lying on top of a concrete platform. I didn't sit up but remained in my prone position staring at the ceiling.

"Do you want to tell me what happened?" she smiled.

"Don't know," I replied.

"You must remember something, Jack, you can tell me, I'm on your side," she finished. I didn't answer, I couldn't, it wasn't that I didn't remember the argument or Marie attacking me, it was just that I couldn't make sense of it all and deep down inside I was hurting in a way I never knew was possible. She did her best did Margaret Turpin, but I mostly ignored her or gave one-word answers. The cell door eventually opened, and a young copper spoke to Margaret.

"It's time to interview him now, can you sit in?" he said ignoring the fact I was even there. I was escorted into a small interview room and as I took my seat at the table I began to think of the last time I was there. I would have given anything to have gone back to that day, just to be with Dad, one more time. Margaret, the social worker took her seat at the side of me, whenever I looked in her direction, she would offer a reassuring smile. It didn't bloody work. I was scared, confused and above all even with her sitting there, I felt alone. We sat in silence for several minutes, just Margaret and me. I had no doubt there was a copper standing outside the room in case I tried to do a runner. God knows, I wanted to.

Margaret cleared her throat. "Jack, when the officers come in they are going to ask you some questions, it would help if you tried your best to be honest with them," she pleaded in a soft tone. She reached out her hand to touch my arm but withdrew it without making contact, perhaps she'd thought better of it.

I was about to answer her when the door opened and in walked two coppers. I took my face out of my hands and looked across the table where the two coppers had seated themselves. One was about fifty with ridiculously red hair cut short about an inch all over. The other was younger maybe in his thirties, with black hair and a porno moustache.

The two coppers both introduced themselves to Margaret. Once again, I was invisible. "Right then young man", said the older copper as though he'd suddenly noticed me. "You've been cautioned earlier when you were arrested but just to remind you, you are still under caution and anything you say will be taken down and can be used in evidence against you, do you understand?" he asked.

I nodded to indicate I understood. The younger copper
142

turned on a tape recorder and spoke into it. "This is an interview with Jack Marriot. Those present are myself, police constable two five five nine, Bolton and police constable three five three one, Chapman." He continued, also present is "Mrs?" he stopped and looked in Margaret's direction.

"Turpin," she said leaning towards the tape recorder. "Mrs Turpin a social worker from Leeds social services," concluded the young copper.

"Right then Jack, why don't you start at the beginning?" asked the older copper who had obviously decided he was going to do the majority of the grilling. It was easier said than done, start at the beginning, where was the beginning? I sure didn't know. I looked down at my hands under the table. I had dried blood spattered across the knuckles and a good way up my wrist. I quickly looked up trying to put it out of my mind. "Well?" coaxed the copper as he stood up and walked behind my chair. I hated that. Teachers used to do that at school and suddenly slap you on the back of the head for some misdemeanour. I braced myself, but it never came The copper walked back around and sat heavily in his seat. He clasped his hand to his forehead and slowly ran it down the length of his face coming to rest on his chin. "Would it be easier if I start and if you want to add anything you can just stop me?" he asked as he gave me a half smile that was more menacing than reassuring. He began, "Jack when we arrived at your house we found your stepmother," he paused as if choosing his words carefully, let out a sigh, raised his eyes to look directly into my face and continued, "Badly injured, injuries that she claims you inflicted on her. What do you have to say about that?" I didn't have anything to say, didn't want to say anything and wasn't going to say anything. I looked down away from his gaze.

"Well?" he urged as if to remind me he was speaking. I moved my gaze once again to my hands, the blood under my fingernails had gone a dark brown colour and seemed to shout at me, 'you did it, you did it!' "Jack we can't help you if you don't tell us what happened. We've seen the state of the living room and the kitchen and to be honest it looks like you lost your temper and tried to destroy the house, your Mum says she was trying to stop you and you turned on her, is that what happened?"

I looked up at the older copper as he finished speaking, our eyes met. "She 'ain't my fucking mother," I shouted as I leaned forward into his face. "I fucking hate her, hate her," I repeated as if to emphasise the point.

"Okay, okay, Jack take it easy, just stay calm, it's okay," said the younger copper as he stroked at his moustache.

Margaret the social worker reached out and placed her hand on mine under the table giving it a squeeze.

The older copper recomposed himself took a deep breath and in a gentler manner coaxed, "Sorry Jack I didn't mean to upset you, it's just that we need to know what happened, we need your side, so we can deal with this fairly, you don't want to be punished if it was not your fault do you?" He hadn't finished speaking but I'd stopped listening. Who was he trying to kid, treat me fairly, my side of the story. I knew, as was always the case, that when an adult said things like that it was just to ease their conscience, so they could punish you with impunity, nobody was interested in my side of any story and I wasn't interested in telling it. What was the bloody point?

After a standoff of around two hours I was placed back in my cell with Margaret's words ringing in my ears. "We can't help you Jack, if you don't help yourself". I'd been helping myself all my life, what do you know? I thought as the cell door slammed shut.

Marie had done a right number on me. Her statement was so far-fetched it should have been signed by Hans Christian Anderson. In fairness the courts had been kind enough to furnish me with a solicitor although I just frustrated him as much as the social workers and coppers whom I mostly ignored or gave sarcastic remarks to. It didn't matter to me what anyone thought, and in any event, I'd had experience of Marie's lies and she was always more than plausible, so I resigned myself to whatever shit life was going to throw at me. I was charged with Malicious wounding with intent, intent? I never really understood that part, intent to do what? Hurt the bitch, then damn right, I wanted to hurt her, and she fucking deserved it. I didn't feel guilty or ashamed, she had it coming and twenty-five years later I don't regret that day and never will. I promised myself after that, that I would never let anybody lay a hand on me again and if they tried then that was their look out, this philosophy has served me well and although I would never bully or hurt an innocent person if you crossed me, I would make you pay.

I received a copy of Marie's statement via my solicitor and it made interesting reading to say the least. It was claimed she had returned home and that I started shouting that there was no food in the house and suddenly went crazy smashing up the living room and kitchen. She said that when she tried to stop me, I turned on her and punched her to the floor finally smashing a chair over her back and clubbing her around the head with it. I had no idea whether I punched her or hit her with a chair, it was all a blur. I remember her lying on the floor bleeding and my little brother crying. I remember helping her to her feet and phoning an ambulance and that was it. There was no mention of the beating that she was giving me, no mention of the years of abuse that poisonous cow had inflicted on me, just her warped version of events. I sat on my bed in the cell and laughed loudly as I finished reading her statement. She could never touch me again, she knew it, I knew it and what did it matter where I was sent, prison? Borstal? I had nowhere else to go anyway.

I was placed on remand in Thorpe Arch remand centre, a purpose-built prison for juveniles between the ages of fifteen and eighteen. I remember arriving there on a coach with around forty other poor bastards. I was handcuffed with what resembled some medieval torture device, huge padlocks that hung from your wrists and constricted your blood flow. It was de-humanising, humiliating and what's more uncalled for but that was to be my lot and I just accepted it. The coach was full of chatter, kids bragging about the number of houses they'd screwed or the amount of cars they'd taken and driven away. I sat in silence, the kid at my side had tried to talk to me but the look I gave him must have been enough to put him off, he never spoke again for the rest of the journey. As we neared the prison the bragging subsided and most of the kid's stopped talking, the bravado was long forgotten as the prison loomed into view. A large green mesh fence, around thirty feet high surrounded it, razor wire hung off the top and as we approached, the solid wooden gates opened automatically, and we were sucked into the depths of despair.

We left the coach in two's and were herded into a small annexe where a prison officer, this will be the only time I refer to a prison officer by that term, (they became screws a term they earned as they would happily turn the screws when an opportune moment came their way.)

The screw sat behind a desk, called us forward one at a time. When it was my turn I walked forward. "Name," the screw demanded. He was a small fat bloke with a crew cut and an ego the size of a house. "Marriot," I replied. "Turn out your pockets," he snapped. I did as he asked. It didn't take long. I had nothing in them. "Over there" he pointed indicating a cubicle where another screw stood looking in my direction.

"Strip."

"What," I asked a little confused. "Strip, everything off, now!" snarled the screw as he pushed me into the open cubicle. It had no front just a back and two sides; keeping your modesty is obviously low on Her Majesty's list of priorities. I began to remove my clothing until I was standing in just my underpants. "The lot" the screw said in a manner that said he was bored with the whole thing. I slowly removed my underpants until I was naked and standing in an open cubicle with around fifty people looking at me. I didn't mind being naked it was something I was used to from my times in the showers at the gym and at

146

school, but I felt violated at being ordered to strip naked by another person, it felt like a form of rape. The screw looked me up and down, "Turn around," he ordered. "Squat," I did as I was told; there seemed no point in arguing, it was going to happen anyway.

Once I'd been ritually humiliated, I was given a set of prison issue clothes and told to take a shower. The showers were bloody freezing, so I quickly ducked in and out shivering as I dried myself with a towel. I picked up the clothing I'd been given and began to get dressed. The clothes smelled of starch and detergent and in truth it was quite pleasant to be wearing something clean. I stood in front of a mirror that hung on the wall outside the showers and took a long look at myself. Brown trousers, grey knitted jumper with a blue collar and underneath a blue and white striped shirt. The whole ensemble was completed with a pair of cheap black slip-on shoes. So this is what prisoners really look like I thought.

Chapter 11

School of Hard Knocks

I was led from the reception area down a long corridor with a vinyl floor that shone like a mirror. I wondered how it got so shiny, it seemed to go on for miles, and I screwed my eyes up but still could not see the end of it.

"This way," said the screw who was walking in front of a group of us. We turned into a double door to our left and climbed a flight of stairs. Once at the top of the third flight we entered into another corridor, again the highly polished vinyl floor was blinding and made you half close your eyes as the overhead lighting reflected off it. On each side of the corridor were heavy steel doors with a long thin glass panel in the middle. I knew these were cells, by now I'd been in a few.

"You're in here," signalled the screw and as I entered the cell he called another lad, "And you" he finished, pushing him inside behind me. The cell door closed, and I began to take in its surroundings. A metal bunk bed stood by the wall to the left, a wooden desk was on the right-hand wall on top of which stood two plastic bowls and a water jug. There were two chairs not dissimilar to the kind you have at school, all plastic with two tubular legs; these were at the end of the bunk bed, under the chairs. Staring at me ominously were two plastic piss pots. I threw the pillow case I'd been given in reception, on to the bottom bunk, it contained two sheets a clean pair of underpants and socks, gym shorts, a vest, a pair of black plimsolls, a towel and a toothbrush. I walked over to the window and looked out it was not that inspiring and in order to see anything other than the brick wall opposite you had to stick your head through the bars and although a little awkward if you stuck your head out and twisted at a certain angle you could see a footpath that ran along the outside of the prison. This would be a focal point for me and I spent many hours watching people walk up and down that path. They had something I didn't, freedom, and by watching them, i t was like I could steal some of theirs, stupid I know, but that's the way it was.

"What can ya see?" came a voice from behind me. I'd forgotten momentarily about the kid that was pushed in the cell with me. "Well it 'ain't fucking Blackpool," I said sarcastically.

"Give us a look," pleaded the kid's voice from behind me as he tried to look over my shoulder.

"Hang on, let me get out of the way," I laughed as I pulled my head back in. I'd seen all I needed to; the footpath, the exercise yard, the grass that grew beneath the windows and, oh yeah, the heaps of shit parcels strewn on the grass and hanging from a flat roof opposite, but that's another story.

My cell mates name was Andy Paton and he was sixteen years old. He was a slightly built kid with acne and the worst haircut I'd ever seen, a kind of pudding basin affair that was unkempt dirty and had scissor marks that bore all the hallmarks of a home barber's handy work. I liked Andy he was in for burglary and stealing cars. Andy never bragged about the things he'd done he simply made excuses for it. It was always somebody else who talked him into it, someone else's fault he got caught, or the fact that his parents didn't raise him properly. You had to like him he could think up a fairly reasonable excuse for anything he did and after a while you would start to empathise with him. If Andy had not turned to crime, he would have made a brilliant criminal lawyer. He could have got Jack the Ripper a Community service order.

"Well you know all 'bout me, what's your story?" Andy asked as he reclined on the top bunk sucking heavily on a roll up cigarette.

"Nowt to tell," I said shrugging my shoulders.

"Well yer must have done something, you don't get sent here for getting an O level in chemistry," he laughed.

149

I wanted to tell someone, had to tell someone and besides, I hadn't talked to anyone in days. "Got a spare smoke," I asked. Andy threw me his tobacco tin and as I opened it, I perched on the desk looking up at him and began to tell him my story.

When I'd finished Andy spoke for the first time since I'd started to spill my guts, he was a good listener and knew when his opinion was needed, in my case he just chipped in with the odd "Uh, uh" or "Mm," just to show I had his attention. "Fuck me mate, she was a right cow. I'd have done her too, the bitch," he said as he leapt off the top bunk and grabbed the cigarette from my hand. I'd been trying to roll it unsuccessfully since we started talking. "Need a hand with this," he smiled as he skilfully manipulated the workings in his hands and in no time produced the thinnest cigarette I'd ever seen.

"Now that's how yer roll a fag in ere, yer gotta use as little bacca as poss because it's gotta last, yer know what I mean?" he offered as he grinned lit the roll up took a large drag and passed it to me.

Dinner time soon came which was good because both Andy and I were bloody starving.

"Come on move yer arses, down to dinner," yelled the screw who had just opened our cell door. I hadn't a clue where to go and neither had Andy, so we just followed the thronging mass of inmates as they made their way down the stairs and headed along the corridor. The dining hall was about the size of a school gymnasium, tables and chairs were strategically placed in ten long rows of around eight tables, to the end of each row stood a screw.

I slowly joined the rear of a queue that had formed at a large serving hatch manned by several prisoners dishing out food. "No pushing, stand in line, Wilson back in line or you can get to the back," a screw standing at the front hollered. I looked him up and down. He wasn't what you could call approachable. A peaked cap low over his eyes, head slung back so he could peep out from under it, the sleeves of his

150

uniform shirt were rolled back showing his hairy tattooed forearms and his chest was puffed out like a strutting ostrich. I could spot a bully at ten paces, he didn't prove me wrong. "Wilson, git ere," the screw screamed at the top of his voice. A young lad around my age stepped forward he was well built about six feet tall and muscular. He approached the screw with his head bowed and took up a submissive stance in front of him. I assumed this was Wilson.

"He's fucking for it now," said a voice from the back of the queue.

"Good, fucking twat" said another. I looked behind me but couldn't tell who had been speaking.

"What have I fucking told you about pushing and shoving?" the screw shouted into Wilson's face his nose almost touching his.

"Sorry Sir, I wasn't" stuttered Wilson. I don't know why he bothered apologising; the screw wasn't the forgiving type.

"Get to the fucking back," the screw screamed, his face contorted into a mass of throbbing veins. Wilson turned to do as he was told but the screw hadn't had his pound of flesh yet. Wilson was grabbed from behind by the neck, slapped in the face with the screws free hand and finally kicked up the arse as he tried to make his retreat. The other kids smirked into their hands and began whispering to each other as they looked on. I knew what they were thinking, they were just glad it was someone else and not them. The sad thing is eventually it is you; you can't avoid a bully like that.

Andy and I found a table and sat through our meal without speaking. It was not the most appetising food I'd ever eaten but I still ate everything on my tray.

"You want mine?" Andy said as he pushed his stainless-steel tray towards me.

"You sure?" I asked. He didn't answer, just smiled and took my empty tray and placed it in front of him. When dinner was over, we stacked our trays on a rack near the door and put the plastic knives and forks in a bucket, a screw stood over it counting as utensils were dropped inside. Andy was first out of the dining room and waited for me in the corridor.

"Did ya see that screw bash that Wilson kid?" he said excitedly.

"I saw," I said nonchalantly as I kept walking.

"Fucking unreal" he giggled as he speeded up and headed back to our cell.

It wasn't long before I learned the routine. It wasn't that hard really as there was not much to it. Mornings started at six thirty with slopping out, a degrading procedure that belonged in the dark ages. Each prisoner would empty and rinse his piss pot which undoubtedly had stunk out his cell throughout the night, he would then fill a water jug and take it back to his cell where he would wash with just water. Soap wasn't given to prisoners, they had to buy it and if all you had were prison wages, you could either smell nice or buy half an ounce of tobacco, most prisoners didn't smell nice. Teeth were cleaned, once again with just water, toothpaste wasn't given out either. After you'd had a wash you would get dressed and empty your dirty water and fill up your drinking jugs. You were then ready for breakfast. Breakfast consisted of porridge, a pissy-grey looking colour with no hint of sugar and with more lumps than a teenager with raging acne. A rasher of bacon that was no thicker than a piece of string and finally two slices of bread and margarine. Tea was available but none of the prisoners drank it, it was rumoured that the authorities put bromide in it to stop you wanking and let's be honest in prison there's not much else to occupy your time.

Once you'd had breakfast you went back to your cell where, after about an hour, screws would come round and ask you if you wanted to work. Most prisoners would volunteer for any job going just to get out of their cell. I made that mistake once until I realized how those floors got so fucking shiny, four hours on my hands and knees with a scrubbing brush and a bucket of polish was not my idea of fun and I never made that mistake again. If you didn't want to work and as a remand prisoner you didn't have to, you just remained in your cell until exercise which was half an hour before lunch.

Exercise was a strange spectacle and if you've never been in prison it would strike you as an odd concept. Prison rules state that each prisoner is entitled to a half an hour's exercise each day and in order to satisfy this requirement prisoners would be let out into a big yard where they would walk around in circles. This in itself is not particularly strange but add to this the fact that you had to walk in a clockwise motion and could only walk in groups of two it all gets a little ridiculous. It was like a giant conga chain which occasionally joined together at both ends. The afternoons were the worst as bang up (the time spent in your cell) was longer and you would pace your cell floor until you were let out for tea at around six o clock. Three evenings a week we would get what was called association, this was when you would be let out of your cell in the evening to mix with other prisoners. You could watch TV, play pool, table tennis or just swap house breaking tips with other cons. It always made me smile when the screws would open the cell door and shout, "Everybody down to association." You would think the last thing you would want would be a load of criminals associating with each other, but they didn't just encourage it, they damn well made it compulsory.

The monotony was the worst thing, it suited some people to know what they would be doing a week on Tuesday, but I wasn't one of them. Nothing ever changed, and days just ran into weeks until you didn't even know what day it was. There were odd things that helped you get through, like trips to court where you would get to wear your own clothes and ride in the coach, or prison visits, either by friends, a relative or your solicitor. Everybody liked visits, me included. I only ever saw my solicitor, but he was a nice man who would bring me cigarettes and buy me tea and coffee as we chatted. It was always good to talk to somebody who wasn't either a prisoner or a screw. I made several visits to court whilst I was on remand. A court date was yet to be fixed and therefore every week I was marched before a judge who said the same thing week after week, "No application for bail, I therefore remand you into custody for a further seven days." It was bloody stupid, he may as well have rung up the prison asked to speak to me and told me over the phone. It would have saved all that pissing around, booking me out of prison, packing up what few possessions I'd managed to accumulate, the one-hour journey to court and lastly being strip searched each time on my return. I fucking hated strip searches, besides what were they looking for? I only ever saw my solicitor at court and he wasn't going to supply me with two ounces of cocaine, although I never actually asked him.

"Court tomorrow, Marriot, get your things ready for the morning, you never know you might get bail" said Mr Wakely smiling at me as he closed the cell door after association one Monday evening. I liked Mr Wakely, for a screw he was a nice guy. He was around sixty years old, with greying hair, silver rimmed glasses and smelled of cheap aftershave, he reminded me of a teacher I once had, always laughing and pulling your leg.

"Lucky bastard, wish I were going to court," said Andy as he pulled himself up onto his bunk. Andy no longer went to court. He was waiting to go to crown court and as such no longer had to attend the magistrates court on a weekly basis. The whole system was more than a little flawed. If you were a remand prisoner, that is waiting to be tried by a jury, you were entitled to certain privileges. These included daily visits by family and friends, cigarettes and tobacco, soaps, toothpaste, bottles of pop, sweets and chocolates, newspapers and spending money. All of these items could be brought in for you on your daily visits and after the screws had thoroughly checked them for contraband, they

154

would be delivered by room service directly to your cell. These privileges would cease the moment you were convicted, and you would then serve your sentence in a mainstream prison or young offender's institution. Prisoners who knew they were going to be found guilty would therefore delay their trial as long as possible in order to serve most of their sentence on remand, bearing in mind time served on remand was taken off any sentence you received when you were found guilty. It was not and is still not uncommon for convicted criminals to be released directly from court after a guilty verdict because they had served their sentence on remand. The main idea of the whole remand system is the presumption of innocence until proven guilty. It is only right that someone who has not been convicted of a crime should indeed be treated differently to convicted criminals, but what I never understood was that when you were committed for trial at crown court you were immediately treated as a convicted criminal and all privileges were removed. It would appear that you were then considered guilty even though you had not yet been tried. When I asked anyone, screws included why this was they didn't know and to be honest they didn't care.

When the cell door opened the following morning, I was already sitting on my bunk with my belongings in a clear plastic bag. My bed had been stripped and my sheets were stuffed into my pillowcase along with my gym kit and spare underwear. I would hand these in at reception as I left and upon my return ,they would issue me with new ones.

"See ya mate" called Andy as the screw opened the cell and I lugged my stuff out onto the landing.

"Yeah see ya," I called as the screw closed the door leaving Andy alone in the cell. It was crap when your cell mate went to court. It was a long day banged up alone with nobody to talk to. The worst part of it all was you knew if he got bail you were going to get a new cell mate. A new cell mate was a bad thing, you had no control over who it would be and besides it was kind of like dog training, you'd just

155

trained one and you had to start all over again.

"Come on Marriot, move your arse," the screw hollered up the stairs as I made my way down carrying my pillowcase over my shoulder.

"Better hurry up, he's a right bastard is Gnosher," came a voice from behind me. I turned to look and saw a black kid dressed in grey trousers. The grey trousers told me he had been committed to trial and was up in court today, remand prisoners wore brown trousers.

"You going for trial?" I asked as I quickened my step.

"Yeah, going down I reckon," said the black kid. I didn't answer I was by now three steps in front of him and hurrying as the screw was still shouting for me to get a move on.

Once in reception we were given our own clothes and quickly got dressed. It was a strange feeling, putting on your own clothes, it was like you suddenly became yourself again not just a name and number. It was also a time when you could see what other prisoners were really like, many prisoners build a story that they are successful criminals who were living the high life prior to being caught. It was mostly bullshit and when they were dressed in their old trainers and tatty jeans you knew it for sure. The odd one would be dressed in crisp pressed trousers, silk shirt and crocodile skin shoes. I kept away from these types they were mostly in for street robbery or drug dealing and would cut their granny's throat for a new pair of shoes.

After we had been given our breakfast we were then handcuffed and loaded on to a coach. I drew the short straw and was handcuffed to a screw; the rest of the inmates were handcuffed in pairs to each other. I was really annoyed, being chained to a screw was really going to spoil my day. It was always a bit of a giggle riding through the town and pulling faces at people or eyeing up any pretty girls we caught sight of. In truth after a while they didn't even need to be pretty, just female.

We eventually arrived at the court and as was the usual

156

procedure, a screw would march us, pair by pair into a side entrance, his eyes darting all around nervously. Once inside we would be placed into a holding cell that held a maximum of four prisoners in each, the handcuffs would be removed and there we would wait until either our solicitor came to see us, or we were called into court. The holding cells were located underneath the main magistrate's courts and were not dissimilar to a medieval dungeon. The cells had no natural light and were lit by a dim bulb that was housed in a vandal proof grille high on the domed ceiling. Concrete floors that stunk of urine, no seats and congealed food and dried sputum that hung from the ceiling like stalactites greeted you on each visit. The powers that be were obviously aware that the cells left a lot to be desired. If your solicitor wished to talk to you prior to your appearance in court, you would be led along the musky corridors into a nicely decorated and air-conditioned interview room, talk about double standards.

"What time you up?" asked the black kid I'd seen on the landing earlier.

"Ten thirty," I replied.

"You're fucking lucky, you could be shipped back with the afternoon lot, saves being stuck in this shit hole all day," he finished. I didn't say anything more, I disliked him on sight, he was cocky had too much to say and would turn on anyone who disagreed with him in the blink of an eye. I listened to him talking to another prisoner shortly after we'd been put in the holding cells. He was saying how he was some big shot from a rough part of the city and though he might do time he would be taken care of when he got out by the brothers. I nearly pissed my pants, he was all of seventeen years old and had obviously watched too many gangster films. I hated his arrogance and the fake Jamaican twang he injected into conversation, when he remembered to, of course. I thought it best to let this one lie and sat down in a corner of the cell and shut my eyes. I could still hear the black kid prattling on about this and that, how he would buss up anyone who giv im no respect. I smiled to myself and slipped into a half doze.

"Eh iz talking you man," a voice disturbed my tranquillity. I opened my eyes and looked up. The black kid was standing over me.

"What?" I snapped angrily, annoyed at being disturbed.

"Who you talking at man, yer thinks ya's mean er what?" snarled my new-found friend kicking me in the thigh as he spoke. I couldn't take this idiot seriously and really didn't want any trouble.

"Look just leave me alone," I said, shaking my head. Some people just don't know when to stop, as my father would say teasingly, "You play with the bull and you'll get a horn up your arse." This fucker was about to get gored.

"You want sum, iz gonna wup yer white ass, git up," declared the black kid loud enough for the whole cell block to hear or anyone else who was listening. I wasn't. I'd already decided on the best course of action. I knew if I tried to stand, he would probably kick me in the face or punch me, as I used my hands to lift myself up. With a sweep of my right hand I took out his legs at the knees and he fell backwards onto the concrete floor. I didn't wait, I was up and ready. I'd been taught never to kick a man when he's down, so I waited for him to get to his feet and as he stood I took a good long look at him he was about six feet tall, broad shouldered with scrawny legs and as he moved towards me, I noticed two gold teeth right in the front of his mouth. One appeared to have a red gem stone set in the middle. I couldn't resist it, I hit him with a right cross straight in his jewel encrusted gob. The sound of his head bouncing off the concrete floor echoed throughout the whole cell block and for a moment I thought I'd killed him.

"Fucking hell, is he dead?" asked another prisoner who had wisely pressed himself into the furthest corner away from the action. I leaned over our unusually quiet friend who was now lying on his side a pool of blood about six inches in diameter oozing from his mouth. "You still with us,

158

bigshot?" I said sarcastically. He let out a deep moan and tried to get up, his legs just buckled, and he fell back down on his face knocking himself unconscious.

"Give us a hand," I signalled to the other two prisoners. They didn't argue and helped me drag the limp body into a corner of the cell out of sight of the door. What happened next was weird even by my standards, we just sat in silence all three of us looking at the black kid and waiting for him to come round, not one of us taking our eyes off him. It was probably only a few minutes before signs of life started to show, it began with a low kind of moaning and then his legs started moving kind of like Buster used to do when he was asleep but trying to run.

"I think he's waking up," said one of the other kids, his voice high with excitement. I climbed to my feet and walked across the cell until I was standing over the bleeding mess that used to be the black kid.

"You okay?" I asked not out of concern for him but more so because I wanted to know he hadn't got brain damage. I didn't want any further charges.

"Yeah, I'm okay," he replied as he looked up at my face, the arrogant and cocky look he was wearing earlier was nowhere to be seen, the fire in his eyes had gone out. I'd seen that look a dozen times when I'd beaten someone in the ring, even before the fight was over, they'd lost, and they knew it.

"I'm Winston," said the black kid holding out his hand. He was still squatting in the corner his left hand cupping his mouth. He probably wasn't sure whether he could stand up and figured it best to stay where he was.

"Jack," I grinned as I took his hand and pulled him to his feet. "One thing," I said in a serious voice.

"What," said Winston a worried look on his face.

"Is your name really fucking Winston?" It broke the ice and we both started laughing. We were still laughing when the screws came and called me out to see my solicitor. Winston couldn't hide the huge blood stain that had spread across his silk shirt

"Sorry boss but I fell over and banged my face," he offered in his defence when the screw said, "What the fuck?" as he caught sight of him.

Chapter 12

Home truths

My solicitor's name was Mr Stone and as usual he was full of the joys of spring, he brought me lots of news, none of it good. "Jack we are going to ask the court today if we can have a two-week adjournment in order to gather reports for your defence, do you understand why we need to do this?" he said lifting an eyebrow as though to emphasise his question.

I was nobody's fool and being on remand every barrack room lawyer had given me the benefit of their advice. "Get your brief to ask for a phsyco report, it's easy to fool the prison shrink and if you do a good job you could get off" they'd say.

"Yeah, I nodded, got a fag?"

Mr Stone reached in his pocket and pulled out an unopened pack of cigarettes and a box of matches and threw them on the table. It meant a lot to me, he didn't even smoke. I will always remember the kindness he showed me, it was way beyond his job as a solicitor. I remember he once came out to the remand centre and visited me just because he knew I never had visitors. He never told me that, but he didn't ask me a single thing about my case on that visit, it was more about how I was and if I needed anything. I remember when he left, and I was taken back to my cell I thought what a nice thing to do.

After several minutes the screw came back opened my cell door and said, "Your brief left this for you." It was a plastic carrier bag, I opened it and found six bars of chocolate, three bags of sweets and two packs of cigarettes. I cried for nearly half an hour.

My court appearance was short and sweet, no change there then, no application for bail was made and I was remanded back into custody. The only difference was this time I had been remanded for two weeks, this was so the reports could be carried out that Mr Stone had requested. I arrived back at the remand centre early in the afternoon was stripped of my own clothes issued the standard prison garb and ushered back to my cell. The cell was empty, Andy was probably on work detail, so I settled myself on my bunk and began to read a book, 'Born Free,' how's that for irony?

It was around four o'clock when I heard the jingle of keys approaching my cell and the door swung open. "Marriot get your stuff and come with us," ordered one of the two screws standing outside the cell.

"Where am I going?" I asked.

"You'll see, git moving, Now," he screamed as if shouting louder would make me move faster, it didn't. I climbed off my bunk and began putting my belongings into my pillowcase.

"We haven't got all fucking day, hurry up," said the other screw who up until then I hadn't really looked at. I recognised him immediately. It was the screw who gave Wilson a slap in the dining room. I decided not to rock the boat, besides I knew that bastard had a short fuse and would love me to give him an excuse to kick me down the landing.

"Get moving, quicker," they both barked from behind me as I was frogmarched the entire length of that never-ending corridor. I had never been right to the end, but I knew what was there, it was the punishment block.

"Stand there and wait," said the screw who'd slapped Wilson. I watched him unhook his keys from his belt he chose the right one and pushed it into the lock of the heavy steel door I was standing beside.

"In," he motioned with his thumb. I didn't argue and as I turned to ask what was going on, I was met with the back of the door as it slammed behind me. The inside of a punishment cell does not take long to describe. It consists of four walls, no windows a bare floor and a mattress. If you're lucky and someone's remembered, you may have a jug of water and a piss pot. I took a long look around my new

162

surroundings, let out a deep sigh and flopped heavily onto the plastic covered mattress. I won't pretend I didn't know why I was down the block (punishment cells), I'd already worked out it was over my little run in with Winston. The thing that puzzled me most was why the bastard would go and grass me up, it was a big no-no in prison and besides we'd shook hands and I thought that was the end of the matter. I resigned myself to my lot leaned back against the wall and waited. It was around two hours later when I heard signs of movement in the passage outside. I could hear a trolley clanking and what sounded like a squeaky wheel as it was pushed along. I heard the bolt being drawn back and a hatch in my cell door opened.

"Grub up," smiled the prisoner as he held a tray with my evening meal on through the hatch. I jumped up and quickly took it from him and before I could say a word the hatch closed leaving me once again on my own but on the plus side with a tray of food. I remained in the punishment cell until after breakfast the following morning when I heard the distinctive sound of footsteps and jangling keys as someone approached my cell.

"Out," ordered a screw I knew to be Mr Adams. I'd seen him around but up until now had given him a wide berth. Mr Adams was a Principal Officer, this meant he was in charge of some of the other officers and carried rank. He was one of nature's freaks, a short squat bloke with a balding head and a huge mass of body hair that seemed to engulf his whole body. I always wondered how somebody could be so hairy yet be bald at the same time.

Adams fingered his collar as though trying to push back the bird's nest that was protruding from his white collar. "Against the wall," he said rather matter of factly.

I did as I was told and leant with my back against the wall in the corridor.

"Don't lean boy, you're not waiting for a fucking bus," he spat into my face.

"Right, listen up he continued, you're going in to see the

163

governor and I'm going to tell you how you will act, do you follow?"

I nodded.

"Right when I open the governor's door you will see a desk in front of you behind which the governor will be seated, you will march in hands by your sides and come to a halt two feet in front of it. You will then give your name and number and stand to attention unless instructed to sit. At no time will you interrupt the governor and you will answer only when spoken to, you got that?" he finished his eyes boring into mine.

I nodded my understanding; it did not seem an appropriate time to ask questions. I was sorely tempted to call him a jumped-up prick or make monkey noises like the other prisoners did as he walked past their cells, but it was just one of those childish thoughts and as soon as it entered my head, I dismissed it.

"Quick march," barked Adams as he opened the door to the governor's office. I did as I'd been briefed and stood to attention the mandatory two feet in front of the wooden desk the governor sat behind. I noticed out of the corner of my eye another screw who was already in the room. He moved towards me and flanked my right shoulder. Adams came and took up position on my left. I nearly giggled, what did they think I was going to do launch myself over the desk and squeeze the life out of the governor's scrawny throat. I was fifteen years old, wankers. The governor cleared his throat and I turned to meet his gaze, he cleared his throat again but still said nothing. What the hell was he waiting for?

I studied his face intently taking in every detail. He was about fifty years old and his face carried the lines of a man who had had far too many sleepless nights. His hair was neatly cut into a short back and sides, a neatly trimmed beard completed his appearance. I felt a nudge from Officer Adams and turned to look at him and then it hit me, "Marriot 667198 Sir," I blurted out my face flushed with embarrassment. The whole room seemed to let out a deep breath, the way you do when you wake from a nightmare and wiping the sweat from your forehead realize it was only a dream.

"Marriot you are on report for the offence of assault. It is alleged that whilst in the holding cells of the Magistrates courts you assaulted another inmate namely Winston Brook, how do you plead?" said the governor throwing himself back in his seat and crossing his arms. He had a look on his face like he'd just finished his closing speech at the trial of the century. I had a feeling that whatever I said it would make no difference and that we were just going through the motions. I remained silent.

"Nothing to say for yourself?" the governor coaxed shifting in his seat, I must therefore assume you are guilty," he said triumphantly. "One-week solitary; take him away," and with the words of the governor still ringing in my ears, I was pushed back into the punishment cell and the door slammed behind me.

"Fucking bastards" I shouted as I kicked out at the heavy steel door. The hatch opened, and Adams face grinned in at me

"Any more of that and you'll be on report tomorrow as well, now shut it."

The hatch snapped shut and as I listened to his footsteps getting further away under my breath I repeated, "Fucking bastards, fucking bastards." It was going to be a long week, no fags and nobody to talk to, but I was never one to dwell on things so picking up my book I settled down to read. Before I opened it to the page I'd marked, I studied the front cover, "Born fucking free" I said out loud and began laughing hysterically.

I spent my first official day in solitary plotting my revenge. Winston was going to pay for grassing me up. I know I'd given him a smack in the mouth but at the end of the day if you can't walk the walk then you shouldn't talk the talk that was my philosophy. Anyway we'd shook hands and to me it was sacred, it meant whatever the problem, when you were offered a hand and you took it that was it. I guess not everyone has the same morals as me. I smiled as I thought of how I would make him pay, this time I would hurt him badly and I'd make sure I knocked those gold teeth down his black throat.

I eventually grew bored with planning Winston's comeuppance and my thoughts focused on my father and throughout the rest of the week, I would talk to him under my breath. I figured as long as nobody saw me, and voices didn't start to answer me back, I was reasonably sane. It was difficult to establish what time of day it was in solitary, as I only had artificial light, so I began to form a routine that was based around meal times. I would eat breakfast and then do one hundred press-ups, two hundred sit-ups and three hundred squats. It had been a while since I pushed my body to any degree and for the first few days, every muscle in my body screamed out for rest, it wasn't going to get any, if I didn't exercise what the hell else was I going to do?

After lunch I would have a sleep and if I woke I would do some shadow boxing until I was exhausted and would fall onto my mattress out of breath and sweating heavily. The cell must have stunk, all that sweat and a piss pot brimming to the top stuck in the corner. I never noticed but when you stink you're always the last to know aren't you? Tea time was always welcome it marked the end of another day and although the next day would be exactly the same, it was one less day you had to serve, and it felt good.

It was on the afternoon of the second day that I heard a voice whispering my name under the cell door. "Marriot, Marriot, you there?" it asked.

"I'm here who's that?" I whispered, my face pressed to the ground by the bottom of the cell door.

"I've got somat for ya, I'll put it under the door, Andy says he'll send some more tomorrow," the voice said. I heard a rustling noise and could see something being shoved through the gap at the base of the door. I grabbed it, it was a

166

piece of paper folded in half, I hurriedly unfolded it as I sat on the floor.

"You're a fucking life saver Andy," I laughed as I fingered the tobacco, cigarette papers and four matches lovingly wrapped in toilet paper. Each day the same voice would call out and push my daily cigarette ration under the door. There would be about enough for three smokes each time and I would have one after each meal, I felt like a king as I reclined on my makeshift bed and blew smoke rings into the air. I would look at the cell door and throw two fingers up, "Fuck you screws," I'd giggle. "Solitary, fucking, bring it on!".

The week came to end but I wouldn't say it passed quickly it felt more like a month. The cell door opened, and in a flash, I had grabbed my things and was marched down that bloody long corridor and back into my cell. Andy was out working, and it was dinner time before I saw him. I had just taken a seat in the dining room and was trying to figure out what the gooey mess on my tray was pretending to be when Andy rushed over.

"Good to see ya mate, did ya get the fags I sent?" he asked excitedly.

"Yeah mate thanks, I mean it, thanks," I repeated.

"Ah, think nowt of it," he smirked and gave me a playful dig in the arm.

"Paton, stop yacking and get your dinner or do ya want to go back to your cell without it?" shouted a screw across the room.

"Shit better go mate, save me that seat," Andy said pointing to the empty chair at the side of me. After Andy had been and got his food he practically ran back to my table and threw himself into the chair. "Everybody's talking 'bout you, you know," he grinned as he shovelled mouthfuls of potato into his mouth.

"Talking about me, why?" I asked a little confused.

"Everybody says you dropped Winston wiv one punch, they say he's supposed to be hard and besides nobody likes him," he said as if to emphasise his point.

167

I didn't answer I was too busy looking around the dining room for Winston. I couldn't see him. "Where is he, I want a word with that bastard?" I asked.

"Where's who, you mean Lewis?" said Andy a puzzled look on his face.

"Lewis, who the fuck is Lewis," I asked, now I was confused.

"He's the grass who told the screws about you chinning Winston," Andy declared triumphantly.

"Wait a fucking minute, Winston grassed me up not this Lewis," I said getting more and more impatient.

"No he didn't, it was Lewis, he was one of the others in the cell when you hit Winston. He came back and grassed you to the screws, now do you see?" sighed Andy.

"Where is this Lewis?" I said standing up from my seat. Andy put his hand on my arm.

"Sit down mate he 'ain't 'ere" he said.

"Well, where the fuck is he," I demanded. Andy then went into a long drawn out story as to Lewis's whereabouts, he was in the hospital wing with a broken nose and concussion. It transpired that when Winston had found out what he'd done, he decided he would dish out his own justice.

"Bloody hell, this just gets better and better, so where's Winston I don't see him?" I said as I continued scanning the dining hall. "Winston's down the block, that's the trouble wiv beating up a grass, if ya don't kill him, he grasses you up as well," said Andy shaking his head in mock disgust.

I took a leaf out of Andy's book and made sure Winston was provided with a few smokes each day, it was the least I could do after I'd misjudged him. It wasn't long before I began to notice a change in the general attitude of the other inmates towards me. I was suddenly Mr Popular and the other lads would nod as they passed me on the landing. When I went to the food hatch for my meals, I would get double portions and a wry smile from whoever was piling the food vertically on to my tray. It got more than a little ridiculous, and on several occasions, I returned to my table so laden down with extra food, I could have fed a small village. I had seen all of this before just in other forms and recognised it for what it was. I was glad when after a few days, things calmed down a little, as the saying goes, "Today's headlines tomorrow's fish and chips wrapper."

It was the day Winston was released from solitary that the rest of the inmates finally got the message. I'd heard their pathetic whispering, how I was going to give Winston another hiding when I saw him, how I'd told a kid I'd never even spoken to that I was going to do Winston just because I hated him. What a load of bollocks, I had no intention of harming Winston. I didn't hate him. The rest of the prison population did but that was not my problem and I wasn't going to beat anyone up just to please those cowardly bastards. It was during our exercise period in the yard that I first saw Winston after his release from the block. I was walking around with Andy puffing away on a roll up.

"Hey look, there's Winston," said Andy excitedly. Andy knew I was not interested in Winston and that I was happy to let the rest of the prison believe what they wanted. Because of this, he had done as I asked and said nothing of my plan to anyone.

"I can't wait to see this. It'll be fucking unreal," Andy sniggered. Winston's arrival had not gone unnoticed by the other inmates and as they walked round in ever decreasing circles, they lowered their voices and began looking expectedly at me. I didn't want to disappoint them and broke away from Andy and walked hurriedly towards Winston. He'd seen me coming, and the expression on his face was a mix of confusion and fear. At this point everybody in the yard had stopped talking and every head was turned in my direction. I noticed four screws beginning to twitch, they looked nervously back and forth at each other, each wanting the other to decide what to do. If it followed their usual form they would wait until you'd knocked each other about a bit and then come in mob-handed and overpower you from behind. I was by now around six feet away from Winston and I stopped as his eyes met mine. My face was expressionless my body language giving little away. Winston's eyes widened, and he didn't know whether to smile and greet me or set off running.

"Winston, I want a fucking word with you," I said loud enough for everyone to hear. There was a sharp intake of breath by the whole yard and for a split second you could have heard a gnat fart. Winston stood frozen to the spot his eyes darting around as if seeking a means of escape. It was too late, I was on him. I grabbed his right hand and shook it really firmly.

"Good to see ya mate, how's things?" I smiled and burst out laughing. Winston's face broke into a wide smile his gold crowns glistening in the afternoon sun.

"Tings is good man, ya know," he said as he patted my shoulder with his left hand.

"Come on let's walk, every fuckers watching," I motioned with my head.

"Yeah man," replied Winston as we fell into step. The yard suddenly sprang back into life as though a switch had been thrown, people started talking and resumed their normal walking pace as though nothing had happened, nothing had, I was my own man and they'd just learnt that. As I walked chatting quietly to Winston, I felt good and a couple of screws nodded in my direction as if to say, "Good lad, Good lad."

I spent a lot of time chatting to Winston after that memorable day. I even managed to convince him to drop the attitude and fake Jamaican twang when he spoke to the other prisoners. It took some doing but once I'd explained how unpopular he'd become, I think he realised that his strategy had badly backfired. I understood what drove him to be openly aggressive to others. It's like a small dog that barks and snarls as you approach it, it is saying stay away, not because it will bite you but because it's scared. Winston was that small dog. To say I managed to mould Winston into a new character would be a bit of an exaggeration He would, at times revert to type and I would occasionally overhear him slipping back into his old ways. I would catch his eye and give him a disapproving look as if to say, you're doing it again, and in turn he would shrug his shoulders as if to say, I can't help it. What did I care people were who they were and as the saying goes, you can lead a horse to water!

The shrinks soon got to work on my reports for court and I was called out each afternoon after lunch to visit the prison psychiatrist. It would make me flinch each time a screw would call out across the packed dining room, "Marriot straight to the shrink, after you've finished your lunch." I knew the screws did it on purpose. It gave them some kind of sick pleasure to try and humiliate you. It didn't work, most of the other kids just figured you for a complete phsyco and would give you a very wide berth, which was just what you wanted. The prison psychiatrist was a complete waste of space and would spend the best part of two hours asking stupid questions, questions which I mostly refused to answer.

" So Marriot," he would begin as he crossed his legs and leant back in his chair staring at the ceiling. I always thought he wanted to talk to me, for me to open up, but he couldn't even be bothered to use my first name, fucking wanker! My reports were never going to be favourable, they mostly read uncooperative, aggressive and volatile. I didn't care, it became a source of great fun as I would wind the bastard up and tie him in knots. Dr M. Benning it said on the certificate above his desk BSC and PHD, what a joke, for an educated man he was a bloody imbecile.

"So Marriot, tell me about your mother?" he smiled as he looked under his half-moon gold rimmed glasses. I was sure he wore them to add to his persona as he never seemed to actually look through them.

"I tell you what Doc, you tell me about my mother because I don't know her. She left when I was a nipper," I

171

declared smugly as I sat in the comfy leather chair in his office. Mr Benning blushed and began rummaging through the report that was on his desk in front of him.

"Oh I see sorry about that, I was getting you mixed up with someone else," he apologised his face a lovely crimson colour. "Well let's talk about you and how you feel, yes that's what we'll do, what do you think?" he smiled nervously.

"You want to know how I feel, what I think? I'll tell you what I think, I think you should read my bloody report before you see me next time, don't you?" I scowled. I was going to enjoy this. I wasn't going to let him off that easily and I made sure he knew it.

"Now, now that kind of attitude won't get us anywhere will it? I think perhaps we've reached a point today where we should leave matters, so I'll see you again tomorrow, okay?" he said standing and extending his arm towards the door.

I shook my head and started laughing. I was still laughing as the screw led me back to my cell.

"You will have to visit the shrink more often if he cheers you up this much," laughed Mr Wakely as he opened my cell door. His comment was just too much, and I collapsed into fits of hysterics as I threw myself headlong onto my bunk.

"Kids," said Mr Wakely as he pulled the door closed.

My next court appearance soon arrived and armed with the prison shrinks reports the Magistrate took a brief look and folding his arms smugly across his chest, committed me for trial at crown court. I had always refused to enter a guilty plea, I didn't feel guilty and I sure as hell was not going to plead guilty. Why should I? 'She had it coming,' I thought, my mind twisted with hatred. Mr Stone was fighting a losing battle. I gave him no defence, no excuses and no chance of getting me off. I think he was more than relieved when I was committed to Crown court as this meant my defence case would have to be handled by a barrister. I was returned to the remand centre and issued with a new set of grey clothing.

"Oh Crown court," the other inmates would grin as they looked at your prison greys, happy they were still on full privileges. The loss of my rights to daily visits and goods, I could have brought in, didn't really bother me. I had no visits and I never got anything brought in, as I had nobody on the outside. But it did bother Andy. I'd been having food parcels and cigarettes sent in by his relatives on a weekly basis, they would send them in to me as Andy was in greys and couldn't have them himself. It was a good arrangement I would get his parcel, and he would share it with me. I guess all good things must come to an end, but that's life!

The build up to my trial at Crown court was hectic. I had more reports carried out, social workers, and probation officers and yet more shrinks poking at and analysing me. I felt I was constantly being bombarded with questions, my whole life put under the scrutiny of anyone who wanted to nose around in it. My barrister had decided that an independent psychiatrist was needed in order to rubbish the prison shrinks original report. I, therefore, began to be seen twice weekly by Mr Golati a professor of psychology. Mr Golati was a real gentleman, he was around fifty years old, of Asian origin and always impeccably dressed. I liked him, he had no edge and was genuinely sympathetic towards your predicament. I remember leaving one interview with him after I'd cried throughout the whole hour.

"Be strong, things will always work out, you'll see," he smiled encouragingly as he touched my arm gently. An adult had not shown me such tenderness for longer than I could remember. I don't know how he managed it, he got right inside your head and prised things out you didn't want him to know. When you made a simple comment, he would write something on his note pad and at a well-timed moment drop it into the conversation, I detested that. You could never take something back you'd said, he had it down in black and white, and before you knew it, everything would tumble out and there were no more secrets.

My visits with my barrister were always difficult, he was a snob and tended to look down his perfectly proportioned nose at me. I had no doubt he was good at his job, but that was it, you could tell that to him that was exactly what it was, a job. The thing I enjoyed most about my barrister's visits were the packs of cigarettes he would slip me. They weren't from him they were courtesy of Mr Stone: God bless him.

"Well Jack, we are in court next Thursday and fingers crossed we might get you out of here," said Mr Kenyon my barrister. I looked across the table and shrugged my shoulders.

"You don't want to get out, Jack?" he said his head cocked slightly to one side.

"Where would I go? Nobody wants me," I said my voice a little shaky. Mr Kenyon swallowed hard and for the first time, I thought I could detect some emotion in his sun-tanned face, but all too soon it was gone. He stroked his immaculately styled greying hair and looking at me with his lifeless brown eyes said dismissively, "We'll worry about that if we get you off." I wasn't an idiot and I was sure what he had in mind could only be a care order. It didn't make any difference to me prison, borstal a local authority care home they were all the same, government institutions.

I had become quite settled in my surroundings at the remand centre and didn't really want to go to court. I had friends, and nobody gave me any hassle. I was therefore somewhat sullen the day before my trial.

"Cheer up mate you could be off tomorrow, I'll miss ya," teased Andy poking me with his elbow as we sat down to lunch.

"Fuck off," I smiled, shoving him with my hand, it was a little harder than I'd intended and sent Andy falling backwards onto the floor his chair clattering to the ground beside him. The metallic clanging of chair legs had the whole dining room turning around in their seats to see what the noise was.

"Get up yer daft twat, before the screws see," I said, as I stood up and lifted Andy's chair back on its feet.

"Marriot get your arse over here, now," screamed the screw standing at the end of our row of tables.

"Oh shit, it had to be Tennyson," I said under my breath to Andy as I helped him up. Mr Tennyson was the screw I'd seen on the first day I arrived, the bully who relished any opportunity to dish out his own form of instant justice. I still flinched when I thought back to the way he slapped Wilson. I was not sure I could have let him do that to me and not retaliate. For that reason, I had always avoided any form of contact or interaction between Tennyson and myself, that is up until now.

"So, what have you got to say for yourself Marriot, eh you like throwing your weight around do you?" Tennyson said as he walked up behind me shoving me in the back. 'He was bloody keen' he didn't even give me chance to walk over to him, just couldn't contain himself,' I thought, as I turned to face him. "Well I'm waiting, why did you push Paton over?" he continued pushing his chest out into his trade Jack stance and pressing his nose into mine.

I wasn't going to answer I knew there was little point and I sure as hell was not going to grovel just be humiliated in front of the whole dining room.

"He, he didn't push me Sir, I, I fell, he was just helping me up," stuttered Andy trying his best to come to my defence. It wasn't going to work Tennyson had gone into overdrive and he wanted his pound of flesh.

Tennyson immediately spun around and focused his attention on poor Andy. "You calling me a liar, are you Paton, I'm a liar, am I? I know what I fucking saw," and with these words he went to move towards Andy.

"Yes Sir, I pushed him it was my fault," I said firmly as I stepped in front of Tennyson. He snapped his head in my direction and our eyes met.

175

I could see by his expression that he'd lost all self-control. "You like throwing people around, do you?" he screamed into my face covering me with spit. I turned my head away in disgust and wiped my mouth with the back of my hand. "How do you like it?" he said grabbing me by the throat and pushing me backwards across a table, dinner trays and food flew into the air and all over the kids sitting around it. They jumped to their feet and made a hasty retreat to a safe distance. I wasn't that lucky as I tried to stop myself falling, I put my hand onto the edge of one of the food trays and the contents spewed upwards covering my face and hair, the metal tray hit me in the mouth and blood ran down my chin. I managed to stay on my feet and as I steadied myself, Tennyson tried to grab me again.

I'd had enough. I pushed his hand away and took a step back. "Touch me again and I'll fucking kill you," I snarled my eyes daring him to step towards me. It was in that instant that what I'd always known about bullies was proved to be true. For all his posturing and shouting, Tennyson was a spineless coward, he quickly stepped backward his eyes darting around nervously as he looked for help from the other screws. "Come on then, you fucking wanker," I shouted, as I picked up some poor kids dinner tray and launched its full contents all over Tennyson. I must admit if it had not been so serious it would have been funny. Tennyson was covered from head to toe in mashed potato, gravy and semolina pudding, he looked like he'd been tarred and feathered. I was getting into the swing of things by now and picked up another tray and threw that as well, unfortunately Tennyson ducked, and it sailed over his head hitting some poor kid I didn't know right on the bonce.

During all of this, the rest of the inmates were laughing themselves to tears. Those that weren't laughing began chanting "Marriot, Marriot, Marriot," as they banged on their tables.

It happened so quickly, it is difficult to recall the actual events, but I was suddenly overpowered from behind and

176

dragged to the floor. I knew it was over and didn't resist but this made no difference to the treatment I received, as I was dragged down the corridor on the way to the block. Two screws had hold of my feet and two had hold of my arms, they took great satisfaction in banging my body into every cast iron radiator we passed, and it was during this point that Tennyson took the opportunity to kick me right in the face.

"Not so fucking tough now are you, you fucker!" he grinned as he drew back his foot for a second go.

"That's enough," shouted Mr Wakely who had just walked out of a side office. I could have bloody kissed him.

A minute later I was in a cell nursing a black eye, cut mouth and a nose that resembled the mashed potato that I'd merrily thrown around moments earlier. It dawned on me it probably wasn't one of my best decisions.

I'd only been in the punishment cell for twenty minutes or so and assumed I was about to get a group kicking as I heard the door being unlocked. I jumped to my feet and put my back to the wall to the rear of the cell and clenched my fists my heart beginning to pound heavily as the door began to open wider and wider.

I let out a sigh of relief when I heard Mr Wakely's voice, "It's Mr Wakley, Marriot, you okay lad?" he called out as he put his head around the door.

"Yeah, I'll live Sir," I said, lowering my hands as my whole body relaxed.

Mr Wakely cautiously entered the cell and as he did so he took a closer look at me. "Oh lad, you're in a bit of a state aren't you?" he said as he reached out and held my chin in his hand turning my head into the light to get a better look. "I won't be a minute, I'll be right back," he said, like he'd just remembered he'd left a chip pan on and with that he was gone. It was a few minutes later when Mr Wakely returned he brought a first-aid kit and as he sat beside me on my mattress he gently cleaned up my face with antiseptic. "Ahh," I flinched as the antiseptic stung my lip. It was very badly cut on the inside; my teeth had done most of the damage when Tennyson booted me.

"Ahh, what do you mean Ahh? A big tough lad like you," smiled Mr Wakely a hint of sarcasm, not wasted on me.

"You know lad, you can't win with people like Tennyson. He hides behind his uniform, he's corrupt and if I had anything to do with it, people like him would never be allowed to put on the uniform." He stopped dabbing my face and ran his hand through his silver hair and shook his head. "You know why I came into this job Jack?" he asked, as he pushed his glasses further up his nose. It was the first time a screw had ever used my first name and it sounded really peculiar. He continued "I came into the prison service because I wanted to help kids like you, I wanted to make a difference, to maybe steer some of you onto a different path. The fact is Jack that I never really did that. I got caught up in just doing the job and now it's too late, I retire next month. He paused for a moment and shook his head. "Don't throw your life away Jack, this may seem like it is forever, but it will only be a small part of your life, learn from it, take whatever is offered, take your exams learn a trade, better yourself and don't waste your life, it's precious."

I shifted my position and leaned forward looking into his eyes, "Sir, you don't always have a choice you know. I didn't want to be here. I know what I did was wrong but I had no choice, I was on my own, nobody could help me, I was alone…" my voice trailed off and began to picture my Dad, I missed him so much, my eyes began to fill up and although I tried I couldn't stop myself and the tears began to fall down my cheeks.

"Eh lad, come on, don't let em beat you, your stronger than most, I know I've watched you," said Mr Wakely as he put an arm around my shoulder. I eventually managed to regain some composure and as I wiped my eyes I looked up at this kind and gentle man.

I smiled "If you tell anyone about this I'll have to kill you, you know that?"

Chapter 13

Judgement day

It was only the fact that I was in Crown court the following day that I escaped further punishment. The remand centre had to send me to court and I could therefore not be brought in front of the governor to answer whatever charge they chose to stick on me. It must have really pissed them off as they let me out in the morning knowing that I would very likely not be coming back whatever the outcome of the trial. It appeared for once that luck was on my side, as usual I was wrong.

I arrived at the court around ten o'clock but instead of being placed in the holding cells I was taken directly to the interview room.

"Your barrister will be here in a moment, wait there," said the screw as he opened the door. I heard him walk away and the internal security gate in the corridor close behind him.

'Well today's the day,' I said to myself as I took a seat in one of the three plastic chairs positioned around the wooden table. I had not been in this interview room before and as I scanned it from floor to ceiling, I came to the conclusion it was much the same as any other. I reached into my pocket took out my tobacco and rolling papers and quickly rolled a cigarette. I was quite the expert by now; weeks on remand had taught me something at least. I struck a match and inhaled deeply as the cigarette took hold. I shook the match to extinguish it and flicked it across the room tilting my head back as I slowly breathed out, plumes of smoke danced across the ceiling fanning out until they disappeared. A few seconds later I heard the, by now familiar noises of a screw approaching, the security gate rattled, and Mr Kenyon strutted into the interview room. I hadn't given a thought to my outward appearance it didn't matter after all it wasn't the first time, I'd had a black eye, swollen nose and fat lip.

Mr Kenyon was of a different opinion.

"What on earth has happened to your face? You can't go into court looking like that, what happened?" he asked as he placed a bundle of files on the table in front of me.

"You don't want to know," I said shaking my head and rolling my eyes.

"I bloody do want to know," he said, his voice now quite stern. I'm going into court and will need to explain to the jury why you look like you've been hit by a bus. This is not good Jack, not good," he shook his head in dismay. It wasn't until Mr Kenyon explained the gravity of the situation that the penny eventually dropped. I was on trial for a crime of violence, my defence wanted to convince the jury that it was an isolated incident carried out in the heat of the moment and whilst suffering from temporary insanity. The state of my face would be enough to convince the jury Mr Kenyon was talking out of his arse, and probably for the first time in his career, Mr Kenyon had no idea what he was going to do.

"Can't we get an adjournment?" I said smiling at my own initiative as Mr Kenyon took a seat opposite me and put his face in his hands.

He looked up. "An adjournment? an adjournment?" he repeated. "This is the day of your trial, if we could get an adjournment and I say if because we don't have a valid reason, do you know how long it would take to get a new trial date, bloody weeks, that's what bloody weeks." He stood up and began pacing the floor. "Got to think, think, think," he repeated as he slapped his palm against his temple. "Right you stay there, I'll be back," he said decisively as he grabbed his files and in a flash, headed out of the door the jacket pocket of his pin striped suit tearing on the door handle as he flounced out.

"Bollocks," I heard him curse as his footsteps echoed along the passageway. I remained seated at the table and looking into the air I declared loudly "Oh why me, God, why me?"

It was around an hour and a half later when Mr Kenyon

180

returned minus his jacket and a sense of humour. "It's on, we will have to do our best, I'll be back again to go through the procedure just give me ten minutes, okay?" he asked, closing the door without waiting for a reply.

I stuck two fingers up. "Fuck you," I mouthed silently.

Just then the door swung back open, "Oh yeah, these are for you," he said throwing me a pack of cigarettes. "Courtesy of Mr Stone," he said grumpily.

"Who else?" I smiled and as the door closed again I said quietly "They weren't fucking going to be from you, were they? You stuck up prick." I hurriedly unwrapped the pack of cigarettes, removed one and lit it. I stood up walked over to the wall and leant my shoulder heavily against it. I knew I was in a whole world of trouble and that the jury would without doubt find me guilty. I was worried, scared and extremely pissed off. And then from nowhere like a bolt from the blue it hit me, a plan a bloody big fat perfect lovely plan.

"Right," said Mr Kenyon, as the door opened he was about to continue, but stopped mid-sentence when he saw my predicament. I was curled up on the floor holding my stomach and writhing around as if in agony. "Jack you alright?" he said looking concerned as he stooped over me.

"Oh I'm in agony, I need a doctor, it really hurts" I said, through gritted teeth and that was that, mission accomplished I was on my way to hospital under prison guard before you could say 'Adjournment.' I was quite surprised how easily they were all taken in although Mr Kenyon did smooth the way a little. I heard him saying to the screw in the holding cells that I had obviously been involved in a fight and that I may have internal injuries and that it was his responsibility to ensure that I received the appropriate treatment. I underestimated our Mr Kenyon I know he only went along with the ruse because he didn't want to end up with egg on his face in court, it was never out of concern for me, but it worked, and I couldn't have given a shit as to his motives.

I spent the night in the general infirmary a screw glued to my side even when I took a piss. It was bloody humiliating. I would see the nurses gossiping in a huddle and then, as if on cue they would turn and stare at me before carrying on as though I wasn't there. I had several tests each of them inconclusive, what a surprise! In the end they gave up trying as I had started to get better and anyway, I'm sure they wanted the bed. Later that night I was given some medication and moved into a side room, this was purely to spare other patients the indignity of having to look at a criminal shackled to his bed and not to cover any embarrassment I felt. The morning came far too quickly, it was good not to be sleeping in a prison bed and some of the nurses were actually quite pleasant to me. I liked that it had been a long time since I'd been fussed over. Anyway I thought, I had got my adjournment and that was what I wanted so back to the remand centre it was.

My feet never touched the ground, straight back to bloody solitary confinement and up before the governor the same afternoon. I hadn't forgotten about the dining room incident but in a kind of naïve way, I thought that they might let it drop, no bloody such luck.

"So Marriot what have you got to say about your behaviour?" said the governor as he looked at me questioningly. I was about to protest my innocence but caught sight of Tennyson walking into the room and stand behind me. I turned to look at him and the two screws stood at my side moved nearer to me. Tennyson gave me a sly smirk and quickly looked away.

"Well?" said the governor waiting for a reply. "What's the point Sir, you're not interested in what I've got to say, you've already made up your mind, do what you like I don't care," I said, my voice raised in anger.

"Well I must find the charge proven, solitary two weeks, take him away" said the governor wringing his hands. I was quickly marched back to my cell by the two screws that had been standing by my side with Tennyson following on a few yards behind.

The cell door slammed and as I heard the screws walk away the hatch flung open, it was Tennyson. "You see you little bastard, you fuck with me and I always win." The hatch closed, "Sleep tight, I'll be thinking of you," his voice trailed off and he broke into a whistle as he walked away.

"Not always, not always Tennyson," I scowled as I slid down the wall and hugged my knees. I was going to get even, I didn't know how, but I was, and that thought raised my spirits during those boring days on my own with only my thoughts to keep me company.

It must have been my lucky day. The screw who opened my door on the last morning of my solitary confinement was none other than Mr Wakely.

"Eh Jack, what we going to do with you?" he smiled. "Come on, get your gear, let's get you back on the wing."

"Can I go back in with Paton?" I said in a way that many fathers would recognise when their kids wanted something.

"We'll see, get your stuff and I'll be back in ten minutes," he said, as he pulled the door closed. Twenty minutes later I was back on the wing and Mr Wakely was opening the cell door of Andy's pad.

"Cheers Sir," I called over my shoulder as I threw my pillowcase onto the bed.

"Just keep your nose clean Jack and stay away from Tennyson, you hear me?" he said as he turned away and gently pulled the door closed. As usual Andy was out, he would volunteer for any job going in order to get out of the cell besides how else would he do his trading. Trade was what made life bearable, you could swap anything tobacco, sweets, toothpaste, biscuits and orange juice, you just had to put yourself about, and Andy certainly did that.

The cell door opened around half an hour before lunch and an excited Andy bounded in. He was like an excited puppy when he saw me. "What yer doing back here? I thought you'd got off or been sent down," he said excitedly.

I spent the remainder of the time before lunch telling him

183

the full story.

"Fuck me mate, what you need is cheering up," he said as he climbed off his bunk and rummaged in a draw under the table. "Here, it's yours, have it" he beamed as he held out the biggest bar of chocolate I had ever seen.

"I can't take that mate, besides where'd you get it?" I asked.

"Oh I got another kid in browns getting parcels off me mam," he laughed as he broke a large piece off and threw it at me.

"You're really cut out for this prison caper," I said, shaking my head as I shovelled chocolate into my mouth. Andy told me later that the reason he was so surprised to see me was that he had a cell-mate already and he must have been moved to another cell in order for me to move in, this never happened. I've said it before and I'll say it again, God bless Mr Wakely.

I was soon given a new court date and with it looming up I began to get visits from my barrister again. "I don't want to know Jack, but if you faked that illness to delay your trial, you're one smart kid," Mr Kenyon laughed on his first visit.

I never told him the truth I didn't need to. Besides, he would have been put in a compromising position if I had made him privy to that information. We reached a new understanding after that. Mr Kenyon began to show a kinder more considerate disposition than I'd seen previously and in return I was civil and gave him snippets of information that could help my defence. I began to feel more optimistic with regards to the trial. I knew I would have to be punished in some way if I was found guilty, but Mr Kenyon assured me if that were to happen any sentence would be light with it being my first offence. So with this new-found confidence, I began to look forward to my trial. I wanted it over, one way or another, besides, I couldn't stay indefinitely on remand.

I managed to keep out of trouble for the remainder of my

stay in Thorpe Arch and when the day before my trial arrived, I was relieved I'd not seen the inside of the block for a third time. I'd even kept Tennyson at arms-length and when he was in close proximity, I was careful not to give him an excuse, the excuse I know he was just waiting for. I would be aware of his eyes boring into me from under his peaked cap, the way he puffed out his chest and stiffened his arms as I walked past, none of it was wasted. I took note of it all but let it wash over me. I did have a burning desire to get even but had accepted that I would never get the chance. I'd long since learnt we don't get everything we want in this world!

It was my final bang up in Thorpe Arch, we had just returned from association and the cell doors were ceremoniously closed behind us. We would not be let out until the following morning and then I would be out of there for good.

"Well that's it, Andy, our last night together," I said, as I went over to the barred window and gazed out over the exercise yard.

"Yeah mate, I suppose I'll end up sharing with some right wanker who bores me to death, thanks mate, you could always throw another sicky?" he said patting me on the back.

"You're bloody nuts; as much as I enjoy your company, I'm not going for the record of being the longest prisoner on remand. I'll leave that to you," I chuckled as I turned around and pushed him onto the bottom bunk. "You know the one thing I regret?" I said a serious tone to my voice.

Andy sat up propping a pillow behind his head and looking up at me said, "What's that then mate?"

"Tennyson, I wish I could have sorted that arrogant bastard, he needs sorting the fucking bully," I finished as I pulled out a chair turned it round and sat facing Andy.

"Listen mate, forget that prick, tomorrow he'll just be a distant memory and besides there 'ain't nowt any of us can do, you know what I mean?"

185

I knew Andy was right, but it still didn't make me feel any better. I jumped out of the chair and began pacing the cell. I eventually stopped once again in front of the window, I put my hands on the bars and squeezed, my knuckles turning white. "I fucking hate that bastard, Argh, he gets me so mad," I shouted as I shook the bars several times.

Andy decided that no response was needed and in order to calm me down blurted out, "Game of draughts?" as he jumped off the bunk and groped about under the bed. I shook my head and smiled as Andy straightened up blowing dust from the top of the box he'd just found.

"Draughts, that'll make me feel a whole load better," I laughed "Go on then set em up."

Andy was shit at drafts but insisted we play game after game in an effort to tire me into submission. It was around eleven o'clock when a dull thud at the window startled us both.

"What was that?" I said.

"I didn't hear owt, come on it's your move," said Andy dismissively.

"No, no, I heard something," I repeated as I stood up and walked over to the window and looked out. "Urgh dirty bastards, it's a fucking shit parcel," I said screwing my face up and turning away in disgust. A shit parcel is something anybody who has been in prison would have come across at some point. If you imagine being confined in a cell with no toilet just a piss pot then the last thing you would want to do is take a crap in it, the smell as it languished in the corner of your cell overnight would be enough to make you sick, an ingenious remedy was called for and prisoners are nothing if not ingenious. The shit parcel works like this, you would firstly explore every avenue to avoid having to make one as taking a dump in your cell was a last resort, once you'd rang your bell for the screw and he told you to fuck off or the pain in your stomach was that bad you had no choice you'd go for it. It was a complex procedure, firstly you would tear a square piece of cloth from your blanket and position it in

186

your piss pot in order that it would catch the offending object. You would then put a chair in front of it and hang a sheet over it, so your cell mate didn't have to look at you pulling faces, as you relieved yourself. You would then do the necessary but without taking a piss. You didn't want to piss in the shit parcel otherwise when you lifted it from the pot or you would trail piss all over your cell. Once finished you would tie up the corners of the blanket square and after checking the coast was clear you would launch it out of your cell window.

It didn't matter where it went just as long as it was far enough away from your cell that the screws couldn't pinpoint which cell it came from. It didn't matter if they did a cell search and found big squares missing from your blankets, as by now every blanket in the prison had at least two squares missing, and the stores even issued them like that. And that my friends, is the story of the shit parcel and the etiquette that you must observe when you make one.

"Dirty bastards, get rid of it." said Andy pulling a face and pinching his nose.

"I'm not touching it, you get rid of it," I replied as I looked at the shit parcel hanging on the edge of the outer window sill.

"No way, I'm not touching that, just shut the window, leave it," Andy laughed as he put a pillow over his head. "Dirty bastards," he squealed from under it and continued giggling.

"Oh I'll do it, we can't bloody leave it there," I said, as I walked back over to the window.

"You got owt to pick it up with?" I asked as I looked at the beige blanket square with shit oozing from the sides.

"Like what?" said Andy his head still under the pillow. I was just about to tell him to find something when I heard a gate opening and footsteps on the path below. I glanced down and could see two screws walking together chatting, every now and then they would stop and shine a torch at a dark corner of the fence line and continue walking. They were about a hundred yards away and in the dark of night it was difficult to recognise them. They began to walk across the grass. They paused, one lit a cigarette and in the glow of the light I could make out his face clearly.

"Tennyson, it's fucking Tennyson," I whispered excitedly, my pulse racing.

"What you on about?" said Andy as he jumped off his bed and joined me at the window.

"Turn the light off, turn it off," I snapped at Andy as he looked at me blankly. I kept my eyes firmly fixed on Tennyson. "That's my boy Tennyson, keep coming this way," I said under my breath. Tennyson appeared to look up and I instinctively ducked out of sight.

"What yer doing?" Whispered Andy who was once again behind me.

"I don't know yet, wait, and be fucking quiet," I said putting my fingers to my lips.

Tennyson and the other screw had stopped walking and were laughing loudly, they were by now around twenty feet from our cell block.

"Come on a bit nearer, you bastard," I willed them. It didn't work and as Tennyson stood on his cigarette to put it out, they turned and began to walk away.

"Bollocks, they're going, fuck, fuck, fuck. I don't believe it," I said my face showing my disappointment.

"What do you want with Tennyson. Oh yer not?" said Andy the penny suddenly dropping. "Well let's do it then, get away from the window. I'll get the twat closer, watch and learn," sniggered Andy, almost wetting his pants. "Eh Tennyson who's fucking yer wife this evening" shouted Andy in the best Pakistani accent I've ever heard. "Yeah Tennyson, I heard she likes it wiv two or three at a time, you..."

Andy was about to continue but I'd clasped my hand over his mouth. "That'll do he's walking over this way, now get down," I nodded pushing his head below the window. I could see the outline of the two screws getting closer as they made their way across the grass. Andy was laughing hysterically.

"Sh, sh, they'll hear you," I scowled at him.

"Sorry, sorry," he replied through his hands that were now fixed firmly to his big gob.

"I don't know who said that last remark but if I find him he won't know what hit him, do I make myself clear," shouted Tennyson. He was now directly below the cells and staring angrily up at the windows.

"Fuck off arsehole."

"Yeah fuck off arsehole. Tennyson you tosser," the rest of the cells began to cat call.

"Shut it you lot, or yer all on a charge, you hear me," hollered Tennyson.

"Go on then," egged Andy from his position under the window.

"Not yet, he'll see me, wait and shut up," I said kicking him in the leg. He got the message and fell silent.

I still had my eyes glued to Tennyson. "Go on turn around, you prick, turn around," I said under my breath. It was as if he had heard and almost immediately, he said something to the other screw and they both turned and began to walk away. I grabbed the shit parcel by the corner and lifted it, my whole arm now out of the window. "Please God, if there's any justice, don't let me miss," I prayed as I threw it with all my might in Tennyson's direction. The flying shit parcel was not light I guess the provider had been saving it up for days and as it fell downwards towards the ground it had picked up a hell of a pace, it was not quite terminal velocity, but it was enough to produce the desired effect. Please, please, I thought as it hurtled through the air and then it happened, right at the moment of impact Tennyson turned to look behind him. I will give him his due he had fast reflexes, but in this instance that turned out to be a mistake, as he instinctively raised his hands to protect his face the flying parcel caught his fingers and tore open delivering it's disgusting contents all over him. It was kind

189

of a wet flopping noise, a sound I will never forget, the very thought of it brings tears to my eyes even today.

The shock of this unexpected missile sent him reeling backwards and headlong into the grass. I dropped to the floor, "Got yer, fucking got yer," I beamed.

"You never, you never," said Andy as he nudged me with his elbow.

"I fucking did, I fucking did," I repeated and we both hugged each other laughing silently as the tears streamed down our faces.

Moments later the sound of cell doors being unlocked alerted us that something unusual was occurring, what it was neither of us knew, but I had an enormous sense of foreboding. "Do you hear that? Their opening up on the two's," I said as I stood up keeping out of sight of the window.

"Sounds like their doing cell searches," Andy said nervously. "Fuck em they can't find owt in ere just keep stum and it'll be okay, okay?" I repeated to ensure Andy was with me.

"Goes without saying mate but am I aloud to laugh?" giggled Andy as he scrambled on to his bed. I ignored his last comment I was too busy listening to the hollering voices and the sound of cell doors being slammed shut on the floor below. I quickly realized that the screws were working their way upwards through the block. My suspicions were confirmed as several sets of footsteps pounded their way up the stairs and onto our landing.

"Here they come," I winked at Andy. We know nothing, right?" Andy nodded nervously as we heard our door being unlocked.

"Out of your cell stand against the wall, now," said the screw rather menacingly.

We didn't argue we filed out and stood as we'd been ordered. The screw moved onto the next cell plunged his key in the lock

"Out of your cell stand against the wall," he repeated and

190

continued on to the next until every cell on our side of the landing had been unlocked and its occupants were lined up against the walls as though waiting for a firing squad. I was relieved that we had not been singled out. It meant they really didn't have a clue as to who had done the deed and were just going to get hassled in the hope someone would crack. The kids from the opposite side of our landing were kept locked in their cells. Even the screws were bright enough to know they could not have been responsible. It would have been odds of one hundred million to one that you could throw a shit parcel clean over the roof and hit a screw full in the kisser.

One of the inmates in the cell across from us put his face up to the glass observation strip in his door and mouthed, "What's happening?" I just shrugged my shoulders and pulled a face. I looked at Andy he was sweating, beads of perspiration were dripping off the end of his nose, he wiped it with the back of his hand and gave me a furtive look.

I turned away as I heard a screw shouting at another lad further down the landing, "Get this out now," and then a chair, piss pot and a mattress were thrown into the corridor. They were tearing his cell apart.

"Hold up your blankets," ordered the screw. The young kid he was screaming at looked about ready to burst into tears, his cell mate obviously a bit of an old hand leant against the wall and blew out a large sigh and then yawned.

"This all too much for you, we keeping you up Foggerty?" said another screw sarcastically.

Foggerty just shrugged his shoulders, looked the screw in the face and yawned. I smiled, cocky bastard you can't do better than play the 'I'm really not interested in this bullshit card.' It aggravated the screws no end but as you had not outwardly insulted them, there was not much they could do.

"Back in, the pair of you," said a screw as he strode out of their cell. "And clear that fucking mess up," he finished as he threw their bedding and articles of clothing after them. I could still hear shouting and the scraping of furniture on the floor below, but it was gradually subsiding and being replaced by the slamming of cell doors, their search was nearly over.

"Right you bastards," a voice travelled up the stairwell. "I'm fucking gonner tear your cells apart," the voice screamed as it got ever nearer. I could tell by the sound of the footsteps whoever it was, was coming our way. I was not prepared; indeed I don't think any of the lads on the landing were prepared for what we saw next. Tennyson came racing out of the stairwell and onto our landing covered from head to toe in shit. It hung from the peak of that stupid cap he wore. It was smeared across his nose and face like war paint where he'd feebly tried to wipe it off.

"You bastards," he screamed his voice rattling with emotion. I glanced at Andy he was biting down on his bottom lip; his face contorted his eyes giving away his laughter. I looked away quickly before it became contagious.

"You get yer blankets out of yer cell, now," Tennyson screamed at Mitchell who was in the cell adjacent to ours. "Hurry up you cunt," he continued kicking him up the arse as he made his way into the cell. A second later and Mitchell reappeared holding a set of blankets. Tennyson looked at the blankets and held up the piece of blanket square from the shit parcel he had been carrying in his hand, they were a different colour.

"Back in, fucking move it," he said menacingly Mitchell and his cell mate didn't need telling twice and shot back into their cell like rats up a drainpipe.

"Ah Marriot I bet you had something to do with this didn't ya," Tennyson hollered into my face. He was standing all of a foot in front of me. I screwed up my nose and winced as the acrid rotting smell found its way in my direction. Sounds of stifled laughter could be heard from further down the landing and all at once it spread like a forest fire. "You won't think it's funny you bastards, not when I've fucking finished with yer," barked Tennyson as he turned his attention away from me.

"You think it's funny do you, do you," he said as he lunged at Andy and grabbed him by the neck. Andy didn't have time to reply. Tennyson head butted him full in the face. He'd lost it completely and the giggles of laughter heard moments earlier were replaced with shouts of, "Fucking out of order." "You fucking bully." "No need for that man." Tennyson was oblivious he was a man possessed. Andy was bleeding heavily from his nose and held his hands cupped to his face as though trying to catch every precious drop. I was frozen to the spot. I wanted to do something, wanted to help but couldn't really believe what was happening. Tennyson was still screaming his face looked as though nuclear meltdown was a mere second away. "Funny, is that fucking funny? Is this funny," he said as he aimed a knee into poor Andy's bollocks it connected, and Andy's hands dropped from his face, his knees buckled, and he slid to the floor his head bowed blood running onto his trousers. Tennyson hadn't finished, he took a step backwards and was about to kick Andy in the face. I couldn't watch anymore. I stepped forward and got between them both. "Don't fucking do it Tennyson," I said my voice calm and controlled. "Don't fucking do it!" I repeated.

Tennyson froze his leg still in mid-air and I saw the hatred in his eyes as he glared at me.

"Don't do it," I said gently, my eyes never leaving him. Tennyson didn't answer he lowered his eyes and slowly bent down to retrieve his cap, it was caked in shit. He wiped a big lump off the peak with his hand replaced it on his head and pulling the peak down to cover his eyes walked away his chin up and chest out.

"Back in your cells, back in your cells," the other screws hollered at us. I pulled Andy to his feet and helped him into our cell and laid him on my bunk.

"Fuck mate you alright," I said the concern clear in my voice. Andy's nose had stopped bleeding and the colour was gradually returning to his face.

"Get to sleep you two, it's been a long night," the screw

193

nodded as he pulled the door closed. I ignored him.

"Alright, what do you mean alright?" said Andy through gritted teeth, "I've never seen anything so funny in all my fucking life and when my bollocks finally descend from wherever their hiding I'm going to laugh my fucking nuts off." He put his arm around my neck slapped me on the back and said, "Life's goner be boring without ya mate, bloody boring."

Chapter 14

The day of judgement part 2

"So young Jack, today's the day," said Mr Kenyon as he breezed into the interview room.

"First things first," he smiled as he reached into his suit pocket and threw me a packet of cigarettes.

"I didn't see Mr Stone this morning he smiled, but I thought you'd be needing something to settle your nerves," he said quietly, as though somebody might hear.

"Cheers," I said as I caught them, "By the way, nice suit," I said looking him up and down.

"You think so?" he said, holding out the sides of his jacket as if to show me the silk lining.

"Naw, not really," I giggled cheekily.

Mr Kenyon laughed awkwardly as though he didn't really get the joke. "Erm well let's get down to the matter at hand," he said changing the subject as he pulled up a chair and sat at the table. "We should be up in about an hour, now we've been through everything whilst you were on remand, so you know what to expect don't you?" he questioned as he raised an eyebrow. I nodded my head. "Good, good now I will see you in court the officers will come and collect you when it's time," he finished as he pushed his chair away from the table and gathered up a pile of notes, he'd brought with him.

"Er, one request, don't let them put me back in the cells, can I wait here?" I said pleadingly.

"I'll tell them I may need to come back and see you that should do the trick," he smiled as he was half way out of the door. He was right, and I remained in the interview room until the screws came to take me up to court. I was led down the gloomy damp passageway to a flight of stone steps.

"Up yer go," said one of the screws as he stepped to the side and allowed me to go first. We climbed four flights of

195

stairs the screws directly behind me, their keys rattling on their chains as they tried to keep up. Once at the top, I was instructed to wait, and a screw went through a wooden door reappearing a moment later. "Yep bring him in their ready for him" he called to the screw stood by me. I was then pushed through the open door and up yet more stairs until I came out in a box that was surrounded by ornate railings. I was in the dock. From this elevated position I could see the whole of the court room, men in short white horsehair wigs and gowns were chatting to each other and passing papers back and forth. A woman in a trouser suit was cheerfully greeting people as they entered via the main doors. She was quite a pretty thing in her early twenties but a little heavy on the powder and paint. I looked away as my attention was drawn to the huge plaster shield hanging on the wall above where the judge would sit, it was a coat of arms heavily decorated with gold red white and blue paint.

I noticed the lettering under it, it read 'dieu et mon droit' or something similar. I was just trying to figure out what it meant when I heard voices. A dozen or so people had entered the main doors where the smiling woman in the trouser suit pointed to a raised area to the left-hand side and they duly walked over and took their seats. I knew this was the public gallery and most of them had come just for a good nosey. I watched an elderly woman with white hair and a pea green dress open a packet of mints and pop one in her mouth and as she shifted in her seat to get comfy. She looked in my direction. I smiled but she quickly looked away as though she'd been caught doing something she shouldn't.

I wanted to shout, "I don't bite," but common sense prevailed, and I held myself in check.

"You ready Jack," came a voice.

It was Mr Kenyon. I didn't see where he'd come from, but he was looking up at me, his head just level with my waist even though he was a good six foot tall.

"Yeah I'm okay," I said my voice quivering as I leaned over the rail to look down at him.

"They will come in shortly and we'll get things underway," he smiled up at me patting my hand that was holding the rail. I hadn't seen Mr Kenyon in his court attire before. He looked very important in his wig and gown and he seemed to carry himself with a great confidence I'd not noticed before. I could understand that to some women he would be considered rather dashing, his tanned complexion and deep brown eyes surely drew many a female's gaze, a fact I'm sure he was well aware of.

"I'm glad he's on my side," I thought as I watched him swagger away.

"All rise," a voice shouted from somewhere in the room and as if the whole room had sat on a drawing pin they all jumped upright from their seats. A curtain from behind the judge's seat whooshed to one side and like a magician appearing from the smoke the judge was standing there. He quickly took his seat nodded at the people in the room and on some unspoken command they all sat back down. It was like a giant game of Simon says. I took a long hard look across at the judge. He had on a long white wig and his robe was a little fancier than the plain black version the barristers and court officials had to wear. I guessed he was about seventy-years old. He had grey side burns that stuck out from the sides of his wig and a red knobbly nose that indicated he wasn't averse to the odd tipple. 'Let's hope he's not got a hangover,' I thought as I returned my gaze to the floor.

"Sit down please." I looked up, it was the judge. "Sit down," he nodded in my direction. The screw behind me pushed a chair into the back of my knees and I sat.

A man directly in front of the judge stood up and announced loudly, "The crown versus Marriot, your honour, in the matter of wounding with intent, contrary to section 10 of common law." He then sat back down.

Another man stood up and this time looking at me said, "Stand please. I hopped off my seat. Are you Jack Andrew Marriot, date of birth twelfth of the seventh nineteen sixty-

197

four? Answer yes or no please."

I cleared my throat, "Yes" I said quietly. "You are aware of the charge you are brought before the court to answer, namely that you did wound with intent, one Marie Anne Marriot contrary to common law, how do you plead?" he finished with relish.

"Not guilty," I replied without hesitation and perhaps a little cockily.

"You may sit back down" he motioned with his hand as he turned to face the judge.

It was now the judge's turn to speak. "Very well could we have the jury please."

He nodded in the direction of the first man who'd spoken and in turn he stood up and shouted, "Send in the jury."

A door opened on a wall behind the judge and in sauntered the twelve good and true. They were mostly ordinary people and as I studied them, I didn't envy them at all. They looked more petrified than I was and avoided my gaze as they took their seats.

"I would like to welcome you this morning," said the judge to the jury. "I assume you have all been sworn in?" he asked looking in the direction of another court official.

"They have your honour," he answered jumping quickly to his feet and immediately sitting back down.

The judge returned his attention to the jurors. "You have selected a foreman?" A middle-aged man seated on the front row put his hand in the air to signal he was indeed the foreman. "Very good," said the judge smiling. "Today you the jury will hear evidence given by the prosecution and the defence, you will also hear testimony from both defence and prosecution witnesses."

He paused and leaned across his bench as if to get nearer to the jurors. "It is important that I make you aware that it is the prosecution who has the burden of proof with regard to the defendant's guilt. It is not for the defendant to prove his innocence and if during this trial you feel that the prosecutor has not convinced you beyond all reasonable doubt of the defendant's guilt, you must find the defendant not guilty and that is the verdict you must return. You must listen to the evidence as it is presented, and your decision must be wholly based on what you hear in court and not any personal feelings you have about the crime with which the defendant stands accused, do you understand?" he asked smiling kindly at them.

"We do your honour," answered the middle-aged man who'd identified himself as the foreman.

"Very well would the prosecution like to outline the case for the court?" the judge finished as he shuffled some papers on his bench. The court official seated in front of the judge nodded in the direction of a barrister who was seated on a bench a few feet from Mr Kenyon. He rose to his feet cleared his throat and respectfully nodded at Mr Kenyon before looking at the jury. He was a middle-aged man, a little portly, clean shaven with stubby little hands. I watched him as he sorted through a file before turning his attention towards the jury.

"The case before you today is a sad one," he began. "You will be shocked by the violence that was perpetrated on an innocent victim, you will hear how she feared for her life in what was a callous and totally unprovoked attack by the accused her step-son." He paused and turning to look at me continued as his eyes tore through me. "Yes indeed her own step-son, the boy she had raised as her own, even after the unfortunate death of her husband......"

I lost interest and as he babbled on, filling the jury full of lies, I looked at the floor and I drifted off to happier times. I was lost deep in thought only the mention of my name from time to time jolted me back into the room, but once I'd realized that they were talking about me not too me I quickly returned to my own thoughts. I was walking along the canal skimming stones over the surface of the water or training in the gym. I was anywhere I could be that took me away from that court room. I was happy in my dreamlike state, but the screw seated behind me had other ideas and kicked my chair violently in an effort to make me pay attention. I turned and mouthed, "Fuck you," as I made an effort to sit up straight and follow what was occurring...

"And that is what the prosecution will prove to you the jury, by the end of this trial," the chubby little barrister said, as he wiped his forehead with a white handkerchief and returned to his seat.

Mr Kenyon then rose to his feet and acknowledging chubby with a polite nod turned to face the jury. My heart began thumping at twice its normal pace. I was convinced that everybody in the room could hear it but as I looked across the court all eyes were firmly fixed on Mr Kenyon as he strode over to where the jury were seated. 'Go on,' I wanted to cheer, 'Let them have it,' but in a moment of sudden clarity a realisation hit me. How the hell could he hope to convince the jury of anything? I'd told him very little. It, somehow, hadn't seemed important at the time, and besides I didn't care what happened to me then, but I bloody did now!

"You the jury have heard from my learned colleague about the charge with which the defendant has been accused. I will however, during the course of this trial, explain the events that led up to this incident. I will show you how this child, and let's not forget that he is indeed a child" Mr Kenyon said, as he pointed towards me, "This child he continued was grief stricken at the loss of his father a man he idolised. How unable to cope with his tragic loss and in a moment of mental instability he uncharacteristically lost control and injured his stepmother. I will tell you how after such an uncharacteristic outburst of violence the defendant helped his stepmother to her feet and immediately called for an ambulance taking care of her until it arrived. I will prove to you that this unfortunate turn of events occurred when the defendant was disturbed and therefore not responsible for his actions..."

'Fuck me, steady on Kenyon,' I thought, you're making me sound like I should be in bloody Broadmoor. The jury

200

were transfixed by the mighty Kenyon and as I stared intently across at them not one juror took their eyes off him as he paced back and forth spouting at times what sounded like poetry. It was difficult not to admire him as he held the jury in the palm of his hand, hanging on his every word, he was the very epitome of charismatic and not once did he pause for breath as he delivered what could only be described as a speech to end all speeches. Once he'd completed his initial address to the jury, he thanked them for listening, spun on his heels like a matador and with a nod to chubby that was more of a 'stick that in your pipe and smoke it than a respectful acknowledgement,' he returned to his seat. I grinned as I looked at my feet to avoid the jury seeing my obvious delight. It would not have been prudent for them to think I was actually starting to enjoy myself. It was one-thirty when the judge adjourned for lunch and I was led back to the interview room where my lunch was served. I was just tucking in to a plate of fish and chips as Mr Kenyon waltzed in, grinning from ear to ear.

"I think that went well Jack, don't you?" he asked seeking my approval. "Yep, I think that jury wants to adopt you," I laughed almost choking on a mouthful of fish. "You eat your lunch and I will see you back upstairs afterwards, is there anything you want?" he enquired as an afterthought.

It was a bit of a dumb question, there were lots of things I wanted. Freedom, a year's supply of cigarettes, a super model girlfriend, the world middle-weight boxing title.

"Naw, I'm fine thanks," I nodded as I hungrily pushed the last few chips into my mouth and wiped my hands on my trousers. "Okay, see ya," said Mr Kenyon as he left the interview room, a noticeable spring in his step.

After lunch it was the turn of any witnesses to be called. The first was a young police woman who had attended the house with the ambulance. She outlined what she had seen on her arrival her tone distinctly hostile whenever she mentioned my name. I knew instantly that Marie had worked her lies and that this poor sucker had swallowed

201

them hook line and sinker, but Mr Kenyon did well in his cross-examination of her and played on the fact that I had given first aid and waited for the ambulance to arrive. A little feeble I know, but hell the guy had nothing else to hit back with, the words 'straws' and 'clutching' sprang to mind. The next witnesses were the coppers who had interviewed me. They both just said I was uncooperative and refused to answer their questions. They described the condition of my clothes, the blood spatter on my arms and hands and for good measure said I was unremorseful. I considered this a bit rough, they didn't know what the hell I'd been thinking and had filled in the blanks themselves, a point that Mr Kenyon pointed out in no uncertain terms. He explained that it was just possible that I was in fact in shock and therefore not in a position to answer a barrage of questions, a fact that perhaps they should have considered during their interview of a juvenile. I smirked as one of the coppers went all red faced and flustered at Mr Kenyon's verbal onslaught, he was definitely my white knight and I had to restrain myself from cheering when he scored points off one of the prosecution witnesses.

The ace up the prosecutor's sleeve was Marie. I wasn't a fool and knew she would be doing an Oscar winning performance at some point in the trial and she didn't disappoint me.

"Next witness, please, call Marie Anne Marriot," the words pierced me to the core as they rang out across the court. The jurors' heads turned in unison and as she flounced into the room, they followed her until she climbed into the witness box. She took an awkward glance in my general direction and quickly looked away.

"Could you tell us, in your own words, about the events leading up to the assault by your stepson Jack?" the stubby prosecutor said gently, as he looked up at her in the witness box.

"I'll er I'll try, but it is still very painful to recall that morning," said Marie taking a handkerchief from her pocket and dabbing her eyes. If it hadn't been such a serious matter, I would have pissed myself laughing at the over dramatic performance she was putting on, but unfortunately the jury were completely taken in by it and as I looked across at them as she was speaking, they were actually nodding their heads and agreeing with her.

One juror even threw me a filthy look as if to say, "How could you?" My heart sank, and in that instant, I knew it was all over. Marie's version of events was memorised from her original statement and as she gave her testimony, she told it verbatim without mention of anything that she did. I had in her words attacked her without any provocation after she had tried to stop me smashing up the house. She said I'd always been out of control and after my father died, I went completely off the rails. I glowered at her from the dock my eyes trying to stab a hole through her callous heart. The more I stared at her the more rubbish spewed from her lying face until I couldn't take it anymore. I sprang to my feet catching the two screws off guard. "You lying, fucking bitch, tell the truth tell them, you fucking cow," I yelled, my face contorted in anger.

The two screws were on me in seconds and as they pulled me backwards, we fell over my chair and collapsed in a struggling heap to the floor of the dock. "Order, order bellowed the judge take him below."

I was dragged kicking and screaming by my feet down the steps, my head bouncing off each one as we progressed downwards.

"Get the fuck off me you bastards," I screamed. I was ignored and as we reached the corridor, I was hauled the length of it and into a cell.

One of the screws turned as he started to shut the door and said softly, "You've done yourself no favours there kid, no favours at all." I curled into a corner and sobbed, "I hate you, I hate you," I shouted as the tears and snot ran down my face. It was some time later when Mr Kenyon appeared.

"Jack, Jack it's Mr Kenyon, are you okay?" he called

through the bars. I wiped my face with my hands and gradually climbed to my feet.

"Yeah I'm alright, I'm sorry," I sniffed "But I hate her she's just a fucking lying bitch" I sniffed.

Mr Kenyon shook his head. "Jack, Jack you have not helped with that outburst, I'm going to have to work hard tomorrow to repair the damage. I just hope I can."

"Tomorrow?" I enquired.

"Yes the court has adjourned until tomorrow and the judge has asked that you remain in the cells here overnight to give you time to reflect on your behaviour," said Mr Kenyon, a disapproving expression on his face.

I smiled.

"What's funny," he said a little confused.

"Time to reflect," I beamed, "What the fuck does he think I've been doing for the past few months twiddling my thumbs."

"I'll see you first thing in the morning, don't worry things will work out," he said reaching through the bars and squeezing my arm. "Get some rest," and with that he walked away the sound of his footsteps echoing down the dim passageways.

It was a long night and I had plenty of time to reflect as the judge in his wisdom had instructed. It was a very quiet place at night. There wasn't the sound of doors unlocking and other inmates shouting from cell to cell to distract me. I had no window to look out of and no cell mate to chat to, so I paced the cell until the early hours smoking and cursing until I had a headache; somehow during that time I made a decision, it was time, time to tell my side of the story. So what if nobody believed me, the way I figured it, I had nothing to lose and if I could wipe the smug look off that bitch's face then all the better.

Mr Kenyon arrived as promised around nine o'clock the next morning. I was just finishing my breakfast. A couple of slices of toast and a cup of tea that had briefly been introduced to a tea bag.

"Looks appetizing," said a voice.

It made me jump and I spilled my tea down the front of my trousers. I looked like I'd pissed myself. I put my half empty mug down and glancing at my sopping trousers, I shook my head and said, "It's just as well the jury can only see me from the waist up when I'm in the dock."

"Sorry, Jack, didn't mean to startle you, you okay?" asked Mr Kenyon apologetically.

"Forget it," I said, brushing my trousers, "I'm fine but I do need to talk to you, I have something to say that you might want to hear." I said excitedly.

"Sounds ominous," Mr Kenyon replied but it will have to wait for half an hour. "I have to be somewhere else in five minutes. I tell you what, let me go deal with that and I'll be back to talk to you, okay? Oh thought you might need these," he finished as he pushed a pack of cigarettes through the bars of the cell door.

I was on tender hooks until Mr Kenyon returned. I'd gone through everything I was going to tell him, the physical abuse the cruelty and above all the events of the day I attacked Marie. I felt an enormous sense of relief, relief that at last I could finally tell the truth, the whole truth after all wasn't that what everybody wanted?

"Come on Marriot lets have you," said the screw as he opened the cell door.

"Where am I going? It's not time for court yet, is it? I have to see Mr Kenyon first," I enquired, the panic evident in my voice. "That's where you're going, daft lad, interview room, get a move on," he replied shaking his head as though I was stupid. I didn't need the screw to show me the way and I quickly walked the short distance arriving at the steel gate before the interview room. I had to stop and wait for it to be unlocked.

"Where's the fire kid?" remarked the screw as he came up behind me.

I didn't answer him. I just wanted him to open the gate and as always when you want someone to hurry up they tit

205

about.

The screw began sorting through the bunch of keys in his hand, "Now which one is it?" he said to himself as he held them up and studied them.

I was losing patience and rattled the gate, my hands gripping the vertical bars.

"Ah, that's the one," said the screw as though he'd just won the lottery. He leaned forward and placed the key in the lock. I didn't wait as soon as I heard the levers move and the tell-tale click of the bolt retracting, I pushed the gate aside and ran towards the interview room. The door was open, and a quick glance told me Mr Kenyon had yet to arrive. I breathed a sigh of relief and as I took a seat at the table, I felt all the tension leave my body. It was happening. I would at last have my say. I'd been like a coiled spring, once I'd made the decision to tell the whole sorry tale, I couldn't wait to unburden myself and holding it in was killing me.

"Your brief won't be long, wait here," said the screw as he locked me in the room.

I don't know where the hell he thought I was going to go but I was used to screws talking crap and just ignored his stupid remark. I took the cigarette packet out of my trousers and lit a cigarette. Once aglow, I flicked the match across the room and watched it fall through the air and land in the corner, its flame extinguished. I inhaled deeply, holding it in momentarily, before exhaling slowly and deliberately.

"Come on, come on," I said aloud as I looked at the locked door through the Smokey haze that was wafting across the room. Where the hell is he? I thought as I began to get annoyed.

It had been the longest twenty minutes of my life when the sound of footsteps approached and finally the door was unlocked.

"Sorry about that Jack, caught up with other matters sorry," Mr Kenyon offered as he strolled in and pulled out a chair opposite me.

"Now what is it you want to talk to me about?"

"I have to tell you something, I want to tell you everything. I mean I don't want her telling lies," I spluttered.

"Whoa Jack steady on, take it slowly, I'm listening," encouraged Mr Kenyon.

"She attacked me first, I was defending myself. I didn't want to hit her, but she just wouldn't stop, she wouldn't, I had to get her off." I stopped talking, my heart was thumping, and my palms were sweaty, I wiped them on my shirt and continued as Mr Kenyon lent closer his chin cupped in his hands. "All those things she says about caring for me, it's not true. She's always hated me, she used to beat me and lock me in my room for days." I was in full flow and the words were spilling out like water from an over flowing bath.

"Are you saying you were abused by your stepmother, Jack, is that what you're telling me?" interrupted Mr Kenyon his face showing concern.

"If that's what you want to call it yeah, all I know is she would find any excuse to beat me, our kid once caught her and warned her off. It didn't stop her, she just waited until he wasn't around, she took pleasure in my fucking misery and I wish she was dead, the bitch," I said jumping to my feet and banging my fist on the wall.

My eyes had started to fill up and the anger I'd held inside was finally beginning to be released. "Don't you see she's won, she's got me out of the way and now she's standing in court lying to you all, nobody will believe me anyway, so I don't know why I'm even bothering to tell you. It don't matter anyway even if you got me off there's nobody who wants me I'm better off in prison nobody bothers me there." I drew a deep breath and turning to face Mr Kenyon I wiped away the tears. "And now you know," I said as I grabbed a cigarette from the table and struck a match It didn't light, I struck it again and it snapped in half. "Oh fuck it, I can't even light a poxy fucking cigarette," I swore as I screwed it up and threw it to the floor and burst into tears. Mr Kenyon was not a natural to empathy and although he walked over and tried to calm me it was awkward and clumsy. "Oh fuck off, leave me alone," I said angrily as I pushed his arm away as he tried to get hold of me.

"Jack listen to me, you've got to get a hold on yourself, she will win if you go into court like this, do you want her to see you in this state? Don't give her the satisfaction, come on let's try and sort this out together but you must calm down, please come and sit here please," he coaxed as he patted the seat of my empty chair. I knew he was right and as I shook my head, I gave out a sigh of resignation and slowly walked over to the table and sat down. "Here," said Mr Kenyon as he pulled out a cigarette from the pack and went to offer it to me, he thought about it and stuck it in his own mouth and striking a match lit it and began coughing uncontrollably as he passed it across the table to me.

"That's bloody awful, ah," he grimaced as he pulled a face. I stared across at him and couldn't hold back a smile. "That's more like it," he said, "Come on, tell me more and let's see if we can't come up with some answers, what do you say?" After that we went through everything. I had not openly spoken to any adult about Marie and I wanted to make sure I left nothing out. I wanted everyone to know what she was capable of and as I went into more and more detail the expression on Mr Kenyon's face went from pity to disgust and finally to outrage. When I'd finished talking Mr Kenyon leaned back in his chair and his deep eyes filled with tears said, "Your right she is a bitch. I just wish you had told me this earlier." He stood up and walked around the table using the opportunity to covertly wipe his eyes and to gather his thoughts.

"I've got to tell you Jack that at this late stage in the proceedings it is going to be extremely difficult to put forward new evidence, we have to follow set procedures and new evidence must be disclosed to the prosecution prior to me using it in your defence, do you understand?" he said softly. I didn't, but nevertheless, I nodded. "You do realize that in order for me to use this," he continued, "I may have to ask the court for an adjournment, it is unlikely we'll get it as the trial has already started and the jury has already heard half of the evidence," he finished with a sudden spark in his eyes that signalled a flash of sudden inspiration.

"Wait here I need to go and talk to the prosecutor. Let's see if we can get them to play ball," and in an instant he was gone only the case files he'd left open on the table and a gold pen with the top off signalled he'd ever been there. I sat and bit my finger nails to the knuckles whilst I awaited Mr Kenyon's return, I was strangely excited, and the anticipation of good news kept me hanging on the edge of my seat as I strained my ears at every sound as I awaited those jangling keys that would announce his return.

"I'm sorry, it's a no-go," said a red-faced and out of breath Mr Kenyon, his normally immaculate hair looking like a windswept piece of candy floss as he entered the room with all the grace of an SAS counter terrorism team.

"What, we can't get an adjournment?" I said, although I knew the answer before I'd even asked the question. It was written all over the perspiring Mr Kenyon's crimson kisser.

"They won't allow the introduction of new case material without witnesses to corroborate your testimony and we would need time to do that. I'm sorry I really tried," he finished as he took off his jacket and hung it on the back of his chair. He had large damp sweat stains under both arms and his breathing was laboured.

I didn't need any more convincing he'd tried and that was enough for me. "Okay so what now," I said nonchalantly.

"Plan A, we stick to my original strategy," he paused and smoothed his by now unkempt grey hair in an effort to restore order. "We have the psychologists report from Mr Golati and that is very favourable, he continued, his breathlessness subsiding. We are not denying that you carried out the assault on your stepmother, but we are denying that at the time you were responsible for your actions. Mr Golati has stated in his professional opinion you were unable to cope with the loss of your father and as a

209

result you had a temporary and tragic breakdown. The jury should be sympathetic to you and if we're lucky you could be acquitted, that's what we're working towards. His eyes never left mine and I could see the sincerity in his words, I trusted him. What we don't want to happen, he continued is to alienate the jury by trying to blacken your step mother's character. You saw her yesterday, Jack, and she had them eating out of her hand, besides at this juncture it would be your word against hers and in my opinion throwing uncorroborated accusations at her will do more harm than good, don't you think?" I nodded my agreement. "Good lad, now please don't repeat yesterday's performance or the judge will have you removed permanently, and you will turn the jury against you," he smiled as he stood up and slipped his jacket back on.

"We're up in around half an hour. Remember, stay calm Jack, don't blow it, for God's sake, don't blow it, you listening?" he said as he paused with his hand on the door knob.

"I hear you," I replied.

At the appointed time the screws once again took me down those long corridors up the stairs and seated me in the dock. The court was much the same as the day before, lots of general chit chat and the passing of notes and files. The young woman who had been on the door the day before had been replaced by an elderly man who resembled a bumbling headmaster. I watched him for several minutes, he seemed to be a little confused when anybody asked him anything. I smiled at his inadequacy and turned away to survey the rest of the court. I could see Mr Kenyon talking to a middle-aged woman who wore a black gown. She was not particularly attractive but was batting her eyes and hanging on Mr Kenyon's every word, he was oblivious to her clumsy flirting and brushing her off began to walk away. The middle-aged woman's eyes followed Mr Kenyon's tall tanned figure as he crossed the room and took up his seat on a bench at the front. The muffled voices of a group of people entering the main doors drew my attention and exactly like the day before they seated themselves in the public gallery. A few of them had a right good gawp at me and one old bag had the audacity to nudge the fat cow she'd come with and then point at me. I mouthed, "fuck you," when our eyes met. It was worthwhile, she went bright red and screwed her face up like she'd just bitten into an onion.

After everybody had taken their places and the usher had announced loudly, "All stand," the judge flounced in and began by giving Mr Kenyon a warning about his client's behaviour the day before.

"I trust we will not be treated to a repeat performance today," said the judge as he felled me with a killer stare. I just grinned like an imbecile, but it was enough for the judge and he asked for the jury to be brought in. First up was Mr Golati and after Mr Kenyon had taken his turn at questioning the chubby prosecutor stood up ringing his hands as he approached the witness box.

Mr Golati had an elegant turn of phrase and soft voice that seemed to hypnotise the jury. "I Found Jack to be a very polite but withdrawn child, he has been through a terrible trauma. I believe the loss of his father so suddenly and the isolation he felt were a contributory factor in his temporary breakdown," Mr Golati said in his softly spoken voice.

"Are you saying that you can be one hundred percent sure that the defendant was unaware of his actions at the time of the offence?" asked the little chubby prosecutor. Mr Golati thought for a few seconds before he delivered his reply, the jury shuffled and leaned forward in their seats in anticipation of his answer.

"One can only be sure about something one has witnessed so therefore any conclusion must be arrived at by the application of any expert knowledge and previous case history that is available to one's self," Mr Golati smiled. "So you're not one hundred percent sure of your diagnosis of the defendant? That's what your saying isn't it?" barked the prosecutor as he turned to look at the jury. "No Sir,

211

interrupted Mr Golati that is what you are saying. I don't believe I actually said those words." He smiled politely, his perfect Oxford educated voice masking his Indian origin. The jury giggled, and the judge even let slip a wry smile.

The chubby prosecutor went a little red and turned to continue his cross examination. "Er let me clarify my last question, I'm sorry if I confused you," he said trying to score back a few points from Mr Golati.

"Oh I'm not confused, Sir," Mr Golati chipped in and once again the jury smiled. If the prosecutor had noticed he'd started a fight he couldn't win, he didn't let it show.

. "Okay let me rephrase my last question if you could please just answer yes or no, are you one hundred percent positive that your considered opinion of the defendant is that he underwent a temporary breakdown?" said Chubby as he turned back to look at the jury and for a split second I thought he was going to take a bow, he had a smug grin on his face that said he was convinced he'd delivered the killer question.

"Oh yes, Sir," said Mr Golati softly, "I am one hundred percent sure that in my considered opinion the defendant had a breakdown, one should always be one hundred percent sure of his own opinion or he should not offer one." It was too much for the jurors and a flurry of giggles rang out.

"Could the prosecution please make their questions more concise?" said the judge, a tone that showed he was growing impatient, clearly evident in his words.

"Mr Golati could you please tell the court what experience and qualifications you hold in order that they may assess your ability to come to such an opinion?" asked a rather agitated prosecutor.

"I have been a consultant psychologist for over twenty-eight years. I have also held the position of senior lecturer at Leeds University for some sixteen years. It is during this time I have been an expert witness in many cases both for the defence and prosecution. I hold a PHD and BSc in

212

psychology and also carry out work for the Home Office as their criminal psychologist."

"I, I'll stop you there if I may?" the prosecutor cut in. I think the court is satisfied as to your expertise, you may sit down, no more questions your honour," he said, turning to the judge.

"Mr Kenyon would the defence like to re-examine the witness?" the judge enquired.

Mr Kenyon rose to his feet and looking directly at the jury, he smiled as he said, "No thank you your honour. I believe my learned colleague has covered any points relevant to our defence."

Laughter was heard from the public gallery and gradually spread throughout the whole court. The judge hung his head to hide his mirth but his shoulders jiggling up and down, gave him away. "This may be a good time to adjourn for lunch, back here for one thirty gentlemen, court adjourned," said the judge in a moment of composure, and with these words he rose and left the court.

"That could not have gone better, I think we're making good ground," smiled Mr Kenyon as he leant against the bars of my cell door. I'd been placed back in the holding cell until after lunch and was seated on the floor eating off a plastic plate.

I stood up casting aside my half-eaten lunch. "You think we're going to win?" I asked, as I stood and walking over to the cell door, gazed up at him.

"Well let's not count our chickens yet Jack, but I'm very optimistic after this morning. Let's just keep our fingers crossed that we do as well this afternoon. Anyway I'm going to get some lunch myself, so I'll see you back up there, keep your chin up things look good," he said as he turned to walk away.

"Mr Kenyon," I called.

"Yes" he replied as he turned to look at me.

"Thanks, thank you," I smiled offering my outstretched arm through the bars. Mr Kenyon took my hand and gently

213

shook it

"You're very welcome Jack, very welcome," he replied rather awkwardly, "Now eat your dinner, it's getting cold".

The defence and the prosecution began their summing up shortly after lunch. It was like watching two story tellers telling the same story but with different interpretations. The chubby prosecutor had a vivid imagination and as he strode backwards and forwards occasionally pausing in front of the jury, he slowly began to spin his web of lies. He was good and as I listened to his relentless assassination of my character, I began to believe him myself. I caught sight of Marie sitting at the back of the court she was lapping it up and the more the chubby prosecutor tarnished my already ragged reputation, the more she smirked into her hands. I stared and stared at her willing the bitch to look in my direction, but she didn't, she was too busy hanging on the prosecutor's every word.

When the prosecution had finished it was our turn and I had to stop myself cheering as Mr Kenyon got up from his seat and approached the jury. "This has been a trial with many ups and downs he began, a story of great tragedy and of tremendous sadness. The defendant a young child who in despair and the turmoil of grief for one moment lost control and acted completely out of character. You have heard the testimony of Mr Golati an expert in the field of Psychology, you have heard how he concluded that the defendant could not have been responsible for his actions, how the tremendous pressure had caused a temporary breakdown." Mr Kenyon paused and walking away from the jury he glanced down at a file on his bench. "You have heard from the victim herself," he said turning back to the jury. "You have heard how she claims the defendant was a bad child, how he was always in trouble and how in a moment of blind rage he attacked her without reason. I accept that when you heard these remarks you felt compassion for the victim, for the terrible physical assault she suffered; you empathised with her predicament, who wouldn't? But I ask you to spare

214

some of that sympathy for the defendant, a boy, a young child who was torn apart with grief, who even today grieves the father he lost so suddenly. You must also consider that the victim's testimony could be fuelled by bitterness and that the whole truth has never actually been told. I don't dispute that she has a right to be bitter, after all she was severely beaten by the defendant in what she claims was an unprovoked attack, but ask yourselves this question, do you honestly believe that a young child who according to the victim carried out a totally unprovoked attack could have done so whilst of sound mind, I think not! The defendant does not need punishment he needs compassion and understanding. I ask you the jury to find him not guilty, not guilty, not because you feel sorry for him, but not guilty because he was not responsible for his actions and therefore cannot be found guilty as is the law of our land. Thank you." He nodded at the jurors and quickly returned to his seat.

'Short and to the point,' I said under my breath as I sat head bowed my eyes fixed on the dock floor.

The judge now began his summing up and as he began to speak, I dared to take a quick peek at the jurors, it was of no use they were giving nothing away and simply sat stony-faced as they looked up at the judge. "It is now my responsibility to sum up this case," said the judge as he turned in his high-backed swivel chair to look at the jury. "I must give you, the jury, direction and assistance in coming to the correct verdict as prescribed by law," he continued. "You have heard testimonies from both defence and prosecution counsels, you have heard from defence and prosecution witnesses and now it is time for you to consider the evidence you have heard and to reach your verdict. That verdict must be either guilty or not guilty. It is not a question of, if the defendant carried out the serious charge of wounding with intent, after all this has never been disputed by defence council or the defendant in his police interview. What is being disputed is whether the defendant was of sound mind when the alleged offence was instigated. If you decide that the defendant had indeed undergone some temporary imbalance of the mind and is therefore not accountable for his actions, you have a duty to find him not guilty of the charges laid against him. If on the other hand you believe that the defendant was of sound mind at the time of the offence and acted out of anger and malice, then you must return a guilty verdict. Do you understand?" The judge asked as he scratched his bulbous red nose.

The jury nodded in unison. "Very well you will now leave the court and consider your verdict. It is now three-thirty, you may return your verdict up until five-thirty. If by that time you are still deliberating you will return to court tomorrow and continue your deliberations.

"Lead them out!" the judge ordered in a loud voice, "Court adjourned." I watched as the jury filed out, every now and then one of them would dare to look in my direction but turn away when our eyes met. I tried to give them a weak smile, but it was probably more of a scowl, nerves can do that to you.

Chapter 15

Case closed!

I won't bore you with the details or tell you how my faith in justice or people was torn asunder. Your imagination can decide that for itself. I was quietly confident that the next time I climbed the stairs to that dock I would be smiling broadly as I left. I guess the jury had other ideas.

"Guilty," those are the words I still hear as I try to drift off to sleep over twenty years later. I can still see that evil cow, Marie, and her pure delight spreading across her face like margarine.

I flinch when I recall those words I shouted at her as did most of the court. "Your laughing now you bitch, but I promise I'll fucking haunt you for the rest of your life." I would have said more but alas opportunities are fleeting and I never had time to rehearse.

"It'll pass in no time, Jack," comforted Mr Kenyon as he visited me in the cells afterwards.

"Yeah, 'cos six months to two years is just a blink of an eye," I said, shaking my head sarcastically.

"I'm sorry Jack, but your earlier outburst in court must have lodged in the jury's mind, I really tried." I moved closer to the cell door and gazed into Mr Kenyon's brown eyes, they were filled with regret and genuine sincerity.

I offered my hand and as he shook it. I smiled "Guess you can't win em all, eh?"

Mr Kenyon returned my smile and pressed his face right up to the bars and whispered, "Every dog has his day Jack, every dog, you take care and in the best possible way I hope I never see you again."

"See ya" I shouted after him as he walked away, but he never looked back.

I was collected by the screws around half an hour later. "Come on out yer come," a screw barked at me. "Hands," he said sharply as though word rationing had just been declared. I offered both my hands and he swiftly enclosed them in a pair of glistening new handcuffs and led me by them out of the cells. I had no idea where I was going to be taken and nobody seemed too bothered about informing me. Once out into a yard at the back of the courts I was pushed into the rear of a prison van. I'd never been in a prison van before as I'd always been brought to court in a coach. The inside of the van was separated into individual cubicles five on each side.

"In yer get," said a screw as he shoved me into one and locked the door. It was a little like being locked in a mobile Porta-loo and the smell was as bad. There were no windows and a sunken light in the ceiling gave off a dull glow. The seat was moulded plastic and part of the lining of the cubicle. If you were at all claustrophobic this was the last place you would want to be. I noticed graffiti on the walls and ceiling and as I read through them, I couldn't help but wonder where these people were now, not to mention how the hell they managed to get hold of such a variety of different coloured marker pens even after they'd been searched. Prisoners are an ingenious bunch of people and you can't help but think if only they channelled that somewhere else?

The diesel engine of the van clunked into life and as I heard the sound of the handbrake being released, we began to move off. I could hear the other prisoners shouting to each other from their cubicles.

"Billy what you get?" yelled one over the noise of the engine

"Three poxy years, the old fart said, I needed time to reflect on my crimes." I grinned quietly to myself. The judiciary were obviously determined everyone should have enough time to reflect on their behaviour I thought as I remembered Mr Kenyon's words after my outburst in court.

"Three years, 'cor that's a bit rough in it, mate?" replied the first prisoner.

218

"Fuck em, I can do that standing on my head," laughed Billy and besides I was expecting a five stretch he finished. "Who else is in ere? what's yer names?" called Billy from his cubicle.

A couple of voices called out their names and exchanged pleasantries, it was the usual, "What you in for?"

"Which nicks have you been in?" and "Do you know so and so?"

I kept quiet and hoped nobody would realise I hadn't called out my name. I was scared and thought if I spoke it might show in my voice. I'd been on remand long enough to know that any sign of weakness would ultimately bring the prison bullies down on you like a pack of wolves.

"Eh, you kid what's yer name?" came a voice from the next cubicle as he knocked on the dividing wall.

I didn't want to answer but knew it would only cause confrontation if I ignored him. "Jack, Jack Marriot," I replied in my most confident tone.

"I'm John Wickham. I'm doing an eight for robbery with violence, what you in for Jack?" replied the gravelly voice through the partition.

"Wounding with intent," I said cockily, hoping that everybody had heard.

"Oh you a bit of a head case then?" he teased. "I'll have to make sure I don't piss you off!"

"Ere Jack, how old are you?" chipped in Billy from further down the van.

"Fifteen," I replied wishing I was older.

"Fuck me, fifteen and on your way to Armley, you poor cunt," Billy laughed.

"Fuck me, you hear that John?" he called.

"Yeah," John laughed, "Poor little bastard, you must be on yer way to Borstal on a six to two-year apprenticeship, is that it Jack?"

"Yeah borstal, that's what the judge said," I confirmed.

"Anyway, where are we going now? Is it Armley prison?" I asked hoping it was a wind up.

"Aye we're headed for Armley nick alright, you'll get yer first taste of real prison," answered John's gruff voice his amusement clearly detectable.

"But I can't go to a real prison, I'm too young, where are we going really?" I said trying not to sound desperate.

"Eh Billy this one thinks we're having him on. He thinks he's going somewhere else, eh kid, this 'ain't no fucking taxi, it's a prison van and only has one destination and that's fucking Armley, you'll see soon enough," John laughed, and several other prisoners joined in the chorus.

I sat in silence for the rest of the journey, if I was scared before I was bloody petrified by now. My mind was racing with the different scenarios I might face. No matter which one I imagined none of them soothed my frayed nerves. The van suddenly ground to a halt, we'd only been travelling about twenty minutes and I assumed we were at traffic lights or a junction. We began to move off again and I suddenly realised I'd been holding my breath. I inhaled deeply and heard my heart rate begin to slow. The prison van trundled forward for a few feet and stopped once again. This time I heard the handbrake being applied and the sound of the ignition being switched off. The rear doors of the van were thrown open and one by one each cubicle was unlocked.

"Out yer get, out yer get," two screws ordered as I made my way down the two rear steps of the van and into a stone walled court yard. I looked around nervously. The walls were about thirty feet high and as smooth as a baby's arse, an ant wearing crampons couldn't have scaled them. Even if it had, the razor wire strung across the top in large coils would have cut it to pieces. I turned and looked up at the prison building, it was old. I guess it was built in the early nineteenth century and by the look of it that was the last time it had been updated.

"Welcome home kid, nice 'ain't it?" grinned a man of around forty. He had bad teeth and his bald head was covered in scars. I tried not to stare at them, but my eyes were drawn as if by an invisible force.

"Like em?" he said, as he ran a finger across a big red angry scar that stopped just above his left temple. The confused look on my face was enough for him and he broke into a toothy grin. "Billy, I'm Billy," he said as he grabbed my hand and shook it. I smiled but made no reply. "Look kid you take care in ere you got me?" he whispered in a rather sinister manner. "Billy stop frightening the new inmates get inside now," shouted a screw standing in an open doorway.

Billy turned and glanced in the screws direction before returning his stare to me. He grabbed my face with one of his battered and stubby hands and squeezing forcefully he spat, "be careful" as he drew his other hand across his throat in a cutting motion.

If Billy was trying to scare me he needn't have bothered, I was already scared and once you reach a certain point just short of actually shitting your pants nothing else can increase your fear, you're kind of maxed out in the terrified department.

"Take no notice of him he's a fucking phsyco," said a bloke in his mid-twenties as he nudged me with his shoulder as he strode past. I started walking and quickened my step until I was level with him.

"Jack Marriot," I offered.

"I know you dick, I'm John, John Wickham, the van remember?" I smiled as the penny dropped and followed John into the building. Once through the doorway I was met by what was by now a very familiar sight, a large desk. One screw sat behind it calling out names. It must be an unwritten prison law that all inmates are processed in the same manner in similar looking rooms upon their arrival. Perhaps it was to make us feel at home? It didn't bloody work for me!

"Wickham," called the monotone voice of the fat screw sitting behind the desk.

"Yep boss," grinned Wickham in a cool and confident

221

manner as he sauntered forward at a leisurely pace.

"Hurry up Wickham I ain't got all fucking day," said the screw impatiently.

"You're going to G wing, landing 3. Get out of your civvy clothes, get showered and then wait in the next room until Officer Mitchell is ready to take you to the wing, got it?"

"Er boss I'd love to help but I think I might have a problem getting me jumper off wearing these," smirked Wickham holding up his wrists, a lovely pair of heavy cuffs enfolding them.

"Get going Wickham, Officer Mitchell can you remove his cuffs?" The screw nodded at another whom I knew must be Officer Mitchell. I stood silently as I watched each prisoner approach the desk. They gave their names and were then issued with wing and landing allocations. The fat screw didn't bother with small talk, he just systematically processed each prisoner with all the care and concern of an SS officer in a Polish death camp.

"Marriot." I looked up to see the fat screw looking in my direction

"Are you Marriot?" he said, his voice showing his annoyance.

"Yes, er yes, Sir," I stuttered, although I did think it an odd question as I was the only prisoner remaining in the room.

"Get ere then," said the fat screw. I quickly stepped up to the desk and lowered my head. I didn't want him to see my fear and besides that I wanted to hide, hide anywhere. I wanted to be that small that I could go unnoticed. "You listening?" barked the fat screw as he pointed towards the other room.

I hadn't heard a word he'd said. I was too busy listening to another voice, the one in my head that kept saying, 'get me out of here, please God, let this just be a bad dream.'

"Undress and in the shower mate, here's a towel," smiled a prisoner who was wearing a red arm band that indicated he was a trustee; he had kind eyes and reminded me of a

222

television version of the perfect grandad. I took the towel and walking over to a row of benches along one wall, began to undress.

"Put your civvy clothes in here," said the trustee prisoner as he gave me a large box.

"Here, put these on when you get out," he said as he walked back over with a pile of prison issue greys.

"Shoe size?" he enquired as I took the bundle of clothes off him. "Eight," I replied as I placed the clothes on the wooden bench and removing my pants climbed into the shower cubicle. The cold icy water took me back to Dave's gym and I would have given anything at that moment to have opened my eyes and been standing in the showers in that changing room. I finished my shower dried off quickly and began to get dressed. The prison clothes smelt clean and fresh and as my body began to warm and I buttoned up my shirt and adjusted the waistband on my trousers I actually began to feel good.

"Through here, if you're ready," called a screw from another room."

"You best hurry kid, I'll take care of these," smiled the trustee as he picked up the cardboard lid and placed it on top of the box that contained all my worldly goods.

"Oh, don't forget that," he nodded with his head. his hands now clasping the box.

"Oh yeah, cheers," I said quietly as I picked up a pillowcase that I knew would contain a change of underwear two sheets two towels a plastic mug and a piss pot. I walked on into the next room carrying my pillowcase over my shoulder like Father Christmas. I was immediately met by four prison officers and the rest of the inmates who had arrived with me. There was a strong smell of soap and any inmate with a full head of hair had neatly combed it.

"Come on, we're waiting for you," shouted a screw as I entered, he was standing by a steel gate his keys in his hand.

"Yeah, come on, we want our fucking tea," shouted one of the prisoners.

I didn't look up to see who it was I just made my way over to the screw. The screw called out two names and ordered them to go with another screw to their allocated wing and so it went on until I was on my own.

"Come on then, let's get you sorted," smiled the screw who was left with me. I obediently followed as the screw led me down a couple of corridors stopping occasionally to unlock the heavy steel gates, I was by now accustomed too. "This way," he would call over his shoulder without looking back. He didn't need to worry if

I was still behind him, he knew there was nowhere else I could go, and anyway, I was that terrified I would have gladly clamped onto his leg, like a Jewish mother saying goodbye to her child, rather than lose sight of him. The main prison was bigger than anything I'd seen before and as the last steel gate clunked shut behind me, I found I was standing in the middle of a huge open space. If I'd felt small and insignificant before, I certainly did now. My eyes darted around wildly trying to take everything in. The huge hall I was standing in rose to gigantic proportions and at the very top an enormous glass skylight shone light on to me as I gazed open-mouthed at its magnificence. I wondered for a brief moment why the skylight had no bars on it, and quickly realised it didn't need any as the only way to reach it would be with a pair of ladders that were a hundred foot high. Running off the central hall in different directions were the wings. Each wing had six landings starting at ground level and continuing upwards. If you tilted your head back, each landing could be monitored from the ground or indeed from the top landing if you were looking down. Wire chain link mesh hung across the open expanse of each landing I assumed it was to prevent a prisoner falling from the top landing the six floors to his death. It was only later I realised they were also to stop missiles being strategically dropped on to anyone's head as they passed underneath.

"Up yer go," said the screw as we arrived at the bottom of a metal staircase. On the wall a sign in big black letters read

B WING. I made my way up onto the first floor. "This way," said the screw as he pushed past me. We walked along the landing up another set of steps along another landing up yet another set of steps and finally arrived on what the screws affectionately called the threes and the other inmates called the 'youth club.'

"You're in ere," said the screw as he turned the key in the door and flung it open. I looked above the door a stencilled number again in black read **B307**.

"Your new cellmate boys," the screw said matter of factly, at the two prisoners inside who were playing cards.

"What's yer name then?" asked one of the inmates as the door closed behind me. He was sitting on the bottom bunk his mate sitting opposite on a single bed.

"Jack, Jack Marriot," I said quietly.

"Speak up what did you say yer name was?" said the kid sat on the single bed menacingly as he grinned across at his mate.

"Jack Marriot," I repeated a little louder.

"Well Jack Marriot, I'm Wayne and that's Mick," he said pointing to his mate who was shuffling the deck of cards expertly as he drilled me with his hardest stare. Mick was about seventeen years old but looked older. He had huge arms and shoulders that strained his shirt as he leant forward over the makeshift card table. His short cropped bleached blonde hair was spiked and over emphasised his already large head, he looked a tough bastard and I quickly turned to look at Wayne. Wayne was a different cup of tea, I could tell his arrogance stemmed from his alliance with Mick and that separated from his partner in crime his bravado would quickly disappear. Wayne was around the same age as Mick but shorter and lighter in build, he had black shoulder length hair and a goatee beard that resembled pubic hair.

"Don't just stand there, the top bunks yours, get your stuff sorted out before tea," ordered Mick as he exchanged a knowing look with a shifty looking Wayne. I walked the three steps to the bed and threw my pillowcase onto the top bunk opened the end and began to unpack my gear. The first thing out was my plastic piss pot shinny knew with a lid.

"Where should I put this?" I asked nobody in particular. Wayne looked up and without answering pointed to a corner of the cell behind the door. I then pulled out my spare underwear and towels. I looked around for a locker to put them in, it was under the window and in order to reach it I would have had to ask Mick and Wayne to move. I thought better of it and pushed them back inside my pillowcase. I was going to make up my bed but decided to wait until my new-found friends had finished their card school. I climbed up the metal frame at the end of the bunk and slid onto the mattress. I lay back listening to Wayne and Mick.

"Fuck off you cheat, that's mine."

"Naw, it's fucking mine. You can't count that ace, it's not a trump is it?" and so it went on.

I closed my eyes and tried to be somewhere else, but it was no use my imagination was clouded with the events of the day. It could only have been twenty minutes or so when the screws began to open up the cells for tea. Wayne and Mick jumped up and were out of the cell door the moment it opened, they didn't bother waiting for me but that was fine. I wasn't an imbecile and had no desire to try initiating peace talks with two complete twats. I watched them leave and slowly climbed off the top bunk. I walked over to the cell door stuck my head out and as I glimpsed Mick's bulky frame, work its way down the steel staircase, I quickly ducked back into the cell and made up my bed. After I'd finished, I opened the locker under the window and finding an empty shelf put my spare clothes away.

"You not hungry?" said a screw as he stood in the doorway. "Best get a move on or those greedy buggers will eat it all," he smiled and continued walking down the landing. I left my cell and fell into line with the other inmates following their lead. We filed down the landing and down each staircase until we were on the ground floor. A line of food trolleys had been set up and inmates were ladling out food onto prison issue metal trays. Once your tray had been filled you picked up a plastic knife fork and spoon and after being given a mug of tea marched back up to your cell. Wayne and Mick were already eating when I came back. They had set aside the card game and were now facing each other eating like pigs at a trough. I looked around for somewhere to sit but the two other chairs in the cell were either side of the cupboard under the window and there was no sign of my two cell mates moving to allow me to get to one of them. I must have looked really pathetic standing there like Oliver fucking Twist, my tray held in my arms. Wayne and Mick pretended they hadn't noticed my predicament, but their smirking faces told a different story. I gave up and putting my tray on the end of the top bunk ate whilst standing up.

Things didn't improve as the evening turned into night, in fact to say I was being given the cold shoulder would have been the biggest understatement since General Custer said, "Oh look there's a few Indians." I laid on my bunk staring up at the ceiling for the rest of the night listening to the endless babble from down below.

Wayne and Mick would occasionally ask me the odd question.

"What yer in fer?"

"Where you from?" the usual bollocks. I only gave short sharp answers and if I wasn't trying to keep the peace, I wouldn't have bloody answered at all. I appeared just to be the butt of some big joke that my two cell mates seemed to want to keep to themselves. I felt really miserable that night as I put up with the cutting remarks and schoolgirl giggles of those two cruel bastards. I managed to work out through eavesdropping that Wayne and Mick were friends on the outside before being nicked. No wonder they are so bloody tight with each other I thought as I cursed them under my breath.

I didn't sleep very well that night. The other prisoners

were cat-calling and shouting obscenities at each other until the early hours.

Now and again somebody would shout out, "For fucks sake shut it, I'm trying to fucking sleep."

Nobody took any notice and any reply given was more often than not, "Fuck you, wanker."

The following morning we were woken by a bell that resounded throughout the whole nick. I awoke with a start and for a few seconds I could not remember where I was. I rubbed my eyes and as I focused on my surroundings it all came flooding back. I looked over the side of my bunk and could see Wayne asleep on the single bed his hair tangled and matted, and that fucking, stupid goatee beard covered in saliva, where he'd dribbled all night. I scowled at him as he turned over, his eyes still closed, it took all my reserve not to jump out of bed and rag him round the cell until he begged for mercy.

The cell door was eventually unlocked and as it swung open a screw gave us what must have been his usual morning greeting. "Out of bed you lucky boys, it's a new day, same shit same place."

I sat up and pulling on my trousers climbed down on to the floor. Mick was just swinging his legs out of bed and I couldn't help but be drawn to the tattoos he had down both calves.

"Not bad, eh," grinned Mick as he saw me looking. I nodded my head and quickly turned away picking up my shirt from the floor and putting it on. I walked over to the open door and gingerly took a peek out on to the landing. It was a hive of activity. Inmates were slopping out carrying their piss pots back and forth to the toilets on the end of the landing. Jugs of water for washing were being taken back to cells and plastic bowls carried out to be emptied after they'd washed and shaved. A screw was handing out razors and checking them off as each prisoner returned them.

"Out the way," said Mick as he shoved me in the back on his way out, it was far harder than necessary, but I let it go. I

228

had to. I knew it and he knew it. I watched him as he strode across the landing his arms tensed and his chest puffed out and for an instant I was back at Thorpe Arch with Officer Tennyson.

"Come on get yerself washed," said a screw as he brushed past me as he walked along the landing. I quickly went into the cell picked up a water jug and went off to fill it. I stood in line as the three or four prisoners in front of me hurriedly filled their jugs.

"Cheers." I smiled at another kid as he turned the tap back on after seeing I was waiting.

"No probs mate," he winked as he scuttled off. It was the first act of kindness, no consideration I had come across since arriving and it may sound rather lame. but it made me smile and I began to allow myself to believe that perhaps it wouldn't be so bad after all.

Upon my return to the cell Wayne had got his arse out of bed and as I returned, we nearly collided as I walked through the door.

"Watch it," he snapped as he stepped back.

"Sorry," I smiled. I shouldn't have bothered.

"That's okay, cheers for fetching me water," he laughed as he took the jug from my hands. I don't know how I didn't spin him round and knock him out there and then. I could feel the rage begin to stir deep in my belly and my heart rate increase as it pushed extra blood to my muscles.

"That's alright init?" laughed Wayne as he poured the water into a plastic bowl he'd positioned on the seat of a chair. I ignored him and the laughing eyes of Mick as I grabbed another jug and left the cell. I have never been a fool and I had already worked out that if I took on one, I'd have to take them both on. I knew I would win that was never in question. The biggest worry would then be when I slept. I'd seen it for myself and heard some of the horror stories whilst on remand. One poor kid nearly died when his cell mate barricaded the cell door and set fire to his bed as he slumbered on in blissful ignorance. It was only the quick reactions of the screws that saved his life. When they realised the cell door was barricaded, they put a ladder up outside the cell window and put a hose through the bars and extinguished the flames. I pictured that kids face the first time I saw him; his face resembled a melted chocolate bar and one hand was just a lump of skin, his fingers now clenched in a permanent fist. I made a decision that morning that so long as Wayne or Mick didn't actually try to physically assault me, I would let it go. I comforted myself with the knowledge that I would eventually be moved to borstal anyway and they would be just a distant memory. It was a hard choice to live with at times.

The same morning, when I came back from collecting my breakfast, I found my clothes and towels had been thrown out of the locker onto the floor.

"That's our locker and you keep your fucking stuff out of it," said Mick relishing every moment of it. My life became a living hell after that. I was made to fetch their water each morning, empty their piss pots and generally belittled at every given opportunity. Neither of them was very bright and whilst I would gladly fetch and carry their water, I always made a point of filling it up from the toilet as I flushed it. I would smile quietly to myself as I watched them both, splashing the cooling water over their smug faces, or should I say faeces. It didn't surprise me that the bullying grew more and more sadistic and cruel. I'd seen it all my life, first would come the sly dig to see if you'd bite back, when you didn't, they would push more and more believing you were weak. If both of them had known how close they came to being beaten within an inch of their lives they'd have adjusted their attitudes, but I managed to hide that side of me very well. I would decide when it was the right time!

After breakfast that first morning I went before the prison governor who to this day probably had no idea how welcome his words were to my ears. "Yes Marriot you will be shipped out of here within three weeks, we just need a borstal allocation and then you're off, any questions?"

"No Sir," I beamed my happiness plain for all to see. On the way back to the wing I was taken to the prison shop along with the other inmates who'd arrived the day before. We were each told to sign our name in a ledger and then allowed to buy tobacco and whatever else we wanted up to a value of three pounds fifty pence. It was difficult, but I managed to spend it all. Mick was not in the cell when I got back but Wayne was reclining on his bed attempting to read a book. It must have been Janet and John because he had the IQ of cockroach and come to think of it, the looks to match.

"You been to the governor?" he asked as he sat upright and scratched at his goatee beard.

"Yes," I answered as I emptied my pockets on to my bed. I had half an ounce of tobacco some cigarette papers a box of matches and two Mars bars. Wayne jumped to his feet his book falling to the floor.

"Got somert fer me?" he said cockily as he pushed me aside and helped himself.

I grabbed his wrist and looking him straight in the eyes I said, "Put it down, put it fucking down now." The look on that coward's face was a picture, he was puzzled at first. You could see his mind turning over, he couldn't quite believe what he'd heard, he didn't want to believe what he'd heard because that would mean he would have to back up his sneering threats.

"What did you say? did you..."

I cut him off in mid-sentence, "Put it fucking down," I said pushing my face right into his. I could smell the fear on him and he flinched with any small movement I made.

"Okay, okay, I was only jossing, can't you take a joke?" he laughed nervously as he dropped my tobacco back onto the bed. I wasn't surprised by his actions I'd sussed him out within seconds of being in the cell and now my opinion of him was confirmed. I also knew he wasn't going to say anything to Mick upon his return, how could he? He would have to admit he was frightened of a fifteen-year-old boy and fear was something you would never admit to anyone when you were in prison. I really enjoyed the rest of the morning. I sat on my bunk smoking roll ups and looking out of the window. I couldn't help that smug feeling inside as I watched Wayne trying his best not to look in my direction. I would catch him out on the odd occasion and smile as he quickly averted his gaze his discomfort hard for him to hide.

Mick came back to the cell just before lunch and just as I'd suspected, Wayne quickly returned to his old self again. Mick started first, "Can't you keep fucking still up there?" he said angrily kicking the underside of my mattress. I ignored him but didn't miss the look of delight on Wayne's face. I didn't care I'd had my moment of victory and that would keep me going for a while.

The routine in Armley prison was harsh. The boredom was beyond anything I'd had to cope with before. We had no association and were locked up for twenty-three and a half hours a day. The only times we ever left the cells was to collect meals, slop out or for the half an hour's exercise we had each day. I hated exercise I found it intimidating. Most of the prisoners were old lags mid-thirties to early sixties and a bigger bunch of rogues and cut throats I'd never seen. Billy who had travelled with me in the van from court would give me a menacing grin and run his hand across his throat every time he passed me in the yard. I knew he was getting some real thrill out of thinking he was frightening me, but the truth is, after a few days, I was a little disappointed if he didn't acknowledge me in his usual manner as we passed. He must have realised it was no longer working and after a couple of weeks he put aside the cut throat gesture and would just smile or wink at me like two friends passing in the street. This worried me even more as I was now convinced, he wanted to bugger my tight young arse.

The three weeks waiting to be transferred to borstal passed agonisingly slowly. The isolation and despair I felt, I could never put into words. The rest of the prisoners probably found it was different for them, they would spend their twenty-three and a half hours a day playing chess, draughts, monopoly and cards. If they weren't playing board-games they'd be swapping grossly exaggerated stories with their gullible cell mates. I would spend my day's listening to Wayne and Mick laughing and joking. They would just pretend I wasn't there and if they did happen to notice me it was purely as a distraction and I would then become their object of ridicule. Mick would really enjoy being sadistic and several times I thought I might just have to say, "Oh fuck it," and smack him with a right cross. I didn't though he always seemed to take me as far as anyone could and just back off at the right time. Wayne was cautious in his tormenting, he hadn't forgotten the words we'd exchanged, and I have no doubt he was scared that the next time we were alone I might fill him in.

When the day of my move eventually arrived, I'd already given serious consideration to saying goodbye to my two cell mates with a good beating. I'd even planned it to the letter. I was going to wait until the last night when we were banged up. I would wait until they had both fallen asleep and then I would wake Mick first and the moment he opened his eyes I'd hit him and hit him until he begged for mercy. I wasn't worried if Wayne woke up, he would shit himself anyway and I didn't think he'd have the guts to join in, besides I thought in some sick way, it would be better to let him watch, it would increase his fear knowing he was next. The funny thing is after I'd planned and savoured their demise for so long it all ended in what can only be described as an anti-climax. You see I had considered everything except the way I would be feeling. It was true that Wayne and Mick had done everything they could to make my life a living hell. It was true that I lay on my bunk each day and cursed them under my breath. It was true that they were bullies and cowards and needed teaching a lesson. It was also true that on that final night I was that happy at being shipped out the following day, the last thing I wanted to do was hurt anybody. So I just sat on my bunk smoking and smiling contently to myself; sometimes I'm just too bloody forgiving!

233

When the morning finally arrived, I was up and dressed before the screw even opened the door. I didn't wait to be told, I grabbed my pillowcase and headed down the landing leaving my two tormentors slumbering in their beds blissfully unaware that during the night, I'd emptied my piss pot into their clothes drawers.

I was given my breakfast along with some other inmates who were being moved to other prisons and after getting into my civilian clothes I hurriedly boarded the coach.

Chapter 16

Onwards and Upwards

The coach ride was a real pleasure. I had not seen the outside for a few weeks and it was a novelty watching the real world go by. I took in every detail, people rushing about on the streets as they journeyed to work, the postman on a little red bicycle carrying a fluorescent bag full of mail, the school kids being hurried along by their mothers. I would have swapped my life with any of them in a heartbeat. The coach headed down the motorway and as we weaved our way through the morning traffic, I lazed in my seat and allowed myself to daydream about what lay ahead. I knew borstal would not be as bad as main stream prison, and besides at least the majority of prisoners would be around the same age as me. I'd heard whilst on remand that in borstal you got to be out of your cells all day. I looked forward to that, I hated being cooped up. I wondered what kind of job I'd be given. I hoped it would be outside, I really missed the feel of the wind in my face and fresh air in my lungs. If you have never been in prison you cannot imagine how much you yearn to breathe uncontaminated air. You want air that has not been filtered through the lungs of every con on your landing; you want to drag air into your lungs that had been brought on the breeze and that danced and twirled in ecstasy at the joy of its own freedom.

The coach left the motorway at Manchester and as we neared the city centre some of the other prisoners began to look a little subdued. I didn't blame them they were being shipped to Manchester's notorious Strangeways and it had a reputation for being hell on earth. Strangeways prison was a gloomy and desperate place and as we got nearer to its towering brick walls, I thanked God I would not see the inside of it. It seemed to go on forever and the wings could be seen clearly from the outside as you approached. There was a large central dome in the middle and the wings sprang from it like a squid's tentacles. Each wing was at least two hundred feet long and several storey's high. I wondered how many unfortunate bastards were languishing behind its bars, desperate for the chance of a new start.

"Right everybody off," shouted a screw as we stopped inside its intimidating wooden gates.

"Did he say everybody?" I asked the inmate I was shackled to.

"Yep," he replied without looking at me as he began to climb out of his seat. I had no choice but to follow. Once inside the prisons reception we were seated on several benches whilst the screws had a quick chat and handed paperwork back and forth.

"Who's Marriot?" said a screw standing with two others.

"Here Sir," I smiled waving my free hand. This is it I thought they are going to take me out and put me back on the coach and by tea time I'd be settled in borstal.

"Em Marriot," the screw said awkwardly as he walked over to where I was sitting.

"I'm afraid you won't be going on to Portland, there's been a bit of a mix up and you are going to remain here for assessment. I'm sorry kid," he smiled as though that would make things better.

My whole world fell apart there and then.

"But Sir, I thought I was going to borstal today," I pleaded rather pathetically, like a child does when he wants something from one of its parents.

"Sorry nowt I can do," he said dismissively shrugging his shoulders as he walked away.

"Fucking tough break," said the kid I was cuffed to.

"Oh fuck off," I snapped, his face flushed, and he tried to move further along the bench forgetting about the cuffs that joined us together. He looked back at me and smiled nervously as he realised, he wasn't going anywhere. I fixed him with a stare and he hung his head in a fashion that suggested surrender. The rest of what happened went by in a kind of blur and in no time, I found myself in a single cell on the wing and the door securely bolted behind me.

"Fuck, fuck, fuck, fuck," I shouted as I kicked the metal frame of the bed that stood in front of me. I walked across the cell pulled out a chair that was under a wooden desk against the wall and sat down. The cell was sparsely furnished, a tiled floor, one bed, one desk and one chair. High up on the outer wall was a barred window about three feet long by one foot high. I put my head in my hands and as the sheer frustration I felt got the better of me I sobbed like a baby.

The cell door wasn't opened until dinner time and much the same as at Armley, you collected your meals from the ground floor and took them back to your cell. It was Shepherd's Pie and cabbage, dessert was semolina pudding and a large mug of tea. I poured the tea into my piss pot and filled the empty mug with water. I hadn't forgotten about the bromide that the authorities apparently laced our tea with. If I had to look on the bright side, and I did, I comforted myself with the thought that at least I was away from Mick and Wayne and could at last actually eat a meal sitting down. Around half an hour after lunch the door was opened, and I was ordered to place my empty tray outside where it would be collected. The door was then locked and remained so until the evening when it was opened for tea. I killed time by counting the bricks in the cell walls and once I'd done that, I recounted them until I'd reached the same number twice. This didn't happen until the seventh try and it was deduced that my cell held a total of one thousand eight hundred and twenty-two. I made a mental note to remember the count so that I could compare it when I moved to my next cell. It's crazy the things that you can amuse yourself with, when you're confined to a single cell.

I took a look out of the window, it was that high up I had to stand on a chair in order to see out. The view was disappointing to say the least. I couldn't even see over the wall so even my eyes were incarcerated. The prison grounds were as uninteresting as any other I'd seen, cons and screws wandering around aimlessly, shit parcels strewn along the grass verges under the cell blocks, razor wire and pigeons. Oh yeah Strangeways nick was a thriving bird sanctuary for the local pigeon population and as they flapped and fluttered their way from cell block roof to cell block roof, they left the whole prison in a lovely white spattering of shite that made it resemble a badly iced Christmas cake. It was not unusual for a pigeon to land on your window ledge and a good many prisoners had taken to feeding them, they became their pets and would return at meal times and feed from their outstretched hand until they were full, they would then promptly shit all over and flap off.

Not all prisoners were fully signed up members of the RSPB and would find other uses for any poor confused bird that took up a perch outside their cell window. There were some cruel and heartless bastards in Strangeways and they were not happy unless they could watch someone, or something suffer at their hands. These sick individuals would set up traps or coax a bird into their cell and then subject it to such systematic torture it defies description. The screws and the authorities were aware, they had to be, as countless dismembered pigeon carcasses were disposed of each day along with the rubbish and shit parcels that were thrown from the cell blocks. I once saw a pigeon thrown from a cell with its feathers alight and as it frantically flew around the night sky cheers of laughter echoed throughout the block. Another time some callous twat tied a plastic cup to a pigeon's leg and the poor thing got caught up on the razor wire fence and died a slow and agonising death as inmates took bets on how long it would live. I had never seen such outright inhumanity and could never understand what made such people tick. I would later in life bear witness to such acts and worse that were carried out on human beings. I wondered then had these people served their apprenticeships torturing animals and gradually worked their way up the evolutionary scale, it makes me

238

sick to think we allow such people to breath our air.

I quickly gave up the sightseeing and after making up my bed I got myself settled down for a cosy nap.

"Off that fucking bed, where do you think you are, fucking Butlins?" shouted a screw as he peered through the spy hole in the cell door.

I awoke with a start and as the screw said, "Do you fucking hear me?"

I did as he asked. "Sorry Sir" I apologised to just a brown eyeball that appeared magnified through the glass peep hole.

"You fucking will be, if you do it again you're on report," the voice shouted as the metal flap swung across the spy hole and he clattered off down the landing. I was more than a little pissed off at having to sit in a wooden chair just staring at the walls. I couldn't fathom out what difference it made whether I was lying on my bed or hanging from the bloody ceiling. I was still in prison and surely that was all that mattered. It was a very long day and it wasn't until after supper, a cup of medicated tea and a biscuit that I was finally told I could now lay on my bed.

The following morning the sun came shining through the cell window to announce a new day. It needn't have bothered the screws had beaten it to it by about an hour. I quickly washed my face and cleaned my teeth in the plastic bowl that I'd placed on the wooden desk and as I dried my face on the ridiculously small prison towel, I couldn't help but feel sorry for myself. I always had lots of luck, unfortunately all bad. Dad used to say if I fell in a bucket of tits, I'd come up sucking my thumb. At that moment I wouldn't have disagreed with him.

"Come on git yer bowl emptied and make up your bed, mattress against the wall," said a screw as he sauntered past my cell door.

I stuck my head out and shouted after him, "Against the wall?"

The screw stopped and turned towards me, "Yeah put the

mattress on its side against the wall, got it?" he said sarcastically pretending to knock on his head with his fist.

I nodded my understanding although I didn't. I waited until the screw had turned away and took a quick butcher's in the next cell. The blankets were folded into a kind of square bundle and placed at the foot of the bed and the mattress was stood on its side not on the floor but on the bed frame, so it leant against the wall. I ran back to my cell and copied what I'd seen.

"Good, good," said the screw as he looked in on his way back down the landing. "Now git your arse downstairs and get yer breakfast," he finished. Breakfast was never a surprise whatever prison you were in it was like a bad tradition and to change it must have been classed as treason or something along those lines. It consisted of the same ingredients measured out into the same quantities and cooked in the same manner, which was generally just short of inedible. I must confess that the prison cooks were not entirely devoid of imagination and would surprise you with the different dishes they could make from exactly the same ingredients. They could also disguise an earlier meal with a dollop of potato or a sprinkle of cheese and most of the dim wits in prison never even noticed they were having the same thing for tea that they'd had for lunch. I know that the consensus among the general public is that prisoners should count themselves lucky they are being fed at all and we should be given bread and water and hard labour until we drop. I'd like just one of those pompous bastards to be taken away from everything they know and love to be treated like your nothing, beaten and humiliated and left without hope. Then and only then should any person feel entitled to an opinion, as the saying goes, **Walk a mile in my shoes!**

After breakfast I was taken to see the Governor as was the ritual for every prisoner who arrives in a new prison. It's the time when the Governor gets to lay down the law, ask if you've got any problems and then move on to the next subject before you answer. It's a time when if you're lucky

240

you might actually be made aware of what plans were being made for you by the relevant authorities. If you were unlucky it was the time you would have your card marked as you'd already been labelled a trouble causer, what is it they say about a dog and a bad name?

My meeting with the Governor was eye opening if nothing else. It was explained to me that I had been allocated to the wrong borstal whilst in Armley. This was apparently an oversight as the judge's recommendation that I receive psychiatric counselling whilst in borstal had not been taken into account. I would therefore remain on the allocation wing in Strangeways until it was decided where I was to be sent. I was not told how long this would take and to be truthful I didn't ask. I was past caring and would have happily let them subject me to a public flogging without protesting. If your spirit and love of life is gone it becomes less and less important as to what will happen to you and I was half way there.

The routine in Strangeways was exactly the same as Armley. Same meal times, same exercise period, same old fucking story. I hated the regime it was harsh for the sake of it. Prisoners were even put on report if they were caught looking out of their cell windows. I'd have loved to spend an hour alone with the sadistic bastard who came up with that idea. It seemed that not only were we to be locked down for twenty-three and a half hours a day, but our gaze must remain within the control of the establishment as well. Beds were not be used at all until after eight o clock at night and you were to sit at your desk at all times, unless using your piss pot. The whole infrastructure was designed to keep you in your place, to belittle you, to take away any foolish notion you might have to make a decision for yourself. I detested Strangeways and only the distant thought of being shipped out prevented me ending it all there and then. I discovered during my stay that the draconian rules we had to obey only applied to the young offender's wing and not to the general prison population. The lifers and adult cons led a more sedate existence with association and work details that allowed them out of their cells for long periods.

I never made any friends in Strangeways, it would have been impossible anyway I rarely saw another soul. I would nod at a couple of my neighbouring cell-mates when we came out for meals or exercise and in return, they would do the same, that was as far as it went. During exercise I would spend the half an hour breathing in the fresh air alone with my thoughts as I walked robotically behind the other inmates.

Once a week we were taken to the library where we could choose three books. I gave up in the end after I'd tried to read a couple and some clever bastard had seen fit to tear out the last twenty pages in one and a whole chapter in another. So, on the days when the screw would open the cell and holler library, I would just shake my head and he would happily lock the door, leaving me sat at that bloody desk my arse numb right down to my knees.

It was a Friday night just after supper when I heard a screw approach my cell. I vaulted off the bed and stood facing him as he swung back the door. "Marriot, pack yer gear tonight, yer shipping out tomorrow."

I'd been in Strangeways for five weeks and it felt like months. I was so excited that no sooner had the screw shut the door than I'd packed. It wouldn't have taken long anyway, I had very little in the way of belongings. Once I'd neatly placed everything in a pile on top of the wooden desk, I sat back on the bed lit a cigarette and as I blew out the smoke, I smiled for the first time in as long as I could remember.

Chapter 17

Out of the frying pan!

Feltham borstal in Middlesex was a psychiatric borstal. It was where life's young misfits and the misunderstood were sent. A good many of the young offenders had committed serious violent crime or were habitual offenders. It didn't look at all daunting as I first caught sight of it. The first thing I noticed was although it was entirely enclosed by a thirty-foot high security fence, the razor wire was conspicuous by its absence. The grounds were well kept and free from litter and as the coach gunned its engine and crawled through the front gates I smiled as I saw parties of inmates mowing lawns or planting shrubs, they seemed happy they were chatting to each other and smiling. The buildings themselves were not modern but in a good order with fresh paintwork and windows that had no bars just a security mesh that would still allow light in. The whole place looked more like a stately home than a borstal. I quickly climbed off the coach and lined up with the other new arrivals. Most of them looked nervy and bowed their heads in a submissive posture. I didn't, it looked like heaven after what I'd endured over the last few months and I'd already decided to take each new opportunity with an optimistic approach. A screw in civilian clothes came over and after taking some paperwork off one of the uniformed screws who'd brought us, he announced loudly, "Right boys in line, follow me."

We were led down the side of the building along a wide tarmac road with grass borders and flowers around the edges. We filed past two inmates who were trimming a hedge, a screw, again in civilian clothes was standing next to them and they were sharing a joke. The whole place appeared to be on some kind of happy trip and I was really looking forward to seeing the rest of it. The reception area was straight out of the prison interior design book, a desk, a screw, some benches and shower rooms adjacent to it. We were quickly relieved of our belongings and our civilian clothes before being ordered to shower and then seated in a waiting area each wearing the grey trousers, blue and white striped shirt and black slip on shoes we'd been issued with. The screws remained in the main reception area and were engaged in idle chit chat. There were around ten of us that had arrived together and as we sat and waited, we remained silent, deep in our own thoughts.

Occasionally somebody would take a nervous look around at the other inmates but would immediately turn away when their eyes met. After a short time a screw began to call out names and one by one the inmates being called stood up and walked into the next room.

"Right Marriot," said a screw in a friendly tone as I stood in front of him. "You're going to South house so if you stand over there with him," he said pointing towards another kid, "I'll take you over in a bit."

I did as I was asked and watched as the rest of the inmates were given the houses they would be sent to. It became apparent that the borstal was split into houses based around the points of the compass. There was east house, south house, west house, north house, and centre house. The names of the houses had not been made up with any degree of thought as the building itself was anything but round, it was in fact rectangular and centre house was not situated in the middle of it. Before being led our separate ways to our new houses we were each given several changes of clothes, working boots, donkey jackets, gym kit, training shoes and works jeans and jumpers. By the time we'd managed to bundle these things into our arms we were laden down like pack horses and as we were led off down the corridor. You could constantly hear the sound of someone cursing as they had to stop yet again and pick up something they'd dropped.

The screws who were escorting us would open a gate and say, "North house," or "West house," like a bus driver

244

announcing a stop.

The new inmates for the particular house called would file in and the screw would shout after them, "North house, Four on," dependent on the number of new arrivals that entered. "South house, two on," yelled the screw as I walked through the gate with the other kid behind me. The gate was locked behind us and we found ourselves alone standing in a corridor, a toilet to our left and a door to our right.

"Do you think we should go in?" said the kid standing behind me as he motioned towards the door on our right.

"You can if you want, I'm staying here until I'm told otherwise," I said firmly. I had quickly learnt that in prison you were not supposed to think for yourself, you just did as you were told.

"But we can't just stand here," said the kid rather weakly.

"You got somewhere you gotta be?" I smiled at him.

"Rob, my name's Rob," the kid smiled at me. He was about sixteen years old, six stone, wet through and had more spots on his face than an entire copy of war and peace written in Braille.

"Jack, Jack Marriot," I said as I looked away down the corridor.

"Where you from Jack?" asked Rob in a forced way that said he was just trying to make conversation. I wasn't going to answer him anyway but even if I was the screws timing was impeccable.

"Ah, two new ones," smiled a screw as he walked out of the doorway to our right. He was dressed in trousers and a shirt and tie. As with the other screws we'd seen, the only visible sign he was a screw was the long chain and bunch of keys that hung from his belt.

"I'm Mr Staton, come with me boys and we'll get you sorted out. The rest of the boys are at work until four thirty, so I'll show you around the unit when we've seen Mr Beard, okay?" he smiled like a Cheshire cat.

Mr Staton had kindness written all over him. His brown eyes brimmed with energy and the love of life and everything in it. He was about twenty-five years old, clean shaven with neatly trimmed brown hair and as he walked, he spread before him a scent of expensive but overpowering aftershave. "That okay?"

I snapped back to reality.

"That okay?" repeated Mr Staton as he looked right into my face.

"Yes Sir," I nodded and with that we followed the immaculately turned-out Mr Staton back through the doorway down a short passageway and arrived outside an office. To our right, was a large dining room and as I stole a quick peek. I could see a serving hatch to the left of the door as you entered.

Mr Staton opened the office door and poked his head around it "Two on Bob, can you see em now?" he said to whoever was inside, with that we were motioned towards the door and guided inside.

The office looked like a teacher's staff room, lots of comfy chairs half-finished cups of coffee and ashtrays brimming with butt ends.

"Come in lads don't be shy, I'm Mr Beard the Principal Officer for south house," he said from behind a cluttered desk in the corner. Mr Beard was aptly named he was a large man in stature and girth sporting a beard that wouldn't have looked out of place hanging from the chin of a wizard. His face showed the fifty or so years he'd spent on this earth and gave him a look of superior intelligence. "Well boys welcome to South house and the joy that we call borstal," he began, grinning at his own little joke. You will have already noticed that things here are a little different to the remand system and young offender's prisons you've been in," he continued.

'No shit,' I thought everybody here must be on bloody Prozac. I'd never seen so many happy faces since I'd watched the Umpa Lumpas in Willy Wonka's chocolate factory.

"Yes, in here we don't call the officers 'Sir,' 'boss,' 'guv,'

246

or any of that nonsense, we are addressed as Mister at all times do you understand? He asked as he looked at Rob and then at me, we both nodded like we'd lost the power of speech. "Very good," he smiled, "The only two things you need to remember whilst in here is to obey the rules and that we are here to help you. If you have a problem this door is always open," he said as he stopped and looked at his wrist watch before continuing. "Unfortunately lads I'm a little pushed for time right now so why don't you let Mr Staton settle you in the cubicles store your gear and then you can have a quick look round. I will see you both individually after tea, off you go then," he smiled as he waved his hand towards the open door. I was glad he hadn't taken ages giving us the borstal handbook page by page, my arms were killing me with the weight of the gear I'd been carrying since leaving reception. Rob hadn't fared well either, he dropped the whole lot as he walked out of Mr Beards office and hurriedly got to his knees picking everything up like a scolded charlady.

Mr Staton laughed loudly and said, "Come on lad, let's get you upstairs and you can get rid of that lot."

Rob just went a lovely shade of red and scuttled behind us as we climbed a flight of stairs at the end of the corridor.

The cubicles were as near to a prison cell as they had been on the units. They were wooden partition structures with a mesh roof and a wooden door with a safety glass section in the upper half. I counted how many there were as we stopped outside one and it was unlocked. There were twenty in total, ten on each side of a linoleum lined corridor.

"In yer go, get your stuff put away and I'll come back for you in a minute," said Mr Staton as he strode off down the corridor "Come on then," he said impatiently obviously waiting for me to follow.

I was more than happy with my cubicle. It was situated right at the end of the row of ten and as such I only had a neighbour on one wall. I quickly dropped my gear on the single metal bed and took a quick look at my new home. It was quite nicely furnished a wooden wardrobe a chest of drawers a desk and even a rug on the floor. There was no toilet and as I rummaged through the belongings I'd been given in reception, I was slightly mystified as to why I had not been given a piss pot. I made a mental note to ask the nice Mr Staton when he came back for us. In the meantime I explored my new surroundings and was glad to find my cubicle faced the front of the borstal. The view was excellent, and I could see the whole of the main gate and along to the green fence line to the road that ran along the perimeter. As far as views went it wasn't a bad one and I was sure that there would always be something for me to see when I was bored. The view from a cell window is of vital importance to any prisoner and there are a few things that make the scene good or bad. A good view must have an unrestricted path as far as the eye can see, it must also have a couple of focal points somewhere where things are constantly happening, a road is good, a footpath or better still a view of the visitors car park, all of these things are much sought after and prisoners will gladly bribe bully or wrangle their way into cells that occupy premium viewing. A bad view would be one where you can only see inanimate objects, no people no glimpse of the normal world beyond prison walls or fences, these cells should be avoided at all costs especially in a regime where lock down is for prolonged periods.

Once I'd placed everything away in the wardrobes and cupboards. I made up my bed and after plumping up the pillow I threw myself headlong onto the mattress, I sunk my face into the pillow and laughed and laughed like an imbecile. It was a good job the pillow muffled the sound otherwise poor Rob further down the cubicles would have thought I was a complete 'head the ball.' I felt happy and it had been so long since I'd felt that way. I just couldn't help myself. I felt that finally things were looking up, how bad could it be here? The screws were, so far, all nice people. I wasn't going to be banged up all day, I'd get association and I no longer had to be frightened of being bum raped by adult

248

prisoners who fancied a bit of fresh (I know now that it was all in my wild imagination, but at that age you believe all those wind-up merchants when they fill you full of shit). Yeah life was definitely looking up for Jack Marriot and I had hope.

Mr Staton came back after ten minutes and shouted from the top of the stairs, "You boys come on then." I quickly made my way out of the unlocked cubicle and down the corridor. Rob exited his cubicle and fell into step with me.

"How's yer cell, er I mean cubicle?" I said as I patted his shoulder.

"Yeah it's better than the shit hole I came from," said Rob as he itched a yellow zit on his chin. "What jobs do yer think we'll get?" he continued excitedly.

Before I could answer Mr Staton hollered "Come on lads. We'd better move it." I smiled at Rob and we both picked up the pace until we joined a, by now rather pissed off Mr Staton, at the top of the stairs.

"Right, come on you two. I know you've got six months to two years but I'm off-shift in half an hour, so let's move it!" he grumbled.

The grand tour of South house didn't take long although I'm sure Mr Staton rushed through it. We were shown the dining room. "This is where you take all your meals, they are served at regular times and only alter at weekends when they are served a little later, you'll soon get to know the routine so don't worry too much," said Mr Staton, his tone a little friendlier.

We then walked out of the dining room past Mr Beard's office past the stairwell and along another corridor. "This is the quiet room, where if you want to read or just sit and chat quietly you can."

I looked in through a long narrow window with mesh safety glass. The room had comfy low chairs with padded arm rests and a large coffee table with books and magazines neatly stacked on it. The walls were covered in a large mural that snaked its way from wall to ceiling. It was a scene with

249

mystical gothic figures and a large fire breathing dragon that swooped down from the ceiling.

"Who painted that Sir?" I asked.

Mr Staton cleared his throat "Who painted that Mr Staton?" he smiled giving me a knowing look.

"Oh yeah, sorry Sir, I mean Mr Staton," I apologised.

"It was painted by one of the inmates. I think he must have been on drugs at the time," he laughed. "Come on then let's move on" he said as he walked away, and we scurried on behind trying to keep up. The recreation room opened up off the corridor where the quiet room was situated. It was a large open plan space with a snooker table taking pride of place as you entered. A table tennis table that had seen better days was forlornly dumped in the middle of the room and lastly a large television hung high on the wall in one corner with plastic chairs scattered haphazardly in front of it.

"This is where you will have association every night and all day, Saturdays and Sundays," declared Mr Staton as he walked towards a door to our left. "These are the toilets for use during association," he said, pointing to a door opposite and if you look to the bottom of the corridor you can see another door to the left, that is the wash rooms and showers. "You go there each morning, get washed and then return to your cubicles and get dressed. When you get in from your work detail you will also be able to get washed and showered before tea, any questions?" he paused briefly and looked at Rob and then me. "Right he continued if you turn about face you can see the gate where you were brought into the house this morning and the door to the right that leads to the stairwell and Mr Beards office, so as you can see you can't get lost." He let out a large sigh, "And that my boys is that, so if you go back to your cubicles and wait until the others return you can introduce yourselves and get ready for tea, I'll catch you later," and with that he walked away leaving Rob, myself and a distinct smell of Paco Rabbane lingering in the corridor outside the toilets.

"What do yer reckon?" Rob said, his face lit up in

anticipation of what he'd seen.

"Yeah not bad, at least we won't be banged up and the screws are pretty sound, come on let's have a nosey around on our own," I said as I raced off towards the washrooms. The washrooms were huge, they had around twenty showers all in a long line, but no curtains or partitions as dignity was something that you left at the prison gates, or so the establishment believed. There were also six full size roll top baths that when full would be at least three feet deep as well as a row of thirty wash basins that ran the full length of the outside wall with shiny tin mirrors above them. "Well we won't be fighting to get in the bathroom on a morning," I laughed, there's room for a fucking army in here."

"Let's check out the recreation room again," said Rob excitedly as he ran off without waiting for me. When I arrived Rob had set up the snooker table and was whacking balls all over the place.

"What the fuck are you doing you daft twat?" I snarled at him as I picked up the cue ball as he was about to hit it. "What are you trying to do? Get us in the shit if we get caught fucking about in here, we'll end up on fucking report and we've only been here ten fucking minutes, put it the fuck away you fucking knob," I finished as I threw the cue ball across the table and walked off towards the stairwell.

I'd only been in my cubicle a few minutes and was sitting on the bed making a roll up when Rob came creeping in. "Sorry Jack bout that, yer right, I weren't thinking soz mate," he pleaded, his pock marked face looking remorseful.

"I'm not mad at you but for fucks sake Rob, there's a thousand ways I can get into trouble on my own so please, please, please, don't do anything that is going to drag me into the shit with you, okay? Now let's just wait here as we've been told," I said my face softening a little as I handed Rob the roll-up I'd just finished making.

"Budge up mate," he grinned and plonked himself on the bed next to me. "Got a light," he said waving the unlit fag under my nose.

251

I shook my head in mock disbelief and raised my eyes towards the ceiling. "Fucking hell, Rob, I can see your gonna be a right pain in the arse," I declared loudly and we both laughed heartily as I slapped him on the back.

The rest of the inmates signalled their return loudly as at least fifty pairs of boots ran up and down the stairs and corridors. I could hear lots of excited chatter and cursing as they hurried back to their cubicles to get changed.

"Shall we go out?" Rob said rather meekly.

"Well you can if you want, but it's not as though we haven't got plenty of time for introductions," I answered sarcastically.

"Yeah, good point, good point," he repeated and settled himself back on the edge of the bed.

"I'm gonna have a shower," I said as I jumped off the bed and pulled a towel out of my locker.

"I'll come too, I'll just get a towel," said Rob as he headed out of the door.

"Rob, Rob," I called after him, but he'd already gone. The other inmates exchanged the odd nod or wink as we passed each other on my way to the showers but nobody actually spoke to me. I noticed a couple of them look and nudge each other before sharing some private joke, it was nothing new I was a new kid and until I'd proved myself, I would be treated like every new inmate, with clever comments verbal challenges and the early onset of bullying. I ignored nearly everyone who fixed me with their hardest stare apart from one cocky bastard who I just literally laughed at as he gave me his street-wise cock of the walk look; it was supposed to frighten me, but he had a mean stare that just made him look constipated.

The shower rooms were alive with activity and kids were jumping into showers the moment someone stepped out. "You gonna be long in that bath?" said a kid as he looked over the tiled partition that separated it from the next one.

"When I'm fucking ready you'll be the last to know, now fuck off Tinsley" replied an unknown voice from the other side. It was the same at the wash basins.

"Give us some soap Batley," said a tall ginger kid as he snatched the soap off a small blonde kid and shoved him in the chest.

"Yeah Batley fuck off," said another kid as he joined in and pushed the by now trembling Batley away from the wash basin. I looked at Batley as he walked away, he was pathetic, broken but worst of all he didn't even hide it, he might as well have had kick me tattooed on his forehead. I found an empty shower stripped off and after testing the water with my hand climbed in. It was hot, I couldn't remember the last time I'd had a hot shower and as the soothing water fell down my face and onto my back. I closed my eyes and tried to imagine I was somewhere else.

"There you are," said a familiar voice and before I'd opened my eyes, I knew it was Rob.

"Ere, I'm getting out, have this one," I said without looking at him as I stepped out. I grabbed my towel and dried my face before working my way down to my feet. I slipped on my trousers and put my shoes on hanging my towel over my shoulder. I gathered up my shirt socks and underpants and made my way to the door. I was just about in the corridor when a voice made me stop in my tracks.

"Get the fuck out cunt it's my turn," I stepped backwards and looked into the wash room. The big ginger kid was dragging poor Rob out of the shower.

"Go on fuck off," he snarled as he pushed Rob in the back sending him falling over the wooden bench in front of the showers. Rob hit the tiled floor face first his nose issuing a pool of blood that gradually made its way along the open gutter and down the drain.

"See you little cunt, you don't fucking argue with me, got it?" the ginger kid laughed as he began soaping his hair. I stood transfixed to the spot. I wanted to help Rob. I felt sorry for him but at the same time I wasn't being given any shit and I wanted to keep it that way. I scuttled away pretending I'd not seen anything and made my way back to my cubicle.

253

Rob turned up moments later and to my shame I acted all shocked at what had happened to him.

"Oh shit mate, I'm sorry I must have just left," I lied.

"It's okay Jack, it's not your problem anyway," said Rob as he wiped his bloody nose on his towel. If he was trying to make me feel worse, it was bloody well working.

Rob stuck to me like shit to a blanket after that, he was frightened to be out of my sight and if I left him alone, he was like a panicked puppy.

"Where you going? he'd ask pathetically can I come?"

I became a little annoyed with him and as if I didn't already feel guilty enough, I heaped a barrow load more on myself. "Look you pathetic bastard get a fucking grip, I'm going for a piss is that alright? You better sort yourself out Rob, we've only been here a few hours and you're getting yourself into a whole heap of shite. If you don't toughen up, they'll make your life a living hell, so sort it or stop fucking whining, you got me?" I shouted into his face before walking out of my cubicle and down the stairs. I wasn't going anywhere in particular I just couldn't sit there listening to Rob bleating and looking at me like I should do something. Why do all the wimps and mummy's boys seem to think I'm their guardian angel? Why should I be the one? Why should I care? They're nothing to me? I tried to convince myself, but it didn't work. I hated bullying I hated to see people suffer needlessly and what made it worse was every meek bastard I met saw it as plain as the nose on my face. I was like some sort of giant fucking geek magnet.

"Where you off lad?" said a screw I'd not seen before as we met at the foot of the stairs.

"Er I've left something in the showers," I said not too convincingly.

"Well it's nearly tea time so hurry up and get whatever it is," he said. "Go on then move it," he urged as I remained rooted to the spot.

"Yes Sir on my way," I smiled and legged it off towards the short corridor that led to the showers.

"Don't run," the screw called after me. The wash room was deserted, and the only signs of its earlier use were the damp humid air and pools of water where people had dried themselves. I walked over to the shower Rob had been in and sat on the bench outside it. There was a feint red tinge to the floor tiles where the water had diluted Robs crimson offering.

"Oh fuck, fuck, why Dad why? Why did you have to make me into this, the one-man fucking avenger," I said as I stared heavenwards. I heard my father's voice as clear as if he was sat beside me.

I wasn't going nuts I was remembering, remembering the words he'd drummed into me, time after time as I pictured his face seated at the kitchen table. "Never be a bully. God gave you strength to help others, the strong should protect the weak not exploit them."

"If only things were as simple as that, if only," I said aloud, pretending I was actually conversing with my old man. "If only they were that simple," I muttered under my breath as I made my way back to my cubicle.

Teatime was announced by the stampede of hungry inmates filing out of their prospective cubicles and pushing each other out of the way as they tried to be the first down the stairs and into the dining room. I stopped at Rob's cubicle and asked if he was coming. He was lying face down on his bed and as he sat up, I could see by his red eyes he'd been crying. I pretended I hadn't noticed, I was embarrassed and didn't see the need to embarrass him as well. I looked away and said I'd meet him at the top of the stairs, it was a chance for him to wipe his face and regain his composure and it felt like the right thing to do. Whilst killing time waiting for Rob, I noticed a door just off to the left at the top of the stairs. It had the by now familiar safety glass in the upper section. I strode over and looking through the wired glass I could see a large dormitory with around thirty beds in it. I had until that time not really considered that the fifty or so inmates in the unit could not have fitted into only twenty cubicles. The dorm was about the size of a school gym, beds were lined up on opposite walls the footboards facing each other. There was a single wooden locker at the side of each bed and this gave each bed a standard gap between itself and the next one it looked regimented, a little like an army barracks. I heard Rob's footsteps and turned as he came up behind me.

"Eh Rob have you seen this?" I said, pointing through the window.

"Oh yeah, it's a dorm," said Rob, his lack of interest apparent.

"Come on I'm starving," I said as I put my arm on his shoulder and nodded with my head towards the stairs.

"It'll be fine," I grinned as I saw the fear Rob was trying his best to hide.

"Where've you two been?" asked a screw as we walked into the dining room. I was in front of Rob and thought it best I do the talking.

"Sorry we're new and didn't realize it was teatime," I said flashing my best cheeky boy smile.

"Go on get your grub, you're lucky there's anything left with this set of gluttons," the screw replied as his eyes surveyed the rest of the inmates. It didn't take long to work out why there was a mass stampede for meals. The borstal kitchen in their wisdom decided it was better to give the inmates a choice of culinary offerings which in principle is a good idea but in practice quite another. You see the kitchen would make two different dishes for lunch and dinner the problem was one meal was always far superior to the other and that's where the idea fell on its arse. If you arrived in the last half of inmates, you were left with the crap choice that nobody else wanted. The choices of food were far from comparative you could get say a large slice of pizza and chips with baked beans or a slice of corned beef that was so thin you could read a paper through it, served with a dollop of mash potato and a spoonful of marrowfat peas. It was no contest to adolescent boys and as you can imagine the battle to be in the first half of diners was akin to a very rough game of no-rules-killer-ball. I felt sorry for the kids who worked on the servery they were tormented and bullied by the tougher inmates who would gladly beat the shit out of them if they didn't ensure they were saved the meal they'd requested. I watched many times as the servery kids had their own meals taken from them by other inmates and swapped for the less appetising choice, they would just let it happen; that look of beaten resignation visible in their sad eyes.

Rob and I got our meals, the second choice at least I hoped it was because if it was the first the food was going to be worse than I'd thought. There is always a problem to be overcome when you arrive in a new prison, borstal or remand centre. That problem is prison protocol. You see you can't just breeze into a dining hall and take up the first seat available. You must first look for an empty table it's not wise to simply plonk yourself on a table with a group of hardened inmates and introduce yourself. This would be taken as a challenge and considered cocky and the last thing you want to do was invite trouble. If no empty table was available, you would make it obvious that you were waiting for an invite and hopefully somebody would wave you over to an empty seat beside them. If no offers were forthcoming, you had two options. One you would look for a table with a spare seat that was occupied by the weediest bastards you could find and elbow your way in. The only problem with that approach was you could then be seen as weak by the other inmates and targeted for intimidation in order to test your mettle. The second option was to grab any seat and simply say 'fuck you' if somebody objected. It was risky as you never knew who you were talking to, but it was the approach I'd used up until that point and I wasn't going to change now.

"Anyone sitting here?" I asked the two kids who were shovelling food into their mouths. I didn't wait for an answer and just threw myself into a chair. Rob followed my lead and simultaneously we began to eat.

"Where you two from?" asked a kid sitting opposite, his mouth still full of food.

"I'm from Leeds, my mates from Oxford," I said answering for Rob as well.

"What you in fer?"

"Malicious wounding" I answered in-between mouthfuls.

"I'm Jerry and my mate's Ian," said the kid opposite his open mouth still full of food. I nodded and carried on eating. I could tell he was waiting for my name, but he wasn't going to get it. I had already deduced that the two lads I was sharing my table with were what other inmates would call Joe's. A Joe is somebody who is bullied into carrying and fetching for the other inmates and there are only two prisoners that are lower, a grass and a nonce. I had nothing against these two lads, but I didn't want to pal up with two Joes on my first day it would make me look bad in front of the other inmates.

"So what's yer name?" asked Jerry not getting the message. I looked up from my plate and fixed his eyes with mine and returned to eating.

"I'm Rob," said Rob holding out his hand to Jerry. I shook my head in disbelief and continued eating my head bowed. I ate the rest of my meal listening to the pointless drivel that was exchanged between Rob, Jerry and Ian. It was fucking humiliating and I could already feel the eyes of the other lads drilling into me from all directions. They were weighing me up deciding if I was a threat or a new whipping boy. I was glad when tea was finally over and as we all made our way down the corridor and into the recreation room. Rob lagged behind chatting with his new-found friends. Poor bastard I thought he has no idea what he's just let himself in for. Prison or borstal life is about decisions and dependent on what decision you make your life can be easy or hard, but you had better make the right one or only God could help you after that. I pulled up a chair under the television and began watching the news. I took out my tobacco rolled a cig and sat back to relax. I kept an eye on Rob and as he formed

258

a bond with Jerry and Ian. I could see the pack mentality of the other lads beginning to form. It was a little surreal every pair of eyes was trained on them and clusters of inmates were pointing and whispering as they looked on. I stood up and casually walked over to Rob.

"You coming to watch TV?" I asked nonchalantly.

"Naw I'm alright, I'll come over in a bit, I'm okay here mate," replied Rob, his pimpled face breaking into a happy smile.

I turned and walked away, "You stupid, stupid bastard," I said to myself as I returned to the TV and the news. Nobody bothered with me, it was a good sign it indicated they were unsure, but I was not fooling myself that I was on easy street I knew sooner or later somebody would be testing me to see if I had any bottle. I had an advantage though and one I was in no hurry to show. You see, I was not a well-built lad. I was quite slim although muscular; coupled with that, nature had given me a bit of a baby face. I didn't even need to shave yet, so anyone who looked me over wouldn't be too concerned that I might be a scrapper. The only thing that made people uneasy was my general demeanour. I was confident and if pushed I could not hide the fire in my eyes, the fire that some never saw until it was too late, or not at all if they were just plain fucking stupid. It was just getting towards the end of Coronation Street and I'd been watching TV and smoking endless cigarettes for around an hour and half happily being invisible to anyone else.

"Marriot," a screw called from the other side of the recreation room and suddenly my cloaking device failed and the whole unit turned their heads in my direction as I stood up.

"Time for your induction talk, can you go to Mr Beard's office please," smiled the screw pointing down the corridor.

"Come in," called the voice as I knocked on the door. Mr Beard was sat behind his desk as though he'd not moved since I saw him that afternoon. He had a cig burning away in his chubby hand and I noticed his fingers were stained with nicotine which was not surprising as the cig had nearly burnt to the stub.

"This is Mr Mulligan, he will be your personal officer whilst you're with us," he announced looking behind me. I turned and acknowledged the screw who was seated by a radiator slurping noisily from a steaming cup of coffee. He lowered the cup smiled and then continued drinking. "Right Marriot," said Mr Beard loudly making me turn to face him. "I have read your file and can see that you have had a few problems whilst on remand." I drifted back to Thorpe Arch, the fights, my time languishing in solitary and my face slowly began to flush.

"Look, we're not interested in what has taken place before, you have a clean slate here and as such it's up to you to keep it that way, do you understand?" finished Mr Beard as he leaned towards me over his desk his beard dangling in the half empty coffee cup in front of him.

"Yes Mr Beard," I replied trying not to stare at his beard as it began to take on a darker shade of brown on the bottom two inches.

"Good, good," he declared as he leant back in his chair, coffee now running down his silk tie. "Have you anything to add Mr Mulligan," asked Mr Beard as he stroked his damp tie. I turned back towards Mr Mulligan who had stood up and was facing me. He was around forty years old extremely thin with pointy features and a mop of straggly ginger hair.

"Yes Marriot, if you have any problems or questions you can come to me at any time and I will do what I can to help. I will also be writing your monthly assessment which will be used at your monthly review board to see how you're getting on. We hold a review for every inmate each month and how you behave will determine how early we recommend you for release," he paused and looking back at Mr Beard said, "I think that's all for now, what do you think Bob?"

"Erm yes. Oh wait, we nearly forgot said Mr Beard

reaching for a file in front of him that was by now covered in coffee stains, your work placement, you will be on the garden party to begin with so tomorrow morning after breakfast if you get dressed into your work clothes Mr Staton will call out your name once everybody is assembled in the rec room at eight thirty and then you'll be escorted to your work area, any questions?" he smiled throwing the file back onto his desk and folding his arms.

I closed the door to Mr Beard's office behind me and leaning back against it I let out a deep breath and smiled. I was glad I'd been put on the garden party. I so wanted to feel the wind on my face, to walk un-handcuffed and to exercise my stale muscles, things were definitely on the up.

I was just entering the recreation room when a screw I heard the other inmates call Mr Pope, shouted loudly, "Supper." I threw myself against the corridor wall in order to avoid being trampled by the hoard of charging inmates as they made their way towards the dining room. Once the recreation room was nearly empty, I looked around for Rob, but he was nowhere to be seen, but Jerry and Ian were standing by the snooker table looking very sheepish.

I walked over. "Where's Rob?" I enquired not talking to either one in particular.

"We ain't seen him, honest," said Jerry as he looked away across the room. I instinctively knew something was wrong. It was the way Jerry had said 'honest,' people say shit like that at the end of a sentence when their lying through their teeth.

"Just off to the toilet," I called in the direction of the screw who was hurrying up the stragglers as he stood in the doorway. I wasn't at all surprised at what I saw when I entered the toilets, I'd expected something like this would befall Rob, but I must admit I didn't think it would be so soon. Rob was a mess his nose was bloodied and by the look of the boot marks on his face and clothes he'd been worked over good and proper.

"Fucking hell mate you alright?" I asked as I bent over

and lifted him from beside the toilet and the cubicle wall where he was wedged.

"Yeah, yeah I'm fine, leave me alone," he shouted pushing my arm from his shoulder. He was hurting, and his eyes were full of tears that I knew he would let out once the door to his cubicle shut behind him that night.

"Come on, it's supper," I said as though that would make everything alright.

"I'll just wash me face, you go, I'll see you in there," he grimaced. I was about to protest when Rob said, "Go, go, I'm fine go."

If Rob was at all angry it was nothing compared to how I felt. I was angry with myself, angry that twice I should have helped him and twice I'd let him down. I decided that I would not let him down again and anyway I was going to have to prove myself at some time and it may as well serve a dual purpose. My eyes tore through everybody in the dining room as I looked for the bully who'd beaten up Rob. I thought somebody would be acting guilty, that I'd know who it was when I saw them, but I didn't, and as I sat at a table eating a biscuit and pretending to sip my tea the knot in my stomach grew tighter and tighter.

Rob entered the dining room along with Mr Pope. I could instantly tell they'd exchanged words as Mr Pope said softly, "Go on lad get your supper."

Rob avoided looking at anyone, his head trained on the floor. It was the invisibility walk, the one we all knew, the one where you just wished the world would open up and swallow you whole.

"Here," I called patting the seat of the empty chair beside me as Rob turned round from the servery, a cup of tea in one hand, a biscuit in the other. He just completely blanked me, sailed past my table straight over to a kid sitting in the corner and threw his red-hot tea into his face. To say pandemonium erupted would not describe what happened next. The scolded victim squealed like a stuck pig as he fell backwards out of his seat and into a heap on the floor his hands clasping his blistering face. Rob hadn't finished yet and began kicking him in the body legs or any other part of the anatomy where he saw an opening. I was stunned; talk about underestimating someone, Rob had taken us all by surprise. It took three screws to pull Rob off the howling melted turd that minutes before had been a young lad. I never moved the whole time I just couldn't believe what I was seeing, it was great, I loved to see the bully have the tables turned on him, it was what made life worth living.

Chapter 18

Testing times

I didn't see Rob again for four days and when he returned to the unit, he was a different person. Gone was his slouching walk and the nervous eyes. He had found confidence and hope somewhere during his time in the block and I smiled to myself as I knew he was going to make it. It would be a long time before anyone was idiotic enough to chance their luck with 'mad dog,' (The nickname he'd been given in his absence)

Me, I wasn't bothered by anyone for the first week and attended work in the gardens where life was a little more sedate than the hustle and bustle of the inside of the borstal. I enjoyed my work and the other four lads I worked with were okay. I'd begun to let down my barriers and the other inmates sensing this began to initiate conversation.

"What's the first thing you'll do when you get out Jack?" asked Jimmy, a tall well-built lad from the east end of London.

"Give up fucking gardening," I grunted as I shovelled a spade full of soil into a wheel barrow.

Jimmy laughed, "No, serious, man what will ya do?"

"Don't know Jimmy, 'ain't got no plans. I'm just taking each day at a time," I said as I stopped and leant on my shovel.

"Sounds like the best way to me," interrupted Mr Staton who was standing watching as the five of us dug one hole.

"Yeah but you gotta have a plan, I mean a plan gives you something to aim at don't it?" reasoned Jimmy.

"Jimmy, if life should have taught you anything by now it should be that plans 'ain't worth shit," said Mike, a black lad from Brixton as he lifted the handles of the wheel barrow and headed off his huge afro immovable in the afternoon breeze.

264

"You're a fucking cynic, that's what you are, no fucking insight," shouted Jimmy as Mike disappeared around the corner pushing the barrow. I put down my shovel, sat on the edge of the hole. I'd pretty much dug on my own and taking out my tobacco I rolled a fag.

"What you tired already?" grinned Jimmy as he reached for the shovel.

"Fuck you," I smiled as I swung my feet out of the hole and allowed Jimmy to jump in.

"Come on Lederer, let's see you put yer back in it instead of winding everybody else up," teased Mr Staton as he brushed the dust from the top of the wall he was about to sit on. I spread myself out on the grass and putting my hands behind my head I stared up at the cloudless blue sky and puffing away on my cigarette I wondered if life could get much better.

I didn't make any real friends in the early days but would engage in the odd conversation with Jimmy and Mike when we were in the recreation room after tea. Mike was a demon snooker player and took at least six fags off me in one night as we hogged the snooker table. Jimmy loved television and would sit glued to it, whatever crap happened to be on. It was no use talking to him as he partook of his nightly viewing as he would just grunt or nod, his eyes never leaving the screen.

It was during my snooker games with Mike in the first week that I got to know what made south house tick, he was a mine of information and if Mike didn't know about it, it wasn't worth knowing. The chap or cock of the unit was a lad called Channing, he was short in stature but had thick-set features, large shoulders and by the five-o-clock shadow he had at lunch time had started shaving at the same time he went through teething. Mike told me how Channing would take tobacco and anything he wanted off the other inmates if he felt like it and that I should stay out of his way as he would sooner or later try and tax me. Taxing was the term that was given to the weekly mugging that took place

265

throughout the borstal. The toughest inmates would seek out the weaker ones and terrorise them into handing over what few luxury's they'd bought from the canteen on Saturday morning. I knew one thing for sure I would not be handing over anything of mine unless they prised it from my lifeless hand. I watched Channing very closely after Mike had given me the heads up. I learnt who he associated with who his enforcers were and who were his gofers. It was like a little club and wherever Channing went at least four others followed sucking up to him and laughing as he threatened some kid half his size. I recognised the type of people who hung round with Channing they were the same misguided fools who would kiss my arse when I was at school because they were frightened of me. I would meet these people throughout the rest of my life, you'd see them in the pubs on a night out in the works canteens and just about anywhere where there was an established pecking order. Channing didn't frighten me and to be truthful, I certainly didn't frighten him. The only reason he'd not introduced himself to me was simple, he just hadn't got round to it. I would wait until he was ready or found himself with nothing better to do, he was the chap of the house and as such he would call the shots, and in the meantime, I would just keep wondering if today was going to be the day.

It was during supper at the end of my first week that the first test came. I was sitting with Rob, Jimmy and Mike chatting when I suddenly felt hot liquid hit my back and neck. I turned quickly to see what it was but could see nothing and as I turned back around, I felt it again. I wiped the back of my neck with my hand and found it wet with tea.

"What the..?" I frowned as I quickly spun back in my chair. I was just in time to see an ugly fat wretch of a lad called Lyndon spurt tea from his mouth towards me. I slipped to my left and it fell harmlessly onto the table behind me.

"Pack it in you fucking twat," I mouthed at him across the aisle that separated us, but some people just can't be told, and Lyndon was one of them he jumped up from his seat and strode towards my table his chest puffed out and his arms flexed as though he was carrying a carpet under each of them.

"What did you fucking call me, you cunt? Who do you think your fucking talking to new boy? I'll fucking smash yer face in," he snarled under his breath as he lent over me. He stunk of BO and his breath wasn't much better and as I stared at his wobbly fat gut, I knew he was carrying his reputation around his waist.

"Look just fuck off, fatso," I smiled at him just as he threw his right hand into my face. It landed but I turned my head at the last moment and took out some of its sting before springing out of my chair like a jack in a box. My first punch was a left hook to the body that bent him over, a look of pain etched across his face just as my right hand came over the top and tore his left eye wide open and twisted his body like a spinning top. I grabbed the back of his neck and ran him into the corner of the wall his head bouncing off it as I let go. Lyndon was out cold the whole incident over in less than four seconds. I turned to face the two screws making their way towards me and put my hands in the air as I walked over to meet them, the dining room so silent you could hear a pin drop.

"Out Marriot out now," Shouted Mr Pope as Mr Mulligan went to the aid of Lyndon.

"Right Marriot wait here and don't move," ordered Mr Pope as he entered Mr Beard's office. I tried to listen to what was being said but the noise from the now excited chatter of the inmates in the dining room drowned out what little I could hear through the wooden door.

"Right in," said Mr Pope as the door reopened his face twitching the adrenalin he hadn't needed still pulsing through his veins.

"What the bloody hell was that all about Marriot?" An angry Mr Beard yelled across his desk his fat frame wobbling under his shirt.

"Don't know Sir," I answered a little arrogantly. I wasn't about to start telling tales like some schoolboy I wasn't a grass and whatever trouble I was in it would only be compounded by telling tales on the other inmates.

Mr Beard ripped into me. "You don't know, you don't know, don't give me that you've beaten poor Lyndon that badly, Mr Mulligan has had to take him to the hospital wing, so don't fucking tell me you don't know, you hear me?"

He could have yelled all night it wouldn't have done him any good besides I'd already resigned myself to spending a few days in solitary and perhaps the loss of a few days remission, so I stood there saying nothing until a knock at the door stopped Mr Beard's incoherent ranting in its tracks.

"Come," said Mr Beard taking his eyes off me momentarily. It was Mr Mulligan his straggly red hair a little more unkempt than usual.

"Ah Bob, just back from the hospital wing Lyndon needs a few stitches above his eye and he has a concussion, but the doc says he'll be fine by tomorrow," gasped Mr Mulligan a little out of breath.

"Well that's good," said Mr Beard but what are we going to do with Marriot? He refuses to say what happened."

Mr Mulligan pulled a face. "Ah, I might be able to shed a bit of light on that Bob. I saw Lyndon walk across the dining room and after talking to Marriot he hit him in the face. I think it was definitely a case of self-defence and perhaps Lyndon got what he deserved, we both know he's no angel?" finished Mr Mulligan raising his eyebrow as though to emphasise his point.

"This true Marriot?" asked Mr Beard his voice now a tad calmer.

"Mr Mulligan says so," I replied not wanting to confirm or deny anything.

"Marriot get the fuck out of here and count yourself lucky, you hear me? Out, out, out," Mr Beard screamed loud enough for the whole borstal to hear.

I became the subject of much speculation after my fight

268

with Lyndon. I'd done to good a job. Lyndon wasn't the hardest lad in the unit, it was obviously Channing, but Lyndon was still considered to be a bit of a tough nut and the fact that I dispatched him so quickly had begun to set tongues wagging. Kids who earlier had been giving me dirty looks suddenly began smiling at me and nodding if our eyes met. Channing studied me closely when he thought I wasn't looking but I always was. I made a point of knowing what that tow rag was up to. I knew he would have to make a move on me at some time. He would have to dismiss the whispers from other kids that had begun to circulate. "Do you think that new kid Marriot can take Channing?"

"I bet Channing won't fucking try and tax Marriot." It was the kind of gossip that the chap of a house could not let go. It would undermine him. It would weaken his hold on the others and there was no way he would have that! The next few weeks were going to be tricky, and on every corner, I turned, as if just to jog my memory, Channing and his entourage would be standing there smirking and plotting.

"I'm wiv yer Jack, if that arsehole thinks he's gonner do yer wiv his muppets, I'll back yer up man," said Mike as he put his skinny black arm around my shoulder, my head just level with his chest.

"Me too mate, fuck that lot we'll be wiv yer," offered Jimmy. "I'll fucking knock their heads off," he declared punching the air in the worst display of shadow boxing I'd ever seen and all at once I knew I was fucked! It wasn't very long before I was sick of waiting and wondering when something was going to happen. I wasn't looking for trouble. I just wanted the whole thing to go away. I didn't want to go to sleep at night with a knot in my gut and wake up with it still there. I wanted a way out, a way to extinguish the flames of the fire that the other inmates kept fanning, but I knew any effort I made to talk to Channing would be seen by him as weakness and I'd be done for. I had no choice and after three weeks of waiting I made a decision.

Channing would have chosen a time when he could have

been sure of beating me and as the saying goes there's safety in numbers. He'd try to get me on my own with his mates and together they would all do me. They'd be careful that no screws were about and no witnesses after all it would be no good if he couldn't brag that he'd done me on his own. Little did he know that I was about to upset his plans and when I'd finished with him everybody would know that Jack Marriot was no push over. After much thought I chose the washrooms as the most suitable venue for our showdown, it had couple of advantages that put it in front of anywhere else. It was a large area and would enable me to use my footwork to get out of trouble and as it was also at the far end of the unit, hopefully the screws might not hear the commotion that usually went hand in glove with a touch of fisty-cuffs. So I made my mind up and that was that. I would confront Channing after work in the evening. It was the best time as mornings were no good because we were always supervised by the screw who handed out the razors, at night nobody bothered us. It was only on rare occasions a screw would saunter down the corridor and see if all was well, it was a chance I would have to take, and I was sure if we were discovered mid punch-up, the screws would be a little more lenient with me than Channing as he was universally despised by inmates and screws alike. I had given a great deal of thought to the odds and to be totally truthful they did not tip in my favour. I was outnumbered by around five to one and I was a good two stone lighter than Channing. I could do nothing about the differing physical attributes, but I made a calculated guess that if I took on Channing in front of most of the unit his cronies would not dare step in. It is kind of an unwritten rule that if a challenge is made to the chap of the house or borstal, then the chap must deal with the contender on his own. It makes sense if you think about it, you can't lay claim to the title if you don't win it or defend it yourself.

I chose a Monday, the way I figured it, if the bastard beat me senseless, I wouldn't have to look at his smug face for the

270

whole weekend and when the weekend did come things would have hopefully quietened a little. I spent that entire day in a world of my own worrying how that night would end. Would I be the victor? Or would I be spending several nights licking my wounds and being forced to kiss Channings arse. I didn't even want to think about it but could think of nothing else!

"You gonna dig that fucking hole or just look at it?" teased Jimmy in his cockney twang.

"Piss off you lazy bastard, it's about time you did some work, here you take it," I said throwing the shovel at him.

"Now, now, boy's no bitching," smiled Mr Staton as he stood over us swinging his key chain.

"Eh, Mr Staton you got a spare fag?" grinned Jimmy as he began to shovel.

"Dig the hole Lederer and if you break sweat, I might consider it," said Mr Staton his eyes squinting in the midday sun. Mr Staton had lost the tag of screw. He'd earned that right. He was only eight or so years older than us and sometimes it was easy to forget he was a prison officer. I never saw him unhappy and a more cheerful good-looking bastard, I'd never met. We used to tease him about his immaculate clothes, the razor creases in his trousers and his baby-faced complexion.

When we went too far, he would give us a stern look and say, "I think that's enough" and we'd quickly change the subject only to return to it a few minutes later. "Come on Lederer your digging like a girl, put yer back in it" said Mr Staton as he threw me a fag.

"Oh, where's mine Sir?" begged Jimmy.

"Do some work and you can have one then," ordered Mr Staton.

"But he's got one" moaned Jimmy pointing at me like a small child.

"He's been digging like a navvy all day, you on the other hand have barely done a stroke, no wonder you're getting fat," grinned Mr Staton as he winked at me.

"Fat I'm not fat Sir it's this baggy shirt look," said a rather embarrassed Jimmy as he sucked in his gut and pulled his shirt tight.

"You fat bastard Jimmy, you 'ain't never gonna get no pussy when you git outta ere," chipped in Mike from where he was sat, leaning with his back against the wall.

"I can lose the weight, but you will always be a big black ugly mother fucker," Jimmy shot back at Mike. It wasn't a racist remark Mike and Jimmy were like two old maids and were never happy unless they were bickering with each other. I couldn't help but smile as they continued swapping insults, they were the Hinge and Bracket of south house no mistake.

"Right boy's as much as I've enjoyed listening to this riveting but somewhat childish debate of who's ugliest, it's time to pack up so get your tools together," interrupted Mr Staton as he threw his fag butt into the hole we'd been digging. I didn't rush to get back to the unit that day and as I lagged behind Mr Staton kept telling me to keep up. He was unaware of my plight it was alright for him he wasn't about to put everything on the line in one moment of madness, he would soon be at home snuggling up to his wife who was no doubt a vision of angelic feminine beauty. I on the other hand would be facing my demons risking my boyish good looks and the only thing I really cared about, my reputation.

"You alright man? Yous been quiet all day man?" enquired Mike as we made our way to the washroom. I stopped in the middle of the corridor and grabbed his arm.

"Get yer shower later Mike, you don't want to come in there with me today," I said pleadingly as our eyes met.

"What you on bout man? I stinks I need a wash," Mike replied not getting my meaning.

I lost my patience. "For fucks sake Mike, just fucking do as I ask just for once, eh?"

The penny dropped, and Mike put his hand on mine. "You don't have to do this man. Channing is a dickhead, ignore him man, let's both shower later," he reasoned as he

272

tried to pull me back down the corridor.

I broke his grip and after walking a few yards I turned back to him and smiled, "A man's gotta do what a man's gotta do," and with that I ran the rest of the way and through the door of the washrooms. I spotted Channing by the wash basins he was stripped to the waist and I could see the tattoos on his muscular hairy arms as he scooped up handfuls of water and threw it on his face. He looked bigger than he had ever looked before, and I could feel my stomach cartwheel. It was too late now, no going back and as I walked over to Channing he turned to face me. I looked deep into his eyes looking for a chink in his armour, there wasn't any he wasn't afraid he didn't even look concerned. He was more than confident, he was bloody cocky. I hit him with a straight right hand on the bridge of his nose sending him crashing to the floor his hands grasping at the wash basin as he fell. I stepped back and waited for him to get up. I flashed my eyes around the room Channings henchmen had moved back and had formed a semicircle around us. The other lads from the unit had pushed their way forward and were vying for the best viewing position.

Channing climbed to his feet and wiped his nose with his left hand a look of anger and confusion on his face. "I'll fucking kill yer," he screamed as he charged at me his arms flailing. I side stepped him and hit him twice once in the side of the mouth the second above his left temple. He fell face forwards and hit the tiled floor his body sliding on its wet surface.

The washroom was by now filled with chanting. "Fight, fight, fight," and the odd brave soul who called out when he thought nobody was looking,

"Go on Marriot, kill the fucking wanker, kick his face in."
I stood back and looking down at Channing. I began to feel good, it was a mistake. Channing climbed to his feet his eyes menacing and threw himself at me in blind fury. I tried to move out of his reach, but it was too late, he caught me around the waist and threw me to the floor, his body on top

of me. I couldn't move his weight and strength were greater than mine and as he launched punch after punch into my unguarded face, I thought I was going to die. I could feel nothing just the dull thuds as my head was driven into the floor with the ferocity of each bone breaking punch. I drifted off into what must have been a semi-conscious state. I was six years old and playing on a little yellow trike, a woman with black hair was smiling down at me as I peddled around a beautiful flowered garden. I knew that woman was my mother. I saw my father firstly as the big strong man I'd known all my life and then as the walking ravaged skeleton he became before death, and in a way, I can't explain I felt at peace.

"You're going to kill him, stop, Channing stop," the words pulled me back from where I'd been just as another right hand hit my left cheek splitting it open. I saw him pull his arm back and turn his shoulder and instinctively I knew if he hit me with the punch he was winding up, I would be out for the count if not for good. I couldn't move my arms, his whole-body weight was seated on my chest, with my arms pinned under his knees. I had one chance and one chance only and I took it. I waited until the punch was airborne and at the last split second, I moved my head slightly to the right allowing it to sail past and bury itself into the floor. I heard the snap that distinctive noise that tells you a bone has broken like a cheap bar of toffee. Channing didn't only hear it he bloody felt it too. He rolled off me and writhed about on the wet floor holding his wrist and howling like a baby. I didn't waste any time, I rolled over and whilst still on my knees I hit him with a right hand in the side of the mouth. Blood shot across the tiled floor and across the white basins behind us. I staggered to my feet and to my eternal shame did something I'd never done before. I kicked the living daylights out of that bastard only pausing to decide where I'd plant the next drop kick. I had such hatred for Channing for all he stood for and now that I'd let go, I just couldn't stop. Mike eventually pulled me off as the chanting subsided and was replaced with a subdued silence.

"Fuck me man, you gonna give me fucking nightmares," laughed Mike as he led me to a sink and turned on the water. I gently washed my face whilst keeping an eye on Channing who was by now trying to stand up. He looked hurt not just physically but mentally and I was glad. The other inmates ignored him, he had no friends anymore, and it was his turn for a taste of the medicine he'd dished out to everyone else.

I waited until Channing was on his feet and as he walked behind me to make his way out of the washrooms, his head hung in shame. I span around and grabbed him by the throat. "I'm the fucking chap now and if you want more you can fucking have it," I spat in his face my adrenalin still pumping.

"I don't, you're the chap I don't want no more please," he begged pathetically.

"Go on fuck off," I shouted as I went to let him go and as I loosened my grip and he tried to pull away, I pushed him to the floor. "You piece of shit," I screamed, "You fucking stay away from me."

The screws asked their usual questions regarding the battle injuries both Channing and I had incurred and as usual we both admitted our sheer clumsiness and cursed the wet floors in the washrooms. The screws weren't idiots they knew the score but didn't continue to press us with pointless interrogation that they knew would bear no fruit. Channing's injuries were more severe than mine and needed hospital attention. He had a broken wrist a gaping wound in his mouth where his teeth had nearly come through his lip and three broken ribs. I, on the other hand, looked a little like Quasimodo and would have not been out of place swinging from a bell tower calling out for Esmeralda. My nose was twice its regular size one eye was closed and the other had a golf ball sized lump under it with a small cut that oozed blood every time I wiped it and to round things

275

off one ear was so badly bruised it resembled a piece of black pudding.

I contented myself with the fact that my injuries would heal on their own and it was Channing who would spend five days on the hospital wing. I made what changes I considered necessary during Channing's absence and when he returned to the unit, he would find that he had been pushed to the bottom of the food chain. I disbanded his hangers on and warned them in no uncertain terms that if they even spoke to Channing or were found talking to each other they would find themselves on the receiving end of my boot. They were all cowards anyway, and the moment I overthrew Channing they were all running around like headless chickens not knowing what was in store for them. I couldn't help but laugh when they actually tried to befriend me. They needed protection from all the kids they'd bullied mercilessly during Channings reign. They didn't get it from me I have always believed you reap what you sew so I gave anyone else in the unit Carte Blanche to make their lives a living hell until I said otherwise. I didn't just let it be known I would look the other way if they were to meet with an accident on the stairs or a slip in the showers, I positively encouraged it.

Over the following weeks it amused me no end to watch as five or six kids would taunt and shove one of their former tormentors and take their tobacco off them as they returned from the prison shop, the worm had definitely turned!

Chapter 19

The glory days

I bathed in the success of my victory and if I'm truly honest I became more than a little cocky. I decided on a set of rules and made sure each and every inmate understood and obeyed them at all times. I outlawed any form of bullying or taxing with the exception of Channing and his former groupies, they were fair game until further notice. Lastly, I made my most unpopular rule. Meal times were to be operated on a first come first served basis and threats to servers and the holding back of the tastiest choice of meals was to cease immediately. I made one exception to this rule and I'll leave that to your imagination as to what it was, but needless to say, I never ate another plate of corned beef again.

The screws noticed the change that had swept through south house like a typhoon. It would have been hard to miss. There was a kind of calmness and the atmosphere was happy and relaxed. Kids were whistling as they made their way to the showers on a morning and laughing as they made their way to bed at night. It had become a happy place and I liked it a lot. Mr Staton said one day that South House had become a pleasure to work in and that they (meaning the screws) didn't know what had come over everyone. The way he said it and the knowing look he gave me told me otherwise, he knew why it had changed he knew who the new chap was, and he was subtly telling me they approved of my methods.

My life took on a whole new meaning after Channing, I was happy. I enjoyed my work in the gardens and the lads I worked with and my new status meant nobody gave me any shit. Mike and Jimmy became my closest friends and would constantly wind me up or have me giggling at their insane bickering until I laughed so much my ribs hurt. The other

277

lads on the unit liked me and although I tried to discourage any form of sucking up it was inevitable that some would do it anyway. I felt uncomfortable when some spotty faced new kid would introduce himself and no sooner had I said "Hi" than he would be trying to buy me with fags and sweets, of course I took them I wasn't a fucking saint but I made it clear that I would never demand anything off anyone and as long as they towed the line they had nothing to fear from me.

I was moved into the dormitory after two months and was a little sad to say goodbye to the cubicle which I'd lovingly decorated with drawings and posters I'd swiped from night classes. It was hard to settle into the dorm at first, the constant noise of chatter at bedtimes and the footsteps of the screw that did a walk through every half hour kept me awake until the early hours tossing and turning in my narrow bunk. In time you get used to anything, so it wasn't long before I could close my eyes, shut out the noise and drift blissfully off to sleep, so much so that Mike said, "I'd have happily slept on if a brass band had marched through the dorm playing fanfare for the common man."

I denied this of course but just to prove a point I woke up one morning to find Mike had drawn a lovely pair of glasses on my face using an indelible marker pen (The fucking idiot). It wasn't the best idea putting me Mike and Jimmy together all night as now not only did we spend all day laughing hysterically but all night as well and if any of the others moaned, we'd just chorus "Fuck off, go to sleep, dickhead," and carry on regardless.

"You lot need to get some sleep, look at you. You look like you've been on the piss all night," said Mr Mulligan one morning as we made our way to the wash rooms.

"It's his fault Sir, he snores like a train and if he 'ain't snoring he's farting 'ims a stinky noisy bastard," replied Mike pointing at Jimmy. Jimmy ignored him and kept on walking, he thought better of it and stopping a few yards away he turned and shouted.

"Eh Rasta boy, you missing yer beauty sleep that'll never

do, you 'ain't pretty enough to do that, yous got a face like a bull dog chewing a wasp."

"Fuck you Lederer, iz gonna fucking smother you in yer sleep tonight," Mike shouted after Jimmy as he chased him down the corridor and they disappeared into the wash rooms.

"They love each other really Sir," I smiled at Mr Mulligan who shook his head rolled his eyes and walked away laughing to himself.

A couple of months later and I found my third monthly review approaching and I was quite excited at the prospect. My behaviour had been good, and I was hoping that my ERD (Earliest release date) may get brought forward as was the case if you'd kept your nose clean. It would only ever be brought forward a maximum of two weeks at a time, but it was two weeks closer to getting out, it was a carrot that the screws dangled before you in order to keep you in line.

"You've had a good month, Marriot," said my personal officer Mr Mulligan. "I think that perhaps we can consider giving you a better job that pays a little more money, what do you think Bob?" he said turning to Mr Beard who was glued to his usual seat behind the desk. In fact Mr Beard may not have had any legs for all I knew as he'd never stood up in my presence and come to think of it, he was never seen leaving or arriving on the unit, perhaps he was beamed in like Captain Kirk of the Enterprise.

"Yes Nobby let's give young Marriot a go in the prison kitchens, that'll keep him busy, would you like that Marriot?" Mr Beard asked as he smiled up at me his unkempt beard making him look like a talking coconut.

I was about to object to being given another job. I liked it where I was but the mention of working in the prison kitchens helped change my mind. It was one of the best jobs in the borstal and anybody would be mad to turn it down, as much food as you could eat, a larger choice and what's more a whole six pounds sterling a week, bring it on.

"Er yes please Sir, I'd like that," I said trying not to show how thrilled I was.

"Very well then, you can start on Monday, that's that sorted. Now your release date, we have a bit of a problem with that at the moment, nothing for you to concern yourself with," continued Mr Beard.

'Nothing to worry about, what was he saying?' I thought, 'Nothing to worry about. I'm bloody worried alright now, bloody tell me what the problem is,' I thought, my mind racing.

Mr Mulligan who was standing at the side of Mr Beard's desk looking at me noticed my worried expression and stepped towards me placing his hand on my shoulder.

"Oh eh, lad no, it's nothing major, we just can't give you any time back this month but will make it up at your next review," he smiled reassuringly.

"Yes Marriot, you see the judge ordered that you were to have a psychiatric evaluation during your stay here and as the psychiatrist has been busy you haven't seen her yet," chipped in Mr Beard. "We need to wait until we see her report before we can make a decision on your release that's all, so by next month we'll have it and you'll get a double helping of remission if you continue your good behaviour, do you understand?" Mr Beard asked as he leant back in his chair scratched his chin and exhaled loudly.

I nodded meekly, I knew that I wouldn't change things by bleating about them and if I started to say something, I was in danger of screaming at them or worse still collapsing in tears like a big girl.

"Listen Jack, you're a good lad and we all know that since you came the unit has been a better place for it, we're on your side and I personally will do anything I can to get you out of this place as soon as you're ready. I want what's best for you remember that," said Mr Mulligan as we stood outside Mr Beards office afterwards.

I looked at Mr Mulligan my eyes filled with tears, he'd called me Jack. No adult had done that for a long time. "You get along, go on," he smiled giving my head a playful rub as he turned and went back into the office.

My job in the kitchens was great at first and when the screw would come to wake me quietly at five thirty in the morning, I'd already be dressed and sat on the end of my bed. The borstal kitchens were always a hive of activity, there was always something to do and what's more we could make ourselves tea and coffee whenever we wanted. I drank cup after cup of strong sweet tea on my first day, it was a treat and I knew it was free from medicinal additives, not that masturbation was high on my list of priorities and being in a dormitory it was practically impossible.

My first job was on the washing-up and boy, did those bastards go through some. Pots, pans, ladles, steel trays, wooden spoons; no sooner had you cleared one lot then some smirking arsehole would waltz over and chuck a shit load more into the gleaming sink without even acknowledging you existed. I spent that much time with my hands in water on the first week I developed a skin complaint and my hands began to crack across the palms and bleed every time I opened my clenched fist. The borstal doctor informed the civilian chef that I was to be excused washing up and as if by magic, I landed the job of head fryer. I thought this was a step up until I realized that just about everything cooked in a prison kitchen is introduced to the fryer at some stage and it was the busiest station in the kitchen. The other inmates would smile and giggle as I poured over that fucking devil's furnace for hour after hour the sweat falling from my face and hitting the sizzling oil only to spit its bubbling venom straight back at me. I eventually got used to the smell of chip fat that seemed to follow me everywhere I went and the other kids on the unit except Mike and Jimmy didn't push their luck by bringing it to my attention. It didn't seem to matter how long I soaked in one of the giant roll top baths, I constantly stank and I'm sure I sweated it out through my pores.

"Ooh I could just go a bag of chips or a nice piece of

skate," Jimmy would tease, only for Mike to join in.

"Ooh yeah what about a nice bit o rock salmon man, that go down real good me tinks." I would pretend I couldn't hear them and carry on watching the telly or whatever I was doing but they'd keep it up for so long that in the end I'd burst out laughing and tell them both to sod off.

My work in the Kitchen had for the first time brought me into contact with kids from the other houses. I had of course seen them in passing as we made our way to night classes or back down the corridor from work but on the whole, we all kept ourselves to ourselves. The other kitchen workers were largely the older lads from north and east house. They were mostly eighteen or nearly nineteen years old. Paul Bullock and I were the youngest kitchen workers Paul being from West House, the other unit that held younger inmates. Paul was a nice lad he was a car thief and what he didn't know about cars wasn't worth knowing. When we were having a break at the back of the kitchens, a brew in one hand and a fag in the other he would recall the flash cars he'd pinched. It amazed me how much detail he remembered, he knew where he'd stolen a car what colour it was the upholstery, if it was leather or velour and what year each car was. I teased him and said he should think about a career in car sales when he got out.

"Na bollocks to that, I'm gonna save up and buy me a big Jag and cruise the town for girls," he would offer eagerly. It would have been a little more believable if he was older than his fifteen years, so it was a little hard to take him seriously. I was a small fish in a big pond in the kitchens and although the other inmates I worked with knew I was the chap of South House it didn't cut any ice with them. Why would it? I was a waif like fifteen-year-old who didn't even shave and they were practically fully-grown men.

Even the inmates who were bullied on their own units would give me shit just because they were older and felt sure their age and hulking build was enough to frighten me. I wasn't frightened of anyone I was beginning to believe in myself and to be frank I neither cared if I lived or died, if you don't fear death you become a very dangerous person indeed, but it was my secret and a secret I kept to myself. I took the cutting remarks and the antagonistic comments in my stride, the same rules always applied say what you like, do what you like but don't put your hands on me.

This strategy didn't work out too well though as lads from north and east house soon began to think I was a bit of a joke and I'd only been in the kitchens for five weeks when they went just a bit too far. I'd done all I could, I'd taken everything they threw at me and not once had I bitten, not once had I shown my hand, but the pack mentality had taken over and I was in serious danger of being badly beaten, scalded or even stabbed just for a giggle. I didn't plan what happened but there is always someone who gets just too brave for their own good.

It was just before lunch-time on a Friday morning when I was at the fryer sweating, as I heaved one fully laden basket after another of chips into a steel tray. I'd already had a shit morning as somebody had put a dead cockroach in my tea and when I spat it out the whole kitchen pissed themselves laughing and on top of that a kid from East House had accidentally on purpose thrown a full bucket of bleach and detergent all over me as he emptied his bucket outside.

"Oops, sorry, didn't see you there," he said sarcastically as his mates pointed at me, their tormenting faces full of hatred. I was on the edge and what had started out as a good job was slowly but surely becoming a living nightmare. I wondered how long I could take it and had even considered asking Mr Beard for a new job allocation, but my pride got the better of me and I refused to be driven out.

I pulled another basket of chips from the boiling oil and after shaking them I heaped the contents on top of the previous lot. I was about to turn round and get the second basket out of the dual fryer when somebody threw a cup of water into the hot oil. A massive whoosh and a flash sent me reeling as I tried to avoid the searing flames, but it was too late my hair was singed and my neck felt as though it had been stripped of several layers of flesh. To add insult to injury as I stepped back, I slipped on the now oil covered floor and thudded to the ground smashing my face into the red-hot tray of chips I'd just emptied out. I was dazed as I climbed to my feet, but I could already hear the growing laughter of the other inmates before I was even upright. The civilian chef was out the back of the kitchen taking a delivery, so my attacker had planned it well, no witnesses and he knew I would never grass on him. But what he never counted on was that it may just have been the straw that broke the camel's back and unluckily for him it was. I saw him, the plastic cup still dangling from his finger as he laughed so loudly his whole body shook up and down. Redmond was a big ugly waste of space from East House. He had bad teeth, bad skin and a really bad attitude. I flew at him and as I closed the gap between us, I saw the disbelief on his face. It was too late I was on him. I was that angry I forgot my boxing and the rules went out of the window. I landed on him and as we fell backwards onto the floor, I sunk my teeth into his big fat spotty nose until I could taste his warm blood on my tongue. Redmond screamed and screamed but it fell on deaf ears. I released his nose and sat up launching punch after punch into his face as he tried to cover up with his hands. Snap, thud, thud, crack, the noise must have been heard throughout the whole borstal and I found myself on a runaway train that I couldn't stop. I don't know how long I beat up on Redmond, but it felt like a lifetime and for him no doubt even longer. I was in a world of my own and it wasn't until I was dragged off him and hauled to my feet by five screws that I heard the ominous sound of the riot bell ringing. I still didn't calm down and struggled to get back at Redmond as he was helped to his feet by another inmate. He was a mess his face looked like somebody had set off a firework in his mouth and his hands were swollen badly where I'd punched them as he'd tried in vain to protect himself. I struggled to break free, but it

284

was no use and the more I writhed the tighter the screws held on until they held my neck and arms that tightly, I couldn't twitch a muscle.

Redmond had at this time got to his feet and drew back his clenched fist before punching me full force in the mouth. I was powerless to move with the screws still hanging on to me for all they were worth and as I raised my head and spat out my two front teeth a large gasp rang out around the kitchen. If I was pissed before I was fucking pissed then and as the blood fell from my chin onto the screws arm around my neck I twisted away from him and in a flash I was back on top of Redmond gouging my thumbs into his eye sockets that hard they began to bleed. Redmond howled as he tried to pull my hands away, but I just drove my thumbs in deeper and deeper. I didn't care I'd teach that bastard not to fuck with me. I wasn't going to stop until I'd plucked his bulging eyes from his ugly face. The screws were thrown into a panic and as they all tried to tear me away from Redmond, I just dragged him with me as they pulled and tugged in order to get me off.

The darkness came that quickly I didn't even see it coming. When I awoke I was in the block, a lump like an apple on my bonce where some kind screw had turned the lights out and a headache to end all headaches. My mouth hurt like hell now the adrenalin had stopped, and as I probed it with my tongue I found just two stumps where my front teeth used to be, and I hung my head and cried. It was not long afterwards that Mr Mulligan came and opened up the cell.

"Oh Marriot look at the state of you. Let's get you to the hospital and see if we can't sort you out," he said as he helped me up and led me out the door. My day didn't get any better after that as the prison dentist declined to treat my injuries on account of the last time I'd seen him, when I jumped out of his chair and called him a fucking butcher, so I was taken by car handcuffed to Mr Mulligan to the local hospital.

285

Chapter 20

Soup for tea

There was very little the hospital could do apart from remove the broken roots of my teeth from my bloodied and torn gums and slap burn ointment on my neck that was peeling and red raw. I spent over four hours in the dentist chair being x rayed prodded probed and injected with local anaesthetic until I could stand no more. Mr Mulligan stayed by my side the whole time and to his credit showed a genuine concern. I didn't get back to the borstal that night until well after tea, but it didn't matter. I was not in a position to eat anything anyway. I'd been given painkillers and after being pumped full of drugs all day, I just felt extremely tired. Mr Mulligan took me back to the dormitory and as I lay back on my pillow he asked if I needed anything and said he'd see to it I wasn't disturbed until after association. I never answered him I was already drifting off to sleep, my mind playing through the events of the day.

I didn't wake until the following morning and I have a sneaky feeling that the rest of the inmates in the dorm had made an extra effort to be silent as they made their way to their beds the previous night.

I was more than a little surprised the following morning when I was not taken before the governor for adjudication as was the norm if you were caught fighting. It transpired that I couldn't go on adjudication until Redmond was able to attend and he was still being kept in hospital as the doctors worked on a detached retina and burst blood vessels in both his eyes. It didn't look good for me and as I hovered around the unit on sick for the next three days, I had an enormous sense of foreboding. It wasn't fair I hadn't started it, Redmond was the instigator and now it looked as though he would win, and I would lose several weeks remission and if

I went before the board of visitors it could be even worse, I could be charged and taken back to court.

The board of visitors were a group of civilians appointed to oversee the running of prisons and borstals, they were made up of retired magistrates and others from the judiciary and would normally call on you when you were in solitary and ask annoying questions like did you have any complaints. The problem that faced you if you went for adjudication before the board of visitors was that they were empowered to take more remission from you than the prison governor, so to be found guilty by them was an inmate's worst nightmare.

It was a week later when I was finally informed I had an adjudication with the governor. Redmond had been discharged from outside hospital and was now on the hospital wing of the prison and considered fit to attend my trial. Mr Mulligan had spoken to me previously and expressed his disappointment at my behaviour but also said he'd been told by persons he would not reveal, that Redmond had been goading me for weeks. I nodded to confirm he was right but refused to go into further detail. I could not and would not be seen to grass no matter how much I wanted to.

"Good luck Jack and listen, stay calm don't lose your temper with the governor. I've given you a good report from the unit and if he takes that into account you may well escape a board of visitors hearing, okay?" Mr Mulligan smiled as he opened the Governor's office door and we both filed in.

Redmond was already inside he was facing the governor with two screws by his side and another seated in a chair behind him. I glanced at him sideways as I entered but he just kept his gaze fixed forward as though rigor mortise had set in. I was led forward until we were both side by side, screws by now, either side of us as well as behind. It must have looked strange to say the least, Redmond a foot taller than me and over four stone heavier and I was accused of beating him up? The governor cleared his throat after we had given our names and prison numbers and the charges had been read out. "Right Marriot you are brought before me on the charge of assault against Redmond whilst working in the prison kitchens, what do you have to say for yourself?" said the governor smugly as he folded his arms in a manner that said he'd already tried and convicted me. I felt the anger rise from my gut and I knew I couldn't hold it in.

"Oh fuck this you don't want the truth, you just want to dish out the punishment so fucking get on with it, you balding old bastard," I snarled at the governor just as the two screws at the side of me grabbed both my arms in case I leapt over the desk and throttled the self-righteous bastard. I hadn't meant to shout it out loud, it was like a sudden burst of Turrets syndrome and what I'd been thinking just tumbled out.

To my surprise the governor remained calm and softly said, "Now come on Marriot, of course I want to hear your version of events, I want the truth so why don't you calm down and we'll start again."

I was bloody speechless. I'd seen the governor in a new light, he was human after all.

"Can er, can I say something, Sir?" Redmond interrupted before I could say anything and as he spoke, I turned to face him. He was a mess, both of his eyes were totally bloodshot, and he still had the imprint of my teeth on his nose, it was quite fitting really as it was the only evidence remaining that I had at one time had a lovely white set of front gnashers.

"What is it?" demanded the governor a little annoyed that Redmond had interrupted before I could speak.

"Well Sir, it wasn't Marriot's fault. I started it and it don't seem fair that he should get all the blame." Redmond blushed and looked at the floor.

"Oh, is that right Redmond, you don't think Marriot should get all the blame, well I've got news for you Redmond, you're not here as the victim the way I see it, you assaulted Marriot in a cowardly fashion after the fight was over and he was defenceless being held by four prison officers. If there's one thing I cannot abide it's a bully and when I've finished with Marriot you will learn what I have in store for you, so stand there and zip it, you hear me?"

Redmond was practically trembling from the governor's verbal onslaught and I had to try really hard not to smirk or smile at his predicament.

"Now Marriot, it would appear that Redmond has owned up to instigating the fight and he wishes to take his share of the blame; this leaves me with a dilemma," said the governor scratching his head as he thought about what he was going to do. "You see you not only nearly blinded another inmate, but you resisted the attempts of the officers who tried to restrain you and even if Redmond did start the fight the violence you showed in retaliation cannot be considered reasonable force whether in self-defence or not, he continued. In your defence I have to take into account that you only resisted against the officers after Redmond had hit you and in this case I find that understandable. I'm also aware that you also suffered injuries that required hospital treatment." The governor stopped and as he looked me up and down came to a decision. "Right Marriot the facts as I hear them are that Redmond began the fight and you were the innocent party up to the point of using excessive force and for that I cannot be seen to turn a blind eye(I'm sure no pun was intended) but I must also lay the blame fairly at the feet of the individual responsible and because of that I'm going to deal with this myself and not place you before the board of visitors. Two weeks loss of remission take him away," he said without pausing for breath, "oh and Marriot don't let me see you again," he called after me as I was frogmarched out into the corridor.

"Fuck me Sir, what a result," I beamed through my gums at Mr Mulligan as he led me down the corridor and back to the unit.

"Yeah, you've got a fan there alright. I've never seen the governor in such fine form, he must have got a shag last night, but on the other hand I've seen his wife and boy is she ugly," he smiled at me with a twinkle in his eye and together we both broke into laughter.

I wasn't surprised by Redmond's sudden confession. He hadn't owned up because it was the decent thing to do, he'd owned up because he was frightened. He needn't have been. I had no intention of carrying on with some sort of vendetta. The way I saw it; it was over, he wouldn't be causing me any problems in the future. Admittedly he didn't know that, and it worked to my advantage, so I just congratulated myself on my good fortune and decided to make an effort to stay out of trouble.

I lost my job after the fight in the kitchen. I think somebody had decided that it was not a good idea to put an inmate as volatile as me, in an area where I had access to knives, so what did they do? They put me in the carpenters workshop where I could manufacture my own weapons. The powers that be can be really dense at times. The carpenter's workshop was run by a middle-aged civilian contractor and as such we got away with murder. The main drawback was the cut in wages and my weekly earnings dropped to four pounds a week.

"Would you help Patterson with the building please, Jack," said Mr Rowntree as I arrived for work one morning. Mr Rowntree was a lovely man, kind-hearted and a warm personality to boot; you just wanted to hug him like a grandparent and inhale his Blue Stratos aftershave. Being kind and friendly did not always guarantee you an easy ride in borstal and many of the inmates would take the piss by spending all day tossing it off so poor Mr Rowntree would end up working late to complete jobs that we should have finished, but he would simply smile and say, "Get yourselves off. I'll take care of this. Goodnight boys; have a good weekend," bless that poor misguided old man, kindness can sometimes be a curse.

"So what's the score then?" I asked Patterson as I walked over to him at the far end of the workshop. "Ah this is a dog kennel with a run and we've to assemble it to see it fits together," replied Patterson as he showed me the different wooden sections that lay haphazardly about the floor.

"How the fuck do you know what goes where?" I asked kicking a piece of wood across the workshop. "Ah it's easy when you've been doing it a while. I'll show yer just watch me" he said as he picked up a couple of planks of tongue and groove.

I got on well with Patterson he was two years older than me and came from East House. His first name was Alex, he was small for his age but strong and he would think nothing of carrying something that a bigger man might shy away from. He liked his job and unluckily for me worked like a navvy on double time, it was as though there weren't enough hours in the day and his life depended on finishing whatever job he'd started each morning. When it was lunch, he would say, "Coming Sir, just let me get these last two screws in." Anyone else would have just said bollocks and let the bloody thing collapse in a heap on the floor, but not Alex. We talked a lot as we beavered away at the back of the shop and after a couple of weeks, we could anticipate exactly what the other wanted as we bolted sections of frame together. We no longer needed to say hammer, drill, screws, bolts, we could just turn round and the other would be holding whatever you needed.

"You going anywhere at the weekend?" smiled Alex as he handed me a handful of nails.

"Naw, just thought I'd have a quiet weekend in and recharge the batteries," I replied keeping up the pretence.

"Oh shame, I was going down the west end, catch a show, meet a few birds and have a kebab on the way home, but if yer not up for it you'll just have to miss out then," he smiled.

I didn't I'd not been doing much smiling since I'd lost my front teeth and I was very self-conscious, it had also affected my speech and I had developed a slight lisp that at times could make me sound like Violet Elizabeth. Nobody mentioned it at least not to my face, but I was sure that there were a good many impressions being carried out behind my back. The prison dentist was still being an arse and refusing to see me, so I'd been allowed to attend an outside dentist who was in the process of making me a false set. The other kids would tease and say it's alright for you you've got your own private Harley Street dentist and we have to see Dr Death as the borstal dentist was affectionately known.

I enjoyed my dental visits. It got me out of the borstal. Mr Mulligan or Mr Staton would usually accompany me and kindly not use the handcuffs to spare me any embarrassment. I preferred it when Mr Mulligan took me, he had taken a bit of a shine to me and I could tell him anything and also push my luck a bit. I badgered him to buy me chips and cans of pop and as we sat on the wall outside the chippy pushing heavily salted chips into our mouths it was like a day out with my Dad.

I often thought of Dad and I'm not ashamed to say it; some nights, I would cry quietly under my covers whispering his name before falling asleep. It was a pain when Mr Staton escorted me, the dental receptionist would bat her big blue eyes at him and hang on his every word. I swear if he'd have suggested it, she'd have done it on the floor right in front of me there and then. Mr Staton pretended not to notice her very unsubtle advances, but I could tell he was enjoying every minute of it, who wouldn't? So I would just sit there looking at the two pathetic goldfish in the cloudy tank as I sat in the waiting room and waited my turn, at least Mr Mulligan stayed with me and was not what anyone could describe as a babe magnet.

"You gonna hammer that nail in or are you just going to look at it?" said Alex.

"Okay, keep yer hair on, where not on fucking piece work," I said swinging the hammer and missing the nail altogether, I hit the wooden frame and took a big lump out of it.

"Oh eh, look what you've done. I hope they're only going to put big dogs in this one cause a small dog could climb through that." I looked at the hole it was about the size of a fifty pence piece.

"You knob, you fucking do it then, I'm off for a fag," I said tossing the hammer to Patterson. "Oh yeah that's right you let me sort out your fuck ups," he called after me in a mocking tone.

Life on the unit was sweet I didn't get any grief from anyone and even the new inmates stayed out of my way. They were usually warned off by the others the moment they arrived. I'd heard what they were saying "Don't mess with Marriot he nearly pulled a lads eyes out in a fight yer know"

"No I heard he bit his nose off and spat it on the floor," another would say. I didn't quash the rumours why would I? If it meant people left me alone then that was alright by me. I certainly didn't want every new kid thinking he could chin me and decide to take a shot at the title, that would just get me into more trouble and trouble was something I didn't want or need. My counselling had also begun with the borstal psychiatrist and although it was nothing I could actually put my finger on, I gradually began to feel better about myself.

The borstal shrink was a lady around sixty years old with straight white hair and glasses and her name was Mrs Kerr. "So Jack what have you been up to since we last met?" she would ask politely. That's how it was, just polite conversation, nothing heavy but you soon found the crafty old woman hadn't just messed about with your head she'd dissected it and after extracting what she wanted she would neatly put the bits back in a different order.

"So you loved your father a lot Jack, and how did you feel when he died?" she asked pushing her glasses up her nose and smiling sweetly.

I would have thought what a bloody stupid question if it had been asked by anyone else but with her I answered every question she ever asked, because she wasn't just asking she actually wanted to know.

"Your stepmother did she become like a replacement for your real mother?" pried Mrs Kerr. I nearly choked on the cup of tea she'd made me in a nice china cup and saucer.

"Like my real mother, like anyone's mother, no fucking way," I said venomously after quickly swallowing a mouthful of warm tea.

"You seem very hostile when your stepmother is mentioned, why is that Jack?" she said, pushing me a little more. I felt the tears well up in my eyes. I could feel all the pain, all the cruelty she had put me through and as I replayed it over in my mind it was as though I was reliving it all at once.

I stood up and threw the cup and saucer across the room smashing it into tiny pieces as it hit the wall behind Mrs Kerr's desk, she never flinched. "I hate her, hate her," I screamed as I fell to my knees and hanging my head sobbed with frustration.

"There, there, that's right you let it out Jack, let all that hurt out, you don't have to hide it, it's her shame not yours, there, there," said Mrs Kerr as she sat on the floor and cradled me in her arms.

My next monthly review was quite favourable, and it was clear that the incident in the kitchen six weeks before had been forgotten about. It had been a great disappointment to me that not only did I not get any time back as promised at the last review, but I'd also had two weeks added on to my sentence, it felt like I was never going to get out of that place. Things were definitely different this time and as I entered Mr Beards office, Mr Mulligan smiled broadly at me as did Mr Beard, although the only way I could tell was by his eyes, as his facial hair tended to disguise any movement below his ears.

"Marriot, come in, come in grab a seat," said Mr Beard jovially as I paused in the doorway my hand still on the door knob. I smiled nervously back at them both in turn. "I see you've got yer new teeth you're not a bad looking boy at all are you?" joked Mr Beard making me blush.

294

I was mystified as to the sudden favour I had found myself in, it made me uneasy whenever people in authority smiled like that and if I'm honest I readied myself for a major disappointment. I shouldn't have been so sceptical; the whole world wasn't against me and in the following few minutes I was given back my faith in mankind.

"I must tell you Marriot we are very pleased with the way you've pulled your socks up. Mr Mulligan has given you an excellent report and quite frankly, I've seen the change for myself. Well done!" said Mr Beard as he stood up and walked around his desk. He did have legs after all!

"You aren't a bad lad Marriot, but you do get yourself into some scrapes and I know they are not always avoidable, but we think you deserve a chance and we have decided that it may suit you to have a job where you can work on your own that should keep you out of trouble eh?" he smiled as he put both hands on my shoulders and rested his arse on the desk. He was looking right into my eyes and it made me feel a little uncomfortable so I just grinned and shifted in my seat.

"We're going to make you gym orderly," he continued, his hands still either side of my shoulders, you will be given a green pass that allows you to walk around the prison grounds unescorted and your wages will be seven pounds a week, you start on Monday," he beamed. "Oh, and one more thing Marriot, I'm also giving you four weeks remission back, so your release date has been brought forward to July the seventh next year," he declared smugly as he waited for my reaction. He didn't get one, I was stunned and just sat there not able to take any of it in. I didn't think I'd done anything special. I'd just avoided trouble for a few weeks.

"Well what have you got to say?" asked Mr Beard as he walked back around his desk sat down and resting his chin in his hands stared at me.

"Thank you, thank you Sir I won't let you down, I promise," I said my voice all high pitched and excited.

"Just do your best lad, now go on yer way and keep up

295

the good work," he said as I rose from my chair and turned. I looked directly at Mr Mulligan who was standing there, a mass of curly ginger hair and a broad smile from ear to ear.

I startled him by suddenly striding across and grabbing his hand and shaking it firmly. "Thank you, Sir, thank you," I beamed.

"Your welcome Jack, now off you pop," he answered calmly and as I opened the door, they both said in unison, "Oh, one more thing Jack," I stopped, and half turned, "Happy birthday!"

I'd completely forgotten that it was my birthday. It wasn't that important anyway. There would be no cards, no cake, and no Dad to hug me and shower me with presents. I was glad all the same that Mr Beard and Mr Mulligan had bothered to remember, and it now became clearer why they had both been so generous to me that day. I walked around on cloud nine for the whole of the weekend and although I only told Mike and Jimmy the good news it was apparent to everyone that I was in an unusually happy mood.

"You are very chirpy today," commented Mr Carver as I passed him on the stairs on Saturday morning. Mr Carver was the quietist of the eight screws who worked on South House and seemed constantly on edge. I didn't dislike him but as with many of the other screws they didn't play a big part in my borstal life unless it was to tell me to stop running or hurry up.

The weekend was suddenly upon us, but I hated them, they always went slowly for me. It was the time when the other inmates would get visits and mail would be handed out. I never had either and it was hard to hide the fact that it bothered me. I would prick up my ears as whichever screw read out the names of inmates who'd got letters. If I just got one just one, I would have been over the moon.

"Marriot," no I thought, I'm hearing things nobody, would write to me.

"Marriot do you want these or not?" Mr Pope shouted across the recreation room. My heart began pounding and as

I made my way across the floor to where he was standing, I could see every pair of eyes trained upon me.

"Yes Mr Pope," I said trying to play it cool.

Mr Pope smiled and as he handed me a stack of envelopes, he pinched my face and laughed. "Happy birthday Jack. Happy birthday." A round of applause echoed around the recreation room and as I made my way back to my seat in front of the television, I wished the ground would swallow me up.

"Happy birthday man, yeah," said Mike as he leant over the back of my chair his black face grinning so much, he looked like he'd swallowed a piano.

"Did you know about this?" I asked, his face told me he did. "I hate fucking surprises," I laughed and pushed him away in mock disgust. It was hard to contain the emotion I felt inside and as I made my way to the toilets, I kept my gaze on the floor. Once inside the toilet cubicle I tore at the pile of envelopes I was holding and read each card one by one. I had twenty-eight cards in total just over half the unit had taken the trouble to try and make my birthday special and as I read one after the other it was hard not to be touched. I'd never been that popular before and it was good to know that people actually liked me.

The screws had even got me a card and each one had signed it and written a silly message beside it that read, *Keep yer chin up lad. All I want for Christmas is me two front teeth. Them showers sure are slippy! and my favourite, Sixteen and just legal.*

I thought my birthday could not get any better, but it did, it was as if the whole unit would not rest until they'd brought me to tears and as the day wore on it became harder and harder to keep my composure. You see on inmate's birthdays their families were allowed to send a small parcel that could be filled with pre-sanctioned gifts. It would mostly contain a pound of boiled sweets, a bar of chocolate, some soap, a tube of toothpaste and an ounce of tobacco together with the odd magazine, pornographic or otherwise.

297

The lucky boy whose birthday it was would be presented with his parcel just after supper in order that he could take it back to his cubicle and hide it away from jealous inmates who may wish to avail themselves of some of the booty. It was a time when the other inmates would hoot and cheer loudly as the red-faced birthday boy took the long walk across the dining room to collect the bulging package from the smiling screw. I knew each time I watched this spectacle that my turn would never come and that when the Christmas parcels were handed out, I would be remaining in my seat and trying to look like I wasn't bothered.

The other inmates had different ideas and during supper, I detected a distinct atmosphere, groups of lads were whispering and giggling and whenever I looked up, they would guiltily turn away.

"Marriot over here lad," barked Mr Carver as he stood by the servery.

"Go on man," said Mike as he elbowed me in the ribs. "He's calling you." I pushed my chair back and as it scraped eerily across the tiled floor it sounded louder than usual and it was only then that I realized the rest of the inmates had stopped talking and were all looking at me.

"Come on then lad move yer arse," called Mr Carver trying not to smile.

"Yes Sir what is it," I asked nervously as I looked up at him.

"The lads have something they wanted me to give you," he said and with that he reached under the servery and brought out a parcel wrapped in brown paper. He pushed it into my chest and instinctively I clutched it with my trembling arms as my eyes filled with tears and then they began

"Happy birthday to you, happy birthday to you, happy birthday dear Jack, happy birthday to you." A round of applause filled the dining room and as I turned looking for some way out I noticed Mr Mulligan and Mr Beard clapping for all they were worth and blocking my exit as they stood in the doorway.

"Happy birthday lad," they both grinned broadly as they stepped aside, and I ran up those stairs faster than I ever had. The screws did me a favour and kept everyone in the dining room for a full five minutes after my departure. I was grateful for that. It would have not done my reputation any good to have been seen blubbing like a girl as I hugged that parcel to my chest and rocked back and forth on my bed.

Chapter 21

One step forward two steps back

Being the gym orderly was possibly the best thing that had happened to me in a long while. I would use whatever spare time I had to heave weights run around the sports field or do a few rounds on the makeshift punch bag I'd hung in the store room. The punch bag was made up of three pillowcases each inside the other, I'd stuffed them with rags and some old bean bags I'd come across at the bottom of a cupboard and tied it to a metal frame that held up the roof. It was not ideal. I found it a little light and without a pair of bag gloves my knuckles were constantly raw and bleeding from friction burns. I enjoyed my new-found freedom and a chance for solitude that many prisoners crave from time to time. I could go anywhere I wanted within the borstal unescorted and I would just smile and wave my green arm band like a VIP pass at a pop concert, if a screw was to challenge me. I became almost invisible a part of the scenery and after a while nobody took any notice of me as I meandered around whistling to myself without a care in the world.

The two screws who ran the gym were Mr Kellet and Mr Barry and together they formed a comedy double act to rival Morecambe and Wise. They were always winding me up and when I fell for it, they would piss their pants laughing that much I thought I might have to call a doctor. I recall one time when I was mopping the showers after one class had finished and Mr Barry crept in and let off a fire extinguisher covering me from head to toe in foam. He was that busy laughing he didn't have time to get out of the way as I tipped the entire contents of the mop bucket over his head. My victory was short lived and after I'd cleaned up the mess, we'd both made and walked into the gym Mr Kellet was waiting for me and knocked me several yards across the

300

highly polished wooden floor with a powerful fire hose. They both collapsed hysterically, and it was only after I'd showered and changed that they both calmed down.

I thought I was the kid, but I was probably more responsible than both of them put together.

"No, no, Sir, don't," I'd laugh as one or the other would throw me to the floor in a headlock and challenge me to a wrestling match which we both knew would eventually get out of hand. There were quite a few times when another screw would walk in and Mr Kellet myself and Mr Barry would jump to our feet out of breath, red faced and dishevelled after playing killer ball or pirates whilst swinging on the wall bars or ropes like chimpanzees. We'd act all serious and business-like until the other screw had left and then somebody would say, "Right, where were we?" and it would start all over again. It would be wrong to say that Mr Barry and Mr Kellet treated their jobs like one big joke, they didn't, when work had to be done, it was, and they were two of the most popular screws in the entire borstal. They both believed life was for living and as long as the gym ran smoothly then playtime was an added bonus, a sort of perk of the job.

Mr Kellet's favourite saying was, "Work hard, play hard," and they put the same amount of effort into both. I laughed so much on a daily basis, I couldn't wait until Sundays when I could rest my aching ribs and practice my mean and moody look.

Mr Barry even joined me on my daily runs around the sports field and as I lapped him time after time I'd tease, "Getting old Sir, not up to it anymore?" This would encourage him to put on a spurt to try and catch me, but he never could, and I would stop until he nearly caught me and then run off like a naughty puppy.

Mr Barry was in his early thirties and an ex-army PTI. He was slim with a short back and sides and a Mexican style moustache that would resemble a big fat slug after it had been soaked by sweat. Mr Kellet was around the same age but seemed to fight a constant battle between exercise and fresh cream cakes. He was of the opinion that he could eat what he liked as long as he took enough exercise, good in theory but his eating binges tended to last longer than any exercise routine he started. All in all they were two big kids and boredom always led them into mischief. Mr Barry once told me that he and Mr Kellet were amazed they'd kept their jobs as long as they had, but finished by saying "While it lasts, let the good times roll!" and promptly rubbed a half-eaten sandwich in my face before racing off in 'chase-me, chase-me,' mode.

There were times when we had to be serious and it was always me that would say, "Sir we've got a class in five minutes, we better clean this mess up." I would see that look of disappointment on both their faces like children who'd been told to come in for their tea in the middle of a game of football.

"Or just five more minutes, go on?" I grew closer and closer to Mr Kellet and Mr Barry and somewhere, the lines that divided us became blurred. Mondays were my favourite days as I would sit in the office first thing. After I'd made us all a cup of coffee, I'd sit and listen to the things that they'd both got up to at the weekend. Their exploits whilst outside the borstal must have made them both the scourge of family gatherings and parties as their ingenuity to extract the urine out of others knew no bounds.

Mr Kellet told me how they had both been ordered to stay away from each other by their respective wives after a particularly embarrassing incident at a christening. Apparently, they'd both got drunk beforehand, and turned up with the entire rugby team from their local pub and sung disgusting rugby songs, whilst elderly grannies and mothers-in-law looked on aghast. As if that wasn't bad enough, they both then dropped their pants and did moonies. Mr Barry denied it was his fault and said Mr Kellet was the one who led him astray by spiking his lager with vodka. Mr Kellet said Mr Barry had spiked his drinks and he'd merely swapped them over when Mr Barry wasn't looking.

I decided to stay out of it and as they childishly said, "Did," "Didn't," "Did," I made a swift exit to the storeroom and knocked shit out of the punch bag.

My monthly reviews got better and better and each time I came out of Mr Beard's office, I was one step nearer to being released. My new release date was now May the twenty fifth and I would have served a total of eleven months in borstal. I could almost taste freedom and for the first time I began to wonder what would lie in store for me when I was released. I had no home and no living relatives. Well none who would want an ex-borstal boy cast into the bosom of their loving family, so I knew life would not suddenly become a bowl of cherries when I walked out of those gates. I pushed it out of my thoughts, it was still a long way off and for the time being I concentrated my efforts on what was going on inside the borstal.

It was nearly Christmas and even inside, it was being met with excited anticipation. The inmates were sending letters informing parents and girlfriends what they could send in their parcels and even the screws were planning games and competitions to amuse us throughout the festive season. I spent less and less time in the unit and whilst the rest of the inmates took part in association each evening, I would be in the gym assisting another screw with five a side football competitions or some other sport. I enjoyed the evenings and with Mr Kellet and Mr Barry safely tucked up at home, I could enjoy some quality quiet time.

When the evening sports classes were over, the screw who had taken the class would lead the inmates back to their units and the gym would become a place just for me, my domain my retreat. I would mop and dry the shower rooms and put away any equipment the previous class had just used. The silence was eerie and alone with my own thoughts, just the echo of my own footsteps reverberated off the walls as I went about my business. I had adopted a routine and it gave me something to look forward to at the end of a long day. I would turn off all the lights except the one in the office and after boiling the kettle, I would help myself to a couple of biscuits from Mr Kellet's secret stash that he had hidden in his clothes locker. After drinking hot sweet tea and dunking several Hob Knobs into my large mug, I would light up a cig and sit quietly smiling to myself before switching off the office light and taking a long slow walk around the borstal, as I took in the night air and gazed at the stars. I loved the night and as I strolled around the sports field I could have been anywhere as I wrapped the night around me like a blanket, as I sat on the grass and located my favourite star. I had a game I played I would choose a star at random and as I concentrated on its distant flicker, I would wonder how many other people around the world were looking upon it's wondrous light as it cut its way through the darkness and shone upon the earth. I had to tear myself away sometimes and on a couple of occasions I was late back to the unit. I would just flash my cheekiest grin and use the fact I didn't have a watch as an excuse. It always worked, and I would be told to hurry along, or I would miss supper. I would smile to myself as the screw opened the security gate and let me into South House, the thought of that big black and white station clock on the gym wall etched into my memory.

The run up to Christmas involved the play-offs of the competitions whose finals were to be held on Christmas day. I'd entered the snooker singles and doubles. In the doubles, Mike was my partner and I'd chosen well as he was the best player in the unit. It was most definitely a sign of his misspent youth and to look at him as he marched around the table sizing up a shot, a fag hanging from the corner of his mouth, he would have been at home in any rough and ready billiards hall. The other competitions didn't interest me much. There was table tennis, darts and for the more intellectual among us, a spelling competition. The spelling competition was entered by every geek and Dwayne Dibley on the unit. and although I believe everybody excels at something, I was of the opinion that some talents are best kept to one's self. Any idiot who was insane enough to enter a spelling competition in borstal was setting himself up for massive amount of ridicule. A very risky thing to do if you are already at the bottom of the food chain.

"Ere Bolton, you're in the spelling contest, aren't you? Spell this then," somebody would shout across the dorm.

"Go on then," the poor sucker would reply waiting to show us how high his IQ was.

"Bollocks," the first kid would shout, and Bolton would plead,

"Naw go on, give us the word, to which the other would laugh and say,

"That is the fucking word arsehole; B-o-l-l-o-c-k-s," and then laugh hysterically to himself as the others joined in.

The week before Christmas was an absolutely mad time for me as the gym orderly. So many sports competitions were running alongside each other, it would have been better if I'd moved my bed into the gym. I was by now working until nearly nine o clock every night and even a reluctant Mr Barry had volunteered to do some overtime as Mr Kellet had gone on leave for his Christmas break. The inter-house competitions were a real hoot and the humour and odd spattering of spontaneous violence made the games much more interesting to watch. Competitions between the different houses were not generally promoted within the borstal as it was akin to pitting two packs of hungry pit-bull terriers against each other and the winners were never the best football or basketball players but simply the best scrappers.

Mr Barry and I were in total agreement that the release of pent-up frustration on the sports field or in the gym was not necessarily a bad thing and we would only intervene if it was reduced to a free-for-all. I did find myself with the unenviable task of refereeing several fights that broke out afterwards, as the inmates continued their arguments from

305

the gym or sports field when they met in the changing rooms. Cleaning the shower rooms ceramic tiled floors after a punch-up always took a bit longer, as the mop just spread the blood around until it resembled a blood bath, a red hue finding its way into the cracks in the grout.

"Cor, Jack, that was a tough one," said Mr Barry as he looked in on me as I was tidying the showers, my mop bucket, a lovely watered-down crimson colour.

"No shit, Sir," I laughed as I squeezed out the mop and dunked it back in the contaminated water. "What's next?" I asked as I sploshed the soaking mop into a corner I'd missed.

"Oh, it's your house versus East House in the five-a-side football semi-finals; should be entertaining!" he laughed as he took a seat on the wooden bench and extracted a pack of cigarettes from his pocket.

"Want one?" he offered.

"You have to ask," I grinned as I helped myself from the outstretched packet. Half an hour later South and East house sidled into the gym.

"Sixteen on, Mr Barry," shouted the screw as he entered after them.

"Cheers Norm, I'll take it from here," replied Mr Barry as he walked out of the gym and into the corridor. To say the atmosphere was tense would be an understatement it was positively bloody menacing. The older lads from East House were already issuing threats to anyone who might have the cheek to score a goal against them, and if South House were to win, a declaration of all-out war had been threatened, no promised.

"Iz don't sweat you, youz a waste of space man and me tinks yous all mouth," shouted Mike as he squeezed his afro through the neck of his t-shirt.

"You'll fucking see who's all mouth, nigger boy. I'm going to snap your fucking legs like a fucking twig," threatened a thick set East House lad with evil eyes and big ears.

306

"See you are getting to know each other," smiled Mr Barry as he looked in on us. "Get a move on lads, we've another match after yours," he finished as he walked away.

When everybody was ready, I followed the two teams into the gym and stood at the back as the players and substitutes were chosen. It was possibly the biggest mismatch since David and Goliath and I didn't fancy our chances at all. South House team consisted of Mike who was the tallest but only because his afro added another foot and a half to his height. Bobby Mitchell a weedy little bastard with legs like bacon rind and a bad case of eczema, Kevin Lowry a Brummie kid with buck teeth and national health glasses but an ability to play football like George Best. Paul Macky, one of the six tough kids in our house and a contender for chap when I left. Paul was tall nearly six foot with a crew-cut hairstyle and hands like shovels. He wore his own shoes as the borstal couldn't find any that were big enough to fit him and most annoying of all he was a really nice kid. I didn't know if he could play football, but I had a feeling he'd been brought in as the hired muscle. And then there was Zippo Simpson, a convicted arsonist hence the name Zippo, he was a small ginger-haired lad with freckles and a look in his eyes that was distant and more than a little disconcerting. I thought he was a dangerous little bastard and gave him a wide berth. I didn't fancy waking in the night to find I'd been hired as an extra in the remake of Towering inferno! Lastly was South House's secret weapon, Simon Flockton, an athletic lad, well-toned, muscular and he could dribble a ball like it was stitched to his foot. His only Achilles heel was his fear of pain and he would let you take the ball from him rather than risk a kick in the shin. I stood and looked them up and down and decided we were fucked!

East House's assembled team looked more like a reunion of cast members from Spartacus and I had a strong suspicion that they had not been chosen for their nimbleness and sportsmanship. The only time any of that lot had kicked anything with accuracy was when they were re-arranging some poor bugger's family jewels. The whistle to start the game should have been replaced with a bell and the two halves split into three-minute rounds as more punches were exchanged in the opening seconds than in any pro fight I'd seen. It was quite comical really as Mr Barry blew his whistle to signal the start and the two players on the centre spot faced each other. Simon Flockton went for the ball, but East House were playing a different game and their player just nutted Simon on the nose leaving him on the floor clutching his face and wiping the tears from his eyes. Mr Barry blew and blew that whistle until the pea nearly fell out, but he was wasting his time. The East House kid just took the ball and in his own sweet time kicked it into the back of our net and turning gave a bow to his team mates.

"You Justin, anymore of that crap and I'll send you off, got me?" snarled Mr Barry as he grabbed the East House kid by his shirt.

"Sorry sir, it was an accident, a clash of heads," Justin grinned as he looked over Mr Barry's shoulder and winked at his team mates.

"Do I look stupid, a fucking accident? You were a fucking accident, Justin, when yer Dad's Jonny split, now fuck off over there," Mr Barry barked as he threw Justin backwards with enough force that he nearly fell over. "Right the rest of you; we will start this match again and please remember it is a football match and not a meeting of Mods and Rockers on Brighton seafront, now let's get on with it!" he ended before blowing his whistle.

It was painful to watch and as goal after goal was scored by East House, it really pissed me off. We were losing because of intimidation and some of the craftiest fouls I'd ever seen. Kevin Lowry was kicked from behind in his knackers as Mr Barry had his back turned. Mike was warned for calling Mr Barry a blind white racist bastard after he missed a foul carried out on him by Justin. The person who had the ball had nothing to worry about as this was where Mr Barry's attention was focused it was anyone who was not

308

up front that suffered as legs were wiped out from under them, elbows were driven into stomachs as kids raced past, and poor Zippo was poked in both eyes by a black kid who just walked up to him. I cringed as I looked on helplessly as we were systematically bullied squashed stamped and bitten into surrender. When the half-time whistle went, you could see the sense of relief wash over South House as they knew they had a brief respite from the hammering they were being given. The score was not a testament to the footballing prowess of East House but to their enthusiasm to win at all costs and fuck the rules. I could understand their motives; the winning team of the competition would be awarded a trophy and an ounce of tobacco to each player and for an ounce of tobacco in borstal you could buy a lot of favours. I don't think it was all about the prizes I'm not that gullible and I'm sure if we had been playing for fun the game would not have been any less brutal.

"Twenty-eight to two, weez getting a whooping and that's fer sure," said Mike as I talked to him as he came out of the toilet.

"Well start giving them some back mate, they foul you, you foul them but fucking harder, you with me?" I smiled as I patted his sweaty back.

A look in Mike's eyes told me he'd had one of his brain waves and I knew it would involve me. "Whoa, I can't fucking play football, I've got two left feet. I won't be any good, besides you've picked your team and I bet I'm not allowed," I said trying to convince Mike and hoping beyond all hope I was right.

"I know man. I'll ask Mr Barry, 'ims a nice bloke, we's gonna see," and with that he raced off ignoring my pleas not to bother. Moments later Mike was back his black face brimming with excitement.

"No don't tell me, let me guess, Mike," I said trying to hide my annoyance at being roped into something, I had no interest in getting involved with.

"Aw man, don't be like that, come on give us a hand,"

Mike said trying to coax me round.

"But I've told you Mike I can't play football, giving me a ball is like giving a cow a gun, give me a break," I said, walking away and into the store room.

Mike wasn't giving up and followed me like a puppy. "You don't need to play football, you've seen it Jack, you can be our chief fouler, what do ya say? Come on man they's killing us," he begged.

"Okay, okay, but just don't expect too much and you fucking owe me Mike, you owe me," I said as I started to remove my clothes and get into my gym kit.

"Oh yes, yes, yes, you beauty," Mike's voice carried through the gym.

"What you so happy bout, we're getting stuffed?" asked Zippo as he came into the stores, his eyes bright red from the fingers he'd had jabbed in them.

"Jack's gonna play for us," said Mike the excitement in his voice spilling over.

"Your fucking kidding, no shit, Jack's gonna play?" asked Zippo not quite believing it.

"Yeah man we's gonna kick some East House butt now, we's gonna be wicked, man, wicked," laughed Mike as he hugged Zippo and they jumped up and down in a celebratory dance.

The game was brutal alright but unfortunately for us we were on the receiving end. East House had obviously given themselves a pep talk at half time and as a result had stepped up a gear. I became public enemy number one and my team mates didn't help by continually giving me the fucking ball. If I heard another bastard say, "Yours Jack," I'd give him a hiding myself and screw the game. Worrell a big lump of a lad from East House was the first to wade in and rabbit punched me in the back of the head as he rushed past. I picked myself off the floor and Zippo gave me a nod to let me know who was responsible. I nodded back and made a mental note of him, he could wait. Mike had the ball and was charging down the left side of the gym with Wilcock

310

from East House on his tail. I could tell any challenge made would exclude any attempt to get the ball so as he ran past me, I matched his speed and stuck my foot out sending him headlong towards the floor. By sheer bad luck, as he fell, he hit the back of Mike's legs and brought him down as well. The ball continued rolling and I ran for it for all I was worth. I never got there, I was sandwiched by two rhinoceroses wearing the blue vests of East House. They ran in from opposite sides and literally crushed the life out of me. I heard the whistle and Mr Barry awarded me a free kick. I was happy to take it and left one of my attackers writhing in agony holding his crotch as I kicked him squarely between the legs.

"Marriot, I meant the ball, the ball," said Mr Barry pointing at the round leather object, tears of laughter filling his eyes.

"Oh yeah, Sir, of course," I grinned cheekily. The ball sailed into the back of the net and nobody could have been more surprised than me especially when I was congratulated with a knee in the thigh that left my whole leg without feeling.

We were never going to win this game, we were too far behind and whilst I didn't mind a bit of rough and tumble, I could not deal with the five lads from East House on my own. I didn't bother with the ball after that I just took whatever opportune moment came my way to settle scores of my own. I took out Justin with an elbow right on the bridge of his nose and when his team mates called, "Oh referee?" Mr Barry just ignored them, it was like a green light and I just couldn't help myself. It was definitely catching and as I fouled anyone wearing a blue vest, the other South House lads found some guts and began giving as good as they got.

Mike ran after Tranter, a tough looking skin head with tree trunk legs, and as Tranter went to score Mike just ran full belt into his back and sent him face first into the gym wall. The whistle blew and as I turned to walk back to our

311

half, I caught sight of Zippo wrestling a guy to the ground and biting his ear. The whole gym began to fill with clusters of inmates tearing lumps out of each other and even the substitutes had got off the benches and were taking part. The sound of Mr Barry's whistle could be heard clearly over the mayhem, but nobody listened, and in the end, Mr Barry just stood a few feet up on the wall bars and waited for it to subside.

Mike was not fairing very well, Tranter was pounding his fist into his face. Mike was trying to wriggle out from under him, his free hands clawing at Tranters lily white face like a mad tiger. I ran over and kneed Tranter right in the mouth both my feet leaving the ground as I supported my weight on one hand that I rested on his shoulder. Tranter was out, and he wouldn't have made it up on a ten count. I pulled Mike to his feet and then I was thrown to the floor from behind and I could feel somebody's breath on my neck. Mike got him off, returning the favour with a punch in the lads ear. He howled like a dog and rolled off me and began crawling away. I sprang to my feet and went to the aid of Paul Macky who had his hands full, he was being kicked in the face by the lads on East House's substitutes' bench and a mean bastard called Knowles was going to work on his body.

I'd never liked Knowles and whenever I'd been in the gym and his unit were present, he walked around as though he owned the place. He was a bully an evil bully and he worried me. Knowles was a freak. I thought maybe his mother had been subjected to a dose of radiation whilst she was carrying him because he was so totally out of proportion. He had a huge head that was misshaped and square looking, and his arms were a foot longer than necessary. It was a wonder his knuckles weren't permanently scuffed from dragging on the ground.

"Eh, get off him," I shouted as I took Knowles arm and pulled him back. He spun and at the same time took a cheap shot at my face. I slipped it and head butted him. He reeled

312

backwards, and I hit him with a six-punch combination. He was unconscious by the forth punch but that's always the problem with a combo, it's like Mastermind, once you've started you just have to finish. Mr Barry's whistle croaked back into action and as now most of us had got it out of our system or were just too plain tired to continue.

Mr Barry soon regained control. "Right you lot, that's enough, the games over, match abandoned and consider yourselves lucky I've not rung the fucking riot bell because you'd all be down the block and Christmas would be just a distant memory. Now clean yourselves up," he paused and as he caught sight of Knowles who was flapping about on the floor like a dying fly, he said, "Somebody help him up before he does himself a permanent injury."

That was the end of our journey on the path of footballing glory. We were never to replay that match. Mr Barry disqualified both teams. He told me later that he couldn't risk another brawl and we didn't deserve another chance so that was that. I had to agree with him and didn't lose any sleep over it. We were never going to win anyway. It wasn't all bad news and I made some knew friends that day. The lads from East House had told everybody about the scrap and now I found that even the chap of East House would nod and smile as we passed in the corridor. There were no repercussions Mr Barry made us all shake hands and by the time we'd all showered we were laughing along with each other as we relived the highlights.

"Fucking hell did you see your face when I kicked you in the nuts, I thought yer eyes were gonna pop out," a kid would laugh, and another would say, "You weren't so cocky yourself when I bit yer ear, you screamed like a baby."

"You would too, it fucking hurt, I think you've filed your teeth to a point, you fucking vampire," the kid would say in his defence as we all fell about. Knowles didn't join in the fun he sat there silently, he was ashamed, and he never walked around my gym again as though he owned it.

Chapter 22

Ding dong merrily

It was impossible, impossible to get away from the enforced festive cheer that followed me everywhere on Christmas day like a bad smell.

"For fucks sake leave me alone, I don't want to sing carols, make fancy glittery Christmas cards or take part in another fucking competition, now piss off," I snarled at Mr Mulligan as he knelt down by my side as I remained glued to the TV in my own in the corner.

The look on his face was awful, I'd never spoken to him like that before and he hadn't deserved it now. He looked mortified and it was less than a second before I regretted it.

"Look Sir, I'm sorry, I just want to be on my own, please let me be, please," I said forcing a smile.

"Okay Jack, you just sit and be miserable if that's what you want, but everybody else is enjoying themselves. I just don't understand you," he said shaking his head and giving me the best disappointed look he could muster.

'No you don't understand,' I thought, 'how could you? You aren't banged up, miles away from everything you know, and you've not lost the only person you ever cared about.' I tried to put Dad's smiling face out of my mind, but it just wouldn't go away and as everybody whooped and hollered as they watched the South House snooker final, I just sat staring at the TV screen and choked back the tears that welled up in my eyes. The Christmas season could not end quickly enough for me, then we would be in a new year and my release would be more than a glimmer of hope, somewhere on the horizon. The other lads badgered me so much to join in I finally had to threaten them with violence if they even thought about trying to cheer me up. I was miserable, and I was entitled to be. I had no Christmas wishes from the outside, no food parcel and no visitors and

314

if I wanted to wallow in my own misery then I should bloody well be able to, I convinced myself.

The prison kitchens excelled themselves that day and as I tucked in to a large plate of turkey and all the trimmings, my mood began to lighten, a stomach full of good food can have that effect. I took a large gulp from my plastic mug that was full of orange squash a rare treat, instead of just the water or piss weak tea that accompanied every meal.

"Boy, that was some grub man, me tinks me's gonna bus," declared Mike as he let out an involuntary burp.

"Oh, you fucking dirty bastard, I'm still eating," said Jimmy as he flicked a lump of mashed potato into Mikes face. Mike reached across to Jimmy who was seated to my left and I grabbed his hand mid-way as he stretched across the table.

"Now, now, boys, it's Christmas day, you can't kill each other until tomorrow, okay?" I said making it clear I was not in the mood for their petty arguments.

"Yeah man, okay but im dun gone and start it, he's always messing," said Mike trying to get in the last word.

Jimmy was having none of it. "You should learn some manners, we's not in no fucking jungle now."

"That's it, just fucking pack it in you pair of idiots, I ain't got time for none of this shit today, now fucking grow up!" I said with my voice lowered in a menacing tone that they both knew meant business.

"Sorry man."

"Yeah, sorry," they both replied and then fell silent although I felt Jimmy jump as Mike kicked him under the table. I looked up and Jimmy was mouthing something at Mike but thought better of it as our eyes met.

"So Mike we gonna win this doubles snooker final?" I asked changing the subject in an attempt to take their minds of each other.

"Yeah man, me's won the singles and iz on a roll so we gonna wup some arse man, what you tinks?" he replied.

"Well let's hope so, I could do with cheering up" I shot

315

back.

"No fucking kidding, you miserable git," said Jimmy sticking his oar in. No sooner had he said it he wished he hadn't, then thinking better of it, his face went red his bottom lip quivered and he squeaked, "Sorry Jack, no offence."

"Okay, if you've finished stack your trays and make your way into the recreation room where Mr Beard will hand out your parcels," shouted Mr Pope across the dining room. It was the signal for a stampede and in a micro-second I found myself seated alone holding half a cup of orange. I chuckled as I surveyed the mess the other lads had left behind in their excitement to get their hands on their Christmas goodies. Chairs were pushed back from tables blocking the aisles, and trays were thrown randomly on the table by the door with plastic knives and forks forming a tangled heap near the receptacle they were meant to go in.

"You coming?" asked Mr Beard as he walked out of his office and noticed me still seated at my table by now smoking a fag. It was forbidden to smoke in the dining room and although he saw it he made no comment.

"Yeah Sir two minutes," I said forcing a smile.

"When you're ready lad, no rush," Mr Beard smiled kindly as he wobbled away. I stayed in the dining room for another ten minutes. I wanted to make sure everybody had got their parcels and I wouldn't be standing around like a spare prick at a pros party. I stood up and walked over to the dining room window and stared out, there was no snow, no frost it was just another cold and misty December day. I could see some screws heading out of the main gates they were laughing and wishing each other a merry Christmas. I knew they were heading home and that their families would be waiting to commence their Christmas celebrations. I imagined the twinkling Christmas lights that would festoon the pine trees in their living rooms, the log fires burning smiling relatives and the glasses of mulled wine and port that would be thrust into their hands as soon as they put

316

their foot through the door. I envied them, and I wondered if I would ever have that again, a family, a home and a reason to smile.

"You coming, we's ready for the match?" I heard Mike's dulcet tones from behind me. I didn't turn around I was lost in thought my gaze still riding on the backs of those lucky enough to be walking out of those gates.

"Yeah coming," I replied quietly as I tore myself away, "Come on let's kick arse," I said as cheerfully as I could as I pushed Mike into the hall and down the passageway into the recreation room.

The snooker match was a complete farce. I couldn't concentrate and although Mike played out of his skin, I left so many opportunities for our opponents they cleared up. Mike got really annoyed he didn't like to lose, and he forgot himself several times and snapped at me. I let it go at first but by the end of the match he was going too far, especially as the whole of the house was watching and I couldn't let them think I'd gone soft.

"Fucking hell man, yous playing like a twat, get a fucking grip you wanker," Mike shouted from his seat as I missed another easy red. I straightened up from my shot walked round the table and without a word grabbed him by the throat and hauled him out of his chair. I looked him in the eyes released my grip and pushed him backwards over his chair.

"Whoa, whoa, boys, it's Christmas, stop that shit," reasoned Mr Beard as he stepped in front of me.

"Oh fuck it, let em ave it, I quit," I announced loudly and stormed off. Mike gave me the space I needed to calm down and avoided me like I had a case of rampant leprosy. I couldn't blame him I was on the edge and if the truth be told I didn't know why. The screws kept a very close eye on me, they had come to know by now when there was a strong possibility that I was going to blow and made sure they were all only seconds away from being able to pounce if they needed too. They must have felt a huge sense of relief when

317

it got to two o clock and I had to go to work.

"I hope you will be in a better mood when you return?" said Mr Pope as he unlocked the gate for me to leave the unit.

"Never hurts to hope Sir," I replied as I stepped out into the fresh air. Mr Pope shook his head and raised his eyes before locking the steel gate and leaving me on my own. On my own is what I wanted. Misery might love company, but Jack Marriot likes his own company and it was the way I dealt with shit, the way I'd always dealt with problems whether on my own by the canal or on my own in my bedroom. I dealt with whatever it was on my own and that was the way it was going to stay.

I set off briskly towards the playing fields. I wanted to breathe that crisp cold air and to get away from everything and anyone to enjoy the open skies and above all the silence I craved. I needed to be away from everyone else, the hustle and bustle and constant chatter of the other inmates, just me and my thoughts. I was supposed to be assisting Mr Barry in the finals of the Five-a-side and basketball competitions, but he could wait. I knew he wouldn't rock the boat by ringing the unit to ask where the hell I was. So I strolled around on the damp grass puffing away on a fag and setting the world to rights according to Jack Marriot.

"Come on Jack, everybody will be here in a minute," Mr Barry said as he met me coming through the doorway into the gym. I didn't answer, I made my way straight to the storeroom to get out the equipment that would be needed but as I entered the stores, I was stopped dead in my tracks. My makeshift punch bag was gone, and in its place, hung a genuine leather one. I pushed it with my open hand and it was balanced just right. not too heavy, not to light.

"I thought you might be able to use it, it was just hanging around in my garage," said Mr Barry smiling from ear to ear as he walked into the stores and stood behind me.

"It's great, thanks Sir," I beamed.

"You might need these as well, save yer hands," he

318

finished as he threw me a pair of leather bag gloves. I was about to thank him, but he looked a little embarrassed and cut me off as I opened my mouth. "Anyway you can knock the shit out of it in your own time now get the gear out, come on move it we're running late."

The five-a-side matches, and the basketball competitions dragged on and on and we even ended up playing injury time, which as you can imagine was probably longer than the standard time for each half. I couldn't wait to try out that punch bag and as I robotically went through the motions, I found myself in trouble for not paying attention. It was no big deal it was Christmas day and all the screws seemed to be overly lenient to any misdemeanours that any inmate carried out. I guess it was the season of goodwill and even in borstal it knew no bounds. North House carried off the trophies for the five-a-side and basketball competitions, the younger kids from West House, the victims of intimidation and bone breaking tackles. The violence was at least moderated and not anywhere near the scale of the match we'd played against East House. There was one main reason for this, spectators. The finals were watched by all of the inmates from the houses taking part including the governor, assistant governor and a spattering of principle officers. It would have been very foolish to push your luck too much with that amount of witnesses scrutinising your every move. So, although North House were the victors, West House, escaped a severe battering and when they walked back to their units it was mostly their pride that had taken a beating.

I remained in the gym until ten-o-clock that night. Mr Barry phoned the unit and said I would be back later as there was still some clearing up to do. It was a lie of course and for over an hour Mr Barry and I worked that punch bag over good and proper. I taught him how to throw a four-punch combination, slip and weave and how to increase his punching power through proper weight distribution. When we were finally worn out and sweating heavily, Mr Barry

319

went to the office and brought out two ice cold cans of Coke and as we gulped them down and smoked his cigarettes, I realised I was no longer the moody grumpy bastard who'd walked in to the gym some seven hours earlier.

Chapter 23

Quieter times?

When I got back to the unit from the gym all the other inmates were tucked up in bed. They weren't asleep most of them too excited by the change of routine and the relaxing of rules that accompanied Christmas day. I could see silhouetted faces of inmates lit by the dim light that filtered in from the corridor outside, they were talking their voices hushed but still discernible. As I sat on my bed and removed my shoes, I could see the whites of Mike's eyes peeking out from under his covers and knew he was waiting for me to say something.

"You awake?" I asked already knowing the answer.

"Yeah you alright mate?" Mike whispered, half of his face covered by the blanket he'd pulled up to his nose.

"Yeah I'm fine, sorry bout earlier I shouldn't have lost my rag with you, sorry mate," I apologised sincerely.

"Forgotten already man, iz know yu's pissed man and it 'ain't me yu's mad at, but boy iz I glad yu's not pissed no more, friends?" said Mike as he offered his outstretched hand from under his blankets.

I went to shake it but pulled my hand up short. "What's wrong man," asked Mike his face showing concern. "Tell me you 'ain't had that on yer knob!" I said a smile lighting up my face.

"No man," he said as though he was hurt by the mere suggestion. I took his hand and shook it firmly.

"Well not in the last five minutes anyway," laughed Mike as I pulled my hand away in disgust. It felt good to have made my peace with Mike and whilst I could be a real misery, I had one saving grace and that was my ability to forgive, so as I took off my clothes and climbed into my bed. I closed my eyes and drifted off to sleep with a clear conscience, tomorrow was after all another day and I was definitely going to put on a happy face.

I had the worst night's sleep I'd ever had that night, and in the morning I discovered why. Instigated by Mike a few inmates had each decided to give me a couple of items out of their Christmas parcels, I knew it was shit that they didn't want or like, but it was the thought that counted and when I discovered why my pillow was full of lumps in the early hours of the morning, I couldn't help but feel choked. They'd given me soap, boiled sweets, a bar of chocolate and three Mars bars. I knew the Mars bars were given by Mike as he fucking hated them. He would say, "Nigger don't need to be putting nuffin in his mouth that looks like black man's cock, it even got dem veins running along it!"

Christmas and New Year soon came and went and as we moved into the middle of January, I settled back down to my job in the gym. Mr Barry and Mr Kellet were unchanged by what Christmas leave they'd had, and soon got back to their old ways. It was a constant battle to avoid their wind-ups and general fooling around. I would get so paranoid in the end that everything they asked me to do was viewed with suspicion and they would both have to plead, "No serious, we aren't kidding," or "I promise not to do anything," just to get me to carry out their instructions. Life was good and when I did spend time on the unit, I enjoyed catching up with Mike and Jimmy who would have lots of tales to tell. I needed to keep my finger on the pulse, but it became extremely difficult being absent from the unit so often. Bullying had reared its ugly head again and although I detested it, I let it go. I know it was wrong, but it wasn't affecting me, and I just wanted to stay out of trouble. I never saw any bullying first hand, nobody was brave or stupid enough to rub my face in it and besides they knew that I would be out of the unit so often they could take full advantage of the weaker inmates then.

I had another favourable report at the end of January and as I closed the door behind me when it was over, I was three weeks nearer to my release. I was buzzing it was coming together and it was so near that I could almost smell it. All I had to do was keep my nose clean, avoid any dickheads and I would be riding the train to freedom, a week's dole in my pocket and a single ticket to Leeds clutched in my sweaty palm.

"Come on Jack, get the weights set out, we've got North House coming in ten minutes," called Mr Barry from the office. I was in the store room a fag hanging from my mouth while I punched the bag with one gloved hand.

"Yeah in a minute," I shouted as I stopped and took a drag on my roll up. I'd got a little lazy and slack in my duties as orderly and any other screws would have binned me off, but not Mr Kellet and Mr Barry, they liked me, and I used this to my advantage. It would not be unusual for the two of them to end up mopping the changing rooms because I just hadn't bothered and wasn't likely to if they never told me off, which of course they didn't. The peace was shattered by North House who invaded the gym like a pack of wild animals, they were always a pain in the arse. They would climb up the wall bars swing on the ropes and pull out the trampoline and bounce on it six at a time, they were a nightmare and trying to get them to desist was not one of my easiest tasks. No sooner had you got one group to put down whatever they were playing with, you'd spot another lot endangering their own or somebody else's life by sheer stupidity. It was the worst part of my job and when Mr Kellet or Mr Barry finally came into the gym and blew their whistle to restore order, I would be more than a little relieved. Today was no different. I caught three lads trying to rifle my stores and when I challenged them, they just laughed in my face as they pushed past me and walked out the door. Another group were having a water fight in the changing rooms and after getting carried away one of them went to discharge the fire extinguisher, but I got to him first.

"Eh give me that back," he said as he tried to lever it from my grasp.

"Get off you twat," I snapped as I pulled away.

"Give him it, you wanker"

"Yeah give him it back, it's only a bit of fun, you wanker," chorused the other lads from North House but I had no intention of giving in.

"Give him it back Marriot, you little tosser," said a voice that was strangely familiar from behind me.

"Yeah, you wanna fuck wiv me, ya tosser?" said the voice as an arm went round my neck. I released my grip on the extinguisher it was no longer important I had other matters to deal with. I struggled and although I felt the arm grow tighter and tighter around my neck, I twisted to face my unknown attacker. I went as white as a sheet, that spikey blonde hair those enormous shoulders and that abnormally large head and as I felt all the strength leave my body I was transported back to that cell in Armley and the laughing faces of both my tormentors.

I was scared. "Mick?" was the only word I could get out as my vocal chords tightened involuntarily.

"Yeah Mick, bet you thought you'd never see me again, now fuck off," he shouted and threw me backwards into the wall, my head thundered into it and momentarily I was dazed. I wanted to fight back I wanted to tear him apart, but my irrational fear had sapped my strength and I was as weak as a kitten. I was saved by the footsteps of Mr Barry that were heard approaching.

"Screw, screw," somebody shouted and as Mr Barry entered the changing rooms, Mick stepped away and began undoing his shirt his back to me.

"Right lads in the gym two minutes," said Mr Barry and in a flash was gone. Mick turned back to me. I hadn't moved. I was still pushed up to the wall like a rabbit caught in headlights. I wanted to run but my legs just wouldn't move.

"You'll fucking keep, Marriot, you pansy," he said pushing me with the palm of his hand in the face as he walked out of the door. My heart was pounding, and I could hear it thud thudding louder and louder and as the last

324

person walked out and into the gym, I slid down the wall and pulling my knees up to my chest I hugged them and began rocking back and forth, my whole body quivering. I replayed every moment of my time in Armley, those meals that I ate standing up whilst Wayne and Mick smirked at each other, the cutting comments the verbal onslaught and that feeling of utter worthlessness that they'd had hammered into me each vile day I'd endured.

I eventually climbed to my feet and hanging my head in the sink, I splashed water into my face, I paused, and looking up into the mirror I spoke to myself. "What are you doing, you're not frightened of anyone," but at the same time my mind was picturing my limp body as Mick kicked me half to death whilst his housemates laughed and egged him on. I knew I had to do something but had no idea what, could I beat him? Should I just avoid him? Why was he here? Why hadn't we met before? There were so many questions and as I looked into my own eyes reflected in the mirror, I could find no answers. I would have happily stayed in that changing room for the whole lesson, but I was summoned by Mr Kellet to help clear the weights and set up the basketball nets.

"Just coming," I said as I took one more look in the mirror drew a deep breath and straightening my shoulders walked out and into the gym. It was everything I'd imagined it would be, the whole of North House took the piss out of me and laughed as they accidentally on purpose thundered into me whenever the chance arose.

"Here," one of them would call and as the basketball was thrown in my direction and I would have to side step the charge that was aimed at me. It was hopeless my self-respect, my standing, my confidence had gone. I got out of the gym as soon as I could and once inside my beloved storeroom, I closed the door and breathed a sigh of relief. My pulse was still racing, and I could not rid my hands of the trembling that had taken over them. I could hear the game in the gym continuing, the ball bouncing, the cheers when

325

somebody scored and the occasional shrill noise from Mr Barry's whistle. My stomach could have won gold at the Olympics for the acrobatics that were taking place inside and in my weakened state as I hit the punch bag with my bare hands it hardly moved. I was pathetic a waste of space and as I wrapped my arms around the bag, I buried my face into it and cried with frustration. I heard the final whistle blow and the sound of footsteps as North House made a dash for the showers. The anger I'd been smothering unshackled itself and broke free rising from the pit of my stomach like a torpedo from the depths of the ocean and I lost control. I hit the bag with all my strength, but it hardly moved so I hit it again and again and as the fear released its hold on me the bag began to lift until I was hitting it like I'd never hit it before, the fear had gone and now I was in control. I didn't weigh up my options or decide on my next move as I pulled open the door to the stores and walked across the gym towards the changing rooms. I had no idea what I was going to do.

"Oh look who it isn't," said a smirking kid as I came through the door, he shouldn't have. I hit him straight in the mouth sending him to the floor. I then ran forward and hit another kid behind his left ear as he tried to climb into his trousers, I hadn't picked him at random he was a gobshite and he'd think twice before joining in next time. I scanned the changing room for Mick and caught sight of him as he stepped forward from between the group of kids who had now formed a semicircle at the far end of the room. He was grinning and had a look of confidence on his face that said he was going to take me apart without breaking sweat. The poor fucker he had no idea that he'd unleashed a dragon that even I couldn't control so he had no chance. I hit him on the bridge of his nose with such force it disintegrated, it would have been enough ordinarily, but I was filled with rage and I wanted to hurt him like he'd never imagined he could be hurt. I moved onto him as he flew back with the force of the blow he'd received, I didn't wait. I was on him

326

three body blows two to the right and one to the left, the tell-tale snap told me his ribs had gone, he was against the wall now his face contorted, and body half turned trying to cover his battered features with his hands. I drove my knee into his ribcage and as more air escaped his lungs blood shot out of his mouth, it was foaming and bright red. He could no longer stand and as his body slid down the tiled wall towards the floor, I helped him with a right hand in the mouth an explosion of blood decorating the walls. There was no shouting no jeering and no cheering just a deadly silence as I straightened up from Mick's broken body. I prodded him with my foot and grinned like a mad man. "Anyone of you fuckers want to call me a wanker, now?" I challenged as I turned to walk out, it was then I saw them, Mr Barry and Mr Kellet standing in the doorway the expression on their faces was akin to two people who'd witnessed a horrific car accident. They were not sure whether it was real or whether they had just imagined it and as they remained rooted to the spot, I slid past them and made my way back to the store room.

Retribution was swift, and I was immediately taken to the block where I spent a week in solitary licking my wounds. I was not to escape a hearing by the board of visitors this time and I knew I was in serious trouble.

"You wait until Mr Mulligan hears about this, he's going to be so disappointed in you," reasoned Mr Pope as he stood with me outside the governor's office. I had never really held a conversation with Mr Pope, but he was beginning to grow on me.

"Yeah I know Sir, but I had no choice, you can't understand what it's like sometimes you just have to fight back," I offered, trying to justify myself.

Mr Pope gave me a knowing look that told me he thought I was talking bollocks.

"But you do Sir," I said, still hoping he'd see my side of the argument.

"Jack, you put a lad in the hospital with three broken ribs

327

a broken nose and a punctured lung. In anybody's book that's a little more than self-defence, don't you think?" he said emphatically.

He had a point and running out of mitigating reasons for my actions I thought it best to stay silent.

"Don't you think that you could have killed that boy, you could have been in court on a manslaughter charge or worse, you can't tell me you wouldn't be bothered about that can you?" Mr Pope continued. I still didn't give him a response I suppose I didn't know what he expected me to say, but Mr Pope wanted an answer and wasn't letting me off that lightly. "Well what if you'd killed him?" he persisted.

I thought of that big piece of shit and the things he'd done to me. I imagined him lying under a sheet in a hospital morgue a cardboard tag on his toe and his mother weeping over his lifeless body, and to be truthful I wouldn't have given a fucking toss. Yeah, I'd have been sorry for myself, sorry for the years that I'd spend behind bars, but I wouldn't have wasted a moment on him.

"Yeah Sir I'd have been really sorry," I lied not too convincingly but it was enough for the gullible Mr Pope.

"Come on let's get you in" he smiled as he knocked on the governor's door.

In the governor's office the board of visitors had already been assembled, and were seated around an oval table, the governor seated at one end. The board was made up of a woman and two men. The woman was probably sixty-years-old, her brown greying hair pulled tightly to the back of her head and wearing a ridiculous pair of glasses that hung from her neck on a gold chain. She lifted her glasses and stared through them as she looked me up and down as though I'd trodden in shit and trailed it in with me. She'd obviously read the report of my charges and decided I was an animal. Already, it was written all over her face and I quickly looked away not wanting to antagonise her further. The two men were pretty ordinary looking, middle-aged, dressed in shirts and ties, their hair parted to the side, they looked like

Tweedle Dee and Tweedle Dum.

"Marriot, we find ourselves yet again in trouble," said the governor breaking the silence. I nearly said why what have you done? but managed to keep myself in check fixing my eyes on a spot behind him on the wall.

"You are today to have your adjudication heard by the board of visitors," he continued. "This is because of the serious nature of the charges against you. If the board feels that even their powers are not broad enough to punish you, we may well decide to instigate criminal charges against you in the Crown court so make no mistake young man you are in very serious trouble, do you understand?" I nodded trying to look contrite. "Very well let us begin," finished the governor as he turned to look at the board. The evidence presented against me was overwhelming and as the charges were read, I could visualise myself becoming the only adult still serving a borstal sentence. I had one piece of good luck the other two kids I'd hit hadn't made a complaint. I hadn't given it much thought, but I suppose Mr Barry and Mr Kellet had not witnessed their assault and as such the lads themselves were not inclined to grass me up. Mr Kellet was the first screw to give evidence and as he did so I could see he wasn't enjoying it. I never expected him to lie for me and he didn't, but he certainly made every attempt to play down the carnage he had witnessed. Mr Barry became my white knight he was amazing and gave me such a glowing reference, I felt myself blush.

Mr Barry's army days had hardened him and in his opinion 'boys would be boys.' He said that although the injuries sustained were serious he believed my attack was not pre-planned and that I had gone calmly and quietly to the block when the other officers arrived in the gym to take me away. By the time Mr Barry had finished, I was convinced I could have stood for Pope and the white smoke from the Vatican chimney would have been sent out in minutes signalling my victory. The board of visitors on the other hand would need a little more convincing. The poker-faced old bag gave nothing away whilst the two men at least nodded and gave the odd grunt as an indication that they were at least listening.

A report was read revealing a few facts about my victim and they were certainly more than eye opening, in fact compared to him I was a fucking choir boy. Mick had been shipped out of his last borstal after running a protection racket and stabbing a lad in the eye with a sharpened tooth brush. He had lost over six month's remission already and had been on report for fighting over nine times. Nobody had a good word to say about him and I couldn't help smirking as I watched the woman on the board turn up her nose at each derogatory fact as it was revealed in all its glory. When all the witnesses had been seen and the reports poured over by the board the room fell silent except for the odd page of some document being ominously turned. Nobody looked at me I just stood there listening to the clock ticking on the wall and praying harder than I'd ever prayed before.

"Now we have heard the evidence and the facts we would like you to have the chance to offer your side of events, so what do you have to say?" said the woman on the board. She had decided she was going to take charge and I knew if I was going to get them to treat me leniently then she was the one I needed to work on.

"Er, yes miss," I said politely. "I would like you to know that I sincerely regret my actions and ask you to give me another chance to prove myself." I looked her in the eyes she was leaning nearer to me and had cupped her chin in her hand her elbow on the table.

"Go on," she nodded at me, we're listening," as if to encourage me to say more.

"I er tried to avoid fighting miss, but I had no choice he was bigger than me and was pushing me around. I had no choice," I repeated as I gave her my softest doe eyed look.

"Thank you, if you can wait outside, we will discuss this further and call you back in a moment, thank you, young man," she said the stern look starting to dissolve. I smiled a sad smile and left the room my head bowed submissively. It wouldn't have been clever to have shown an inch of nonchalance, she had to believe I was sorry and as the two screws stood outside in the corridor with me, I said another prayer. I hadn't just found God, I'd always believed but as with most people I only prayed when I needed something.

It felt like an eternity until that door opened again. It wasn't helped by the two screws standing with me who never said a word either to me or each other. When they were ready for me, I was marched back in and as the two screws shut the door behind me I swallowed hard, here we go I thought.

The woman cleared her throat, adjusted the glasses she was now wearing and began to speak. "The board has made the decision that we will indeed hear your case and in doing so we hope you realise that you are being given your final chance, do you understand?" She paused to await my reaction. I didn't know what to say, it was good news, but I wasn't going to run over and kiss her weathered old face.

"Yes," I mumbled as I adjusted my stance.

"Very well, you are to lose six weeks remission and spend a further week in segregation before you are returned to your unit, and don't let us see you again or we will not be so lenient young man and consider yourself very fortunate". "Now if that's all," she turned to look at the governor.

"Oh yes," he said, as though he'd just been disturbed from his sleep, take him away."

Chapter 24

A taste of freedom

My release from solitary was met with much jubilation by the lads from South House. I was a hero in their eyes and they all wanted to be in my company. The word had spread around the other houses too, it was a big deal and at first I didn't know why I'd had fights before and they had never been met with such sycophantic behaviour.

"What's wrong with that lot?" I asked as I sat behind Mike as he watched TV during association.

He turned to look at me. "You don't know man, you really don't know?" he said, his eyes widening.

"Know what, stop bloody talking in riddles, know what?" I demanded.

"That kid from North House you wup, he the chap of North House and some said maybe the whole borstal, don't you see yous untouchable 'ain't nobody who gonna want to fuck wit ya now!" said Mike pushing me in the chest and grinning from ear to ear. I wasn't as glad to hear what he was saying as he obviously thought I might be, and the look on my face must have shown what I was thinking.

"Wassup man, 'ain't you pleased?" Mike asked his grin beginning to subside.

"Pleased, are you fucking kidding me, no I'm not fucking pleased, this just means now not only will every new kid who comes on to the house want a pop at the title, but every new kid in the borstal who thinks he's hard will want a go too, no it's definitely not made my fucking day!" I snapped, standing up and throwing my chair across the floor.

"Fucking great…." I said loudly as I stormed of in a huff leaving Mike open mouthed and wishing he'd kept it shut.

I kept my head down over the next few weeks. I didn't want any more trouble and enjoying my own company was

332

the best way I could achieve that. I was given another job after being sacked from the gym and just to show how out of favour I was, I was placed on the unit as a house cleaner. It was the shittest job that they had and was generally reserved for newcomers until they'd proved themselves worthy of something better. I would spend most of the day scrubbing floors cleaning toilets and any other crap job they could think of for me to do. The other drawback of such a lowly job were the wages they were two pounds fifty a week and I found myself going without some of the luxuries I'd grown accustomed to like soap and toothpaste. It would have been easy to subsidise my meagre wages by taking what I wanted, taxing the weaker inmates but I had some principles and I would never do that.

Whilst I was on cleaning duties, I found myself working alongside the new inmates as they arrived on the unit and my day was full of inane questions which made me feel like some kind of borstal agony aunt.

"So who's the cock of the house? Who should I avoid?" asked Menzies the first day after his arrival. I had to stop myself laughing.

"Don't know really, I don't get any hassle off anyone, so I just let the others worry about who the chap is. I'm just keeping a low profile, that works for me," I answered turning away and sloshing another mop full of water on the dining room floor.

"But I heard that the cock of the house usually picks on the new kids to test them, ya know?" continued Menzies. "One thing, the cock of the house as you call him, is in fact the chap of the house, we call him the chap not the cock, so before you go looking for him at least learn the correct term you wally," I said splashing water from the mop on to his shoes.

"Right, right, the chap, the chap," Menzies said to himself trying to memorise it. I had to walk away and once I was safely out of his earshot, I laughed to myself until tears filled my eyes. I enjoyed my first day with Menzies immensely, he was so easy to take the piss out of and as I watched him clumsily put his foot in it time and time again, I forgot about the things that played heavily on my own mind. Menzies followed me around that day hanging on my every word and by the time I'd finished winding him up he must have been seriously considering suicide as a possible option. I didn't dislike the kid at all, but he was green and kids like that would sink or swim and nothing I could say or do would make much difference, besides hopefully, I would be leaving borstal well before him and he'd be on his own, so to take him under my wing would only leave him vulnerable later on.

"What happens on association?" Menzies asked as we both emptied our mop buckets down the toilet.

"Happens?" I said rather puzzled by his question.

"You know, when is it? How often? And what do we get to do?" he said clarifying his last question.

"Wait and see, it'll be fine stop worrying, just keep that shut," I said," pointing to his mouth, and you'll be okay". Menzies didn't ask much else after that and as I watched his skinny frame wield his mop around the toilet floor, I knew that the other kids would tear him apart, but at least he was happy now and as they say, ignorance is bliss. I did keep an eye out for him for his first few days and as usual he made his friends amongst the weakest inmates in the unit, it was like they had some kind of invisible pull to each other and every dweeb, mummy's boy and weakling was welcomed into their exclusive club no questions asked.

A week later and Menzies was taken off cleaning duties and given a job somewhere else, I didn't ask where, to be truthful, I wasn't bloody interested, and he was starting to get on my nerves anyway.

I found the next inmate on the house a lot easier to get on with, he was called Tim Stabler, but his nickname was Spider. Spider was a wide boy he came from Peterborough and had spent most of his life in care. He told me his mum was a prostitute and his Dad could have been any number of

334

punters that found their way into his mother's bed. He wasn't bitter about his lot, he had no feelings one way or the other and I admired him for that. Spider didn't give a shit about authority and in order to show he would never conform he'd had a large spiders web tattooed over his left eye with a spider crawling down his cheek, it looked awesome and I laughed every time I thought of him sat in a jobcentre as they tried to find him suitable employment. Spider was a real joker and I knew I would have to watch out or he could easily get me into trouble. He wasn't a tough lad he was a vulnerable boy who hid behind tattoos and his ability to make others crease up, it was his defence and although I could see straight through it, others tended to back off when they first saw him, blonde skinhead haircut and a face that would have been at home in some kind of side show. I grew very fond of Spider and I would spend hours with him during association listening to his stories. I wasn't naïve enough to believe everything he told me, but it helped to pass the time and he had a way of telling a story that could keep you on the edge of your seat spellbound by his words. Mike and Jimmy even got a little jealous and would be constantly trying to drag me off to play snooker or table tennis. They did just about anything they could, to get me away from Spider. We became so close in the end that the screws nicknamed us the 'Marriot two' and if they saw one of us without the other, they would always ask, "Where's yer mate?"

I didn't have any guilt over Mike and Jimmy, they were both due for release before me anyway and besides I was my own man and did what I wanted to do and if others didn't like it that was tough. I knuckled down to my work scrubbing the toilets and doing general chivvying for over a month and when my next review came around, I was convinced, I would at least be given a better job and maybe even some remission back. The screws had other ideas, and not only was I left on general cleaning duties, my release date remained unchanged. I was really hacked off and

335

wondered what I would have to do in order to ever leave this place. I'd had a carrot dangled that if I kept up my behaviour, I would be given a better job the next month and they would consider the possibility of some remission, it wasn't good enough and I felt victimised and like all young kids I wanted it now not later and if they wanted to play games then I decided I'd make the rules.

My first idea was to be as insolent and awkward with the screws as I could get away with, without actually being put on report and I was going to enjoy every minute of it.

"Where you going?" asked Mr Pope as I passed him in the corridor.

"Well it ain't fucking home is it?" I laughed in his face and kept on walking.

"Come back here Marriot" he shouted after me, but I just ignored him. I knew Mr Pope would never run after me, he was weak and lazy, putting me on report would mean the filling in of forms and attending adjudications, he wouldn't want that, he didn't want anything that would give him any extra work as he was always the first to leave the unit when his shift was over.

Mr Pope was just marking time until his retirement, he knew it and so did I. The next thing I did had everybody puzzled except Spider who thought it was the best laugh he'd had in ages. I would sit in association and turn the sound on the TV off, so nobody could hear it. None of the other kids dared say anything and when I was asked why the sound was off I sniggered, "I'm trying to learn how to lip read."

"But what about the others, they might want to hear what's happening?" the screw would protest.

"Ask them?" I'd reply and of course when he did, they would all say they weren't bothered about TV anyway. After a couple of days Spider and I were the only ones to be found watching the TV in total silence whilst we giggled uncontrollably as we caught sight of the screws pointing over and shaking their heads. I relented after eight days and

336

turned the volume up, it had stopped being as amusing as it was at first so together Spider and I racked our brains to think of something else to piss the screws off. Spider had managed to wangle his way into the dorm and I'd convinced another kid to swap beds so Spider was in the bed on my left, Mike was still to the right of me but he and Jimmy didn't join in much anymore, they were both to near their release and I suppose they wanted to distance themselves from the path of self-destruction I had embarked on.

It was a Monday morning when our next wind-up took place and as everybody else got up washed and dressed and headed down to breakfast Spider, and I just continued dozing in our beds. It was only after everybody had taken their seats at their tables for breakfast that the screws realised we were missing and began scouring the unit for us.

"What the fuck are you two doing?" demanded poor Mr Pope as he kicked my bed to wake me up.

"Oh sorry Sir, what time is it?" I said yawning and stretching my arms out from under the covers.

"Yeah what time is it? I'm tired," Spider chipped in as he rubbed his eyes with his closed fists.

"You know what fucking time it is, now get yer arses down them stairs pronto," shouted Mr Pope his eyes bulging and spit foaming at the corners of his mouth.

"Sorry Sir nobody woke me up, must have overslept," I smiled cockily. It was the final straw and Mr Pope completely lost it. He grabbed my bed and turned it over and as I rolled along the floor wrapped in my blanket, he kicked me. I quickly threw off the covers and stood up as he backed off.

"Now, now, Sir, that's not nice is it? It's not my fault that you didn't wake us up is it?" I said sarcastically.

Mr Pope was flustered he'd lost control and he didn't like it, he looked from me to Spider and then back at me. "Get yourselves downstairs," he said quietly and walked out of the dorm.

"Fuck me, Jack, I thought he was going to shit his pants

337

when you jumped off the floor," giggled Spider.

"Yeah and I suppose his wife would have sent me a bill for a new pair of skiddies, with luck like mine," I smiled. "Come on, we better go," I urged as I nodded my head towards the open door. We both went without breakfast that morning it didn't seem prudent to push our luck by pointing out we hadn't had any, so by the time it was dinner we were both starving. I didn't have to worry my plate was always overflowing but as the kid on the servery finished dishing a smaller portion onto Spiders plate, I caught his eye and with a nod of my head told him to keep going, he duly obliged.

"Bloody hell Jack, I don't know whether to eat this or fucking climb it," laughed Spider as he tucked into a triple helping of lunch.

"Yeah all this hard work's giving me an appetite," I winked at him and then putting our heads down we raced each other to finish.

"Fuck me I'm stuffed," said Spider as he pushed his seat back and patted his stomach.

"Yeah, you know what I could do with now?" I replied.

"No what's that?" said Spider.

"A nice sleep," I answered a broad grin spreading from ear to ear, and as he got the joke, we both collapsed into fits of laughter.

Winding up the screws had distracted me from what was really on my mind but eventually I couldn't pretend anymore.

"What's up mate yer not too chipper today?" asked Spider as we emptied the bins in the dining room one Monday morning.

"Ah, nowt, I'm just fed up it'll pass," I said dismissively, but it didn't and by the evening the foulest mood I'd ever been in had taken a hold and there was no escaping its grasp.

"You still moping mate? Fucking hell you look ready to kill someone," observed Spider as he sat on his bed before lights out. I just pulled a face and without a word I turned over in my bed and pulling the covers up tried to block out the world. The night passed very slowly and as the other inmates snored and farted their way through to the dawn, I remained awake staring at the ceiling and wishing to be anywhere else but where I was. I got out of bed at around four in the morning and after pouring myself a drink of water from the jug on my locker, I rolled a fag and sat smoking one after another until the sun began to rise sending fingers of light into the dorm.

"You been there all night?" whispered Spider as he peered at me through the half-light now illuminating the room. He sat up and seeing I was smoking said, "Got one fer me mate?"

I threw him my tobacco tin and he wasted no time in helping himself, he lit it and as he inhaled his roll up glowed bathing his face in an orange hue.

All of a sudden his face suddenly changed, like he'd been hit by a thunderbolt. "I've got an idea" he announced waiting for me to ask what it was, but I just raised an eyebrow.

"Why don't we do a runner?" he said as he swung his feet out of his bed and sat leaning his head closer to me all excited like a dog waiting for a pat from its owner. He'd got my attention, not because I was interested but because I'd never heard such a stupid idea.

I shook my head rolled my eyes and said "Spider I always knew you were nuts but now I know for sure your fucking mad, how do you expect us to do a runner we are never out of the unit these days or were you just planning on asking nicely if a screw wouldn't mind opening a gate and looking the other way, you fucking dick?" I cursed at him.

Spider was hurt and went on the defensive "Okay so I haven't got a plan yet, but I'll think of somert, we can do it if we want, what do yer say?" he said shaking my arm excitedly.

"And if we do get out where are we going to go, cos I

339

don't know about you, but I 'ain't no Ronnie Biggs with a stash of money on the outside," I reasoned.

"Argh, leave that to me. I got mates and I know how to survive on the streets, it'll be a laugh, I know we'll get caught in the end but at least we'll have had a giggle, go on say you'll think about it?" he pleaded.

I looked into his face and then around the dorm where the other inmates were starting to wake. "I know I'm going to regret this," I said, "but if you come up with a decent plan, I'll consider it okay. Now get back in your bed before the screw comes in to wake us up."

The dorm lights flickered as the fluorescent tubes warmed up and in an instant, sprang into life. "Let's have you lot out of them beds, come on move yer lazy arses," shouted the night screw. As he paced from one end of the dorm and back again, he would pause now and again to kick the bed of anyone who was not showing signs of life.

"Come on shake a leg, boy," he'd shout cheerfully, too fucking cheerfully for six in the morning. Some inmates began to gather their wash kits and towels and stumble down the stairs to the wash rooms still half-asleep. Others stood up, scratched their knackers or picked their hairy arses like they had all the time in the world. "Come on get a move on boys, down for yer wash," said the screw hurrying us up.

I was in no rush, it was just another day like all the rest so as the dorm slowly emptied, I rolled a fag pulled on my trousers and rummaged through my locker for my wash kit. By the time I'd sorted myself out I was alone in the dorm and as I made my way to the door something caught my eye. It was a central heating pipe that ran up the corner of the wall and into the ceiling. I poked my head out of the door and made sure nobody was coming up the stairs and ducked quickly back into the dorm. I ran over to the pipe and took hold of it with both hands. It was about three inches in diameter and as luck would have it cold to the touch. I pulled on it to test its strength and once satisfied it would bear my weight, I shinned up it until my hands could touch

340

the ceiling. I probed around where the pipe disappeared from view with my finger and after a few tries I managed to insert my finger behind the plasterboard, I pulled and to my amazement a piece of ceiling a foot square just came away in my hand falling downwards and hitting the bed below before bouncing onto the floor. It made a hell of a noise as it hit the linoleum and worried that somebody might come. I slid down the pipe jumped off the bed and ran to the doorway. It was quiet, no footsteps, no voices, now satisfied I was safe, I returned to the pipe and looking up, I studied the hole. I could see into the loft space there was a mesh with four-inch squares and bars of around five millimetres thick screwed to the joists to prevent anyone gaining access. I cursed under my breath, took hold of the pipe and after straining my ears to listen for anyone coming, I shinned back up. Once at ceiling height I hung on with my knees and pushed on the mesh with both hands as hard as I could. I needn't have bothered pushing quite as hard the mesh was solid but the screws holding it to the roof joists had rusted away so as I pushed, I suddenly found myself with the top half of my body in the loft. I screwed my eyes up. It was pitch black but as my eyes adjusted, I could see faint chinks of light coming in where the roof tiles were badly fitted. I knew then that this was to be our way out. I had to find Spider and as I hurried down the stairs towards the bath-house I met him with Mike and Jimmy, walking back towards the dorm. There were a few of the other lads making their way back to the dorm as well, but I wasn't worried they would all act like the three wise monkeys, see no evil, hear no evil and speak no evil.

"Spider quick here," I called from several yards away. He was chatting to Mike and as he heard my voice he looked up and seeing me waving frantically, he set off at a sprint. I grabbed him without saying a word and manhandled him up the stairs and back into the dorm.

"What, where's the fire?" he asked as I released my grip on his shirt pushing him backwards into the dorm.

"Look dickhead," I said pointing at the hole I'd made in the ceiling. "Well you still wanna go?" I shrieked excitedly but before he could answer Mike Jimmy and three of the other lads appeared behind me. I looked at Spider and he just smiled ran over to the pipe and began clambering up his feet disappearing into the loft before I'd even put my shirt and jumper on. I dived into my jumper and as my head popped out of the neck, I felt a hand on my shoulder, it was Mike.

"No man don't be daft, yous only got four months left, man," he said trying to make me see sense. I shrugged him off and ran for the pipe I was up it in seconds and as I reached the top Spider grabbed my hands and helped me into the roof space. Spider was eager to get on with it and began pulling at me to move.

"Wait," I said angrily pulling away and I bent down and stuck my head back through the hole and looking at Mike Jimmy and the other kids I said firmly, "You ain't seen nuffin right?" Mike just smacked his lips and shook his head the others nodded, and I was gone. To say we had any kind of plan would be a massive understatement but determination we had bags of. I punched a hole through the roofing tiles and as soon as it was large enough, I heaved myself out helping Spider to follow suit until we were both breathing the fresh morning air and looking down into the borstal grounds from the rooftop. "What now?" Spider said between gulping mouthfuls of air. I hadn't realised how unfit he was and couldn't help wondering if this was not such a good idea after all. I ran along the parapet that surrounded the roof and finding a cast-iron drainpipe, I called to Spider.

"Here down here," I didn't wait, I was halfway down before Spiders feet came into view as he swung them over the ledge above me. "Come on," I shouted up.

"I'm coming, keep yer hair on," giggled Spider. He could always find something to laugh about in any given situation but at that moment, I couldn't, for the life of me, find anything remotely amusing. The last ten feet of drainpipe before the ground had cement pushed into the gap between itself and the wall, this was to prevent prisoners climbing on the roof from outside and staging a protest.

"Fuck it, we'll have to jump the last few feet," I called up to Spider who was by now nearly standing on my head.

"Go on then I'm slipping," urged Spider, his left foot now level with my ear. I pushed away from the wall with my feet and released my grip on the pipe and as I fell towards the concrete below, I prayed I didn't break an ankle.

"You awright?" called Spider as I rolled over and dusted myself down.

I looked up at the soles of his shoes. "Come on its easy, jump," I whispered with an unmistakable urgency in my voice. Spider always had to do what I asked him, and this was no different, the dumb bastard didn't even give me time to get out of the way and threw himself to the ground cushioning his fall with my body.

"Get off, you fucking wally," I barked at him as I pushed his hand off my face.

"Oh sorry mate," giggled Spider and I must admit at that point, I thought if he giggles once more, I'm going to bloody well hit him. Once we were both on our feet we headed as far away from the main building as we could get.

"This way," I shouted behind me as I sprinted towards the playing fields. I knew once we were on that side of the borstal, we couldn't be seen by anyone. I didn't know how we were going to get over the thirty-foot fence but at that moment I hadn't really thought that far ahead. We didn't stop running until we were both outside the shed that housed the lawnmower for the sports field.

"Here sit down, let's catch our breath," I ordered, and we slumped against the wooden door our heads hanging as we drew in big gasps of air. My heart was racing wildly, and I thought at any time it might explode out of my chest. Spider said nothing he was in worse shape than me, and as I looked at him, by now on all fours gasping like an asthmatic, I knew

343

we had to make a move.

"You alright, can you run?" I said between breaths.

"Run fucking where?" Spider gasped. He had a point and I desperately looked around for an answer, I hadn't escaped just to spend a day running laps of the borstal grounds. It was definitely my lucky day and as I was almost about to say it was hopeless. I spotted a new building going up at the far side of the football pitch, it was just four walls at the moment, but it had scaffolding around it.

"Quick this way," I called without looking back my eyes fixed firmly on the building in the distance. I covered the open ground in less than twenty seconds and ducked inside hiding behind the wall as I waited for Spider.

"Fucking hell, I'm gonna stop smoking, I'm fucked," declared Spider as he collapsed at my side, his face covered in sweat and a pale white colour.

"It's not over yet mate, come on," I said pulling him up. "We've got to find something to get over the fence with, then we're out of here," I continued as I scoured the site for something, anything we could use.

"Do you think we might be able to use that?" said Spider letting out another girlie giggle. "What?" I shouted my temper rising.

"That," repeated Spider pointing at a wooden ladder he'd found under a tarpaulin. I couldn't believe it. I grabbed Spider and planted a big wet kiss on his forehead. "You fucking beauty," I laughed hugging him to me.

"Yeah, yeah, that's enough of that. I'd have stayed behind if I'd known you were a fudge nudger," grinned Spider as he pushed me away.

"I'll give you fudge nudger, get the other end," I said, pointing to the ladder and together we carried it over to the fence. We were over in seconds and as our feet hit the ground on the other side we just ran and ran across open fields and woodland until exhausted we had to stop. We were free!

344

Chapter 25

On the Run!

If only we'd had more time, I thought to myself as Spider and I sat in the bus station in the town centre. We had only been on the run for five hours and already, I was realising that the realty was not as good as the dream.

"What now?" I asked Spider who was busy picking up cig butts from the floor.

"Fucking hell, look at this one, some people are so wasteful," he said holding up a fag that had been died out after a couple of drags.

"Spider," I said in exasperation.

"Oh yeah, sorry mate, let's get out of here, come on," he beckoned as he made his way to the exit.

I caught up with him. "Where we going?" I asked hoping he had been filled with inspiration and may feel the need to share it with me.

"I don't know, but we should get out of here before we're seen," he said, not really concerned about our future prospects.

I took a grip of his arm. "Wait a fucking minute, you said you had friends on the outside, that we'd be alright, please tell me you weren't fucking lying!" I demanded, my hold on his arm tightening.

"Er, well, I didn't really think we'd actually do it, it was just talk yer know?" he said his face draining of its colour.

I released him and pushed him in the chest with the other hand. "You wanker, I don't fucking believe this, now what we gonna do?" I shouted from a few feet away.

Spider quickly moved towards me, "Shh people are looking," he pleaded.

"Let them fucking look, I don't care, you fucking knob," I shouted even louder.

"I know we'll nick a motor and drive to Peterborough, me

345

mam will see us right" said Spider trying to calm me.

I shook my head and as I looked into his eyes I said, "She fucking better, she fucking better."

Stealing a car was a new experience for me and as we tried one car door handle after another, I realised it was also new to Spider.

"Have you ever nicked a car before?" I asked as we continued walking around the shopping centre car park.

"Oh yeah hundreds, we just need the right one that's all," he lied, looking away to hide his face. It was obvious he was lying but I didn't see the point of letting him know I was on to him besides the pressure was on him to come up with the goods not me.

"I know, you wait here," Spider grinned as though he'd just been hit by an idea he was keeping to himself.

"Wait where? What for?" I asked but it was too late, Spider was already running out of the car park and heading down the main street. I had a horrible feeling that that would be the last I'd see of him and he just wanted a reason to get away from me before I gave him a good hiding. I sat myself on the low wall that surrounded the car park took out my tobacco and rolled a cig. The shopping centre was quite busy, and I passed the next twenty minutes watching shoppers load their cars with groceries and soft furnishings they'd purchased for their homes. I wondered where and how these people lived, what their lives were like and if they knew how lucky they really were. I gave up on Spider when he still had not returned an hour later. I cursed him under my breath and made a promise that when we next met, he'd wish we hadn't. I didn't know what I was going to do then and as I climbed off the wall and walked aimlessly through the car park towards the road my thoughts were of the borstal, what people were doing, my warm bed and more to the point lunch. I was starving I hadn't really given it much thought until now, the adrenalin had kept my hunger pangs at bay but now it was all over, my stomach was growling like a tiger. "Oh shit to this," I said out loud as I walked through the town and at that moment, I made the decision that if I saw a copper, I was going to give myself up, so I'd lose some remission end up down the block but at least I'd be fed and watered. It was strange I thought how nobody seemed to notice me. I was wearing prison uniform after all and assumed everybody would know that, but they didn't and as they went about their day, to them I was just some sixteen-year-old kid on the dole with time on his hands. Fifteen minutes later I was on the outskirts of the town hands in pockets head down and cursing the world and everyone in it. The roads were fairly quiet. I suppose everybody was by now at their places of work or wherever they headed to earlier that morning.

I must have walked two or three miles before the car screeched up behind me. I didn't even look round, I knew it would be the coppers and to be honest I was glad. I walked on for a few feet when I heard a familiar voice.

"Eh, yer want to walk or you getting in?" I spun round and broke into a large grin.

"Spider! but I thought, oh forget that," I smiled as I ran over and jumped into the passenger seat. Moments later we were heading down a motorway, don't ask me which one I didn't know and didn't care my spirits had been lifted and with the car stereo pumping out the latest hits and the windows down life was definitely looking up.

"So where we heading?" I asked as I rummaged through the glove box. "Eh, look at this," I giggled as I found a packet of mints, "Want one?"

"Yeah, not many," replied Spider holding out his hand. "We'll head into London and jump a train from there to Peterborough, what do ya reckon?" asked Spider as he rolled a mint around his mouth sucking noisily.

"But why don't we just drive all the way there? We've got a car and it seems daft not to use it," I offered whilst unwrapping another mint and stuffing it into my mouth.

"Good idea mate but fer two things," smiled Spider. "One, we 'ain't got enough juice." He pointed at the fuel gauge, "And second, I don't know the fucking way."

"You don't know the way?" I asked a little confused.

"Naw, they brought me here in a prison van and before you ask they didn't let me drive," he giggled punching me in the thigh.

I looked across at him and elbowing him in the ribs I laughed, "London it is then." Finding our way into London wasn't difficult it was as though every sign we passed had twenty different ways into the city, so after about an hour's drive, we pulled up in a side street and turning the engine off, Spider looked at me and said, "Everybody out".

We locked the doors like any other careful car owner and began to walk away when I suddenly grabbed Spiders shoulder.

"Wait a minute, give me the keys," I demanded. Spider didn't ask why but did as I asked and handed them over. I walked back to the car and putting the key in the lock opened the boot. "Bingo" I giggled as I gazed upon a row of plastic carrier bags bursting with shopping.

"Fuck me, how did ya know they were there?" said Spider as he dived into the boot and began tipping the bags out.

"Easy you told me you nicked it from the petrol station outside the supermarket. I just took a guess that they may have been shopping, now let's have a gander." I finished pushing him out of the way.

London was amazing, it just went on and on and as we meandered through the streets, we were both in total awe.

"Where are we?" Spider asked as we trundled down yet another street that seemed endless. I had no idea I had never been to London and could not have been more lost if I'd been parachuted into the Malaysian jungle.

"Give us a bit of that," I said snatching a meat pie out of Spider's grubby mits.

"Oh, you had the Jaffa cakes and the cheese biscuits, gim me some," he pleaded like a small child. I broke the pie in half and held it out for him, but Spider was already rifling

348

the remains of the rest of the shopping we'd put into one carrier bag. We'd discarded the household products and items that required cooking.

"Naw, keep it mate, I've got somert better," he said as he turned his back and started fiddling with a wrapper.

"Ere let me see," I said excitedly but he began running off down the street and I had to give chase. "Okay what you got?" I asked breathing heavily as I caught him up and got hold of his jumper, he tried to pull away and as he did so a family size trifle fell from his grasp splattering all over the pavement. The look on Spiders face was a picture, he could not have been more upset if I'd told him his mum had died.

"I was enjoying that," he whimpered, fresh cream all around his mouth and jelly running down his chin.

"Sorry mate," I said trying not to laugh.

Spider looked at me all wide eyed and seeing the humour of the situation he replied, "What did you say? You'll have to speak up I'm a trifle deaf." We soon devoured all of our ill-gotten gains and as we shared a pint of milk straight from the carton, we were both fit to burst.

"Want anymore?" I said holding the milk out. Spider shook his head and I cast it aside into the gutter a stream of milk running along the road.

"Eh, you'll get us dun fer littering," teased Spider and arms around each other's shoulders we quickened our step and headed further into the city.

"I don't like this place much," said Spider as we walked along a dirty back street. It was in a run-down area and during the half an hour we'd been in the neighbourhood we hadn't seen a white face.

"No I feel a bit uneasy and have you noticed how everyone we pass is looking at us?" I replied.

We continued on and winding our way past terraced houses and barking dogs chained up in filthy backyards we kept our heads down. It wasn't long until we turned a corner and met a group of Asians sitting on a garden wall. They were about eighteen years of age and there was a good twelve of them.

"Just keep walking and say nothing," I said under my breath to Spider who was counting cracks in the pavement, his head bowed and oblivious to the potential danger of the situation.

Just then one of the Asians shouted "Eh yus got no business round here, yous best git the fuck out."

"Ignore him," I urged Spider from between my teeth. Again the voice called out "Hey I'm talking to you two, you best git moving you 'ain't got no business here, this is our manor you hear?"

I looked up at the group of youths we were now only five yards away and I was trying to work out if we stood half a chance if they started on us, it only took a milli-second for me to establish we wouldn't have a hope in hell.

Just when I thought things could not get any worse one of the Asians caught sight of Spiders face, his tattoo and his skinhead haircut. "Get them they's skins," shouted an excited voice and all at once the whole group ran towards us there faces contorted with hatred.

"Run fucking run," I shouted pushing Spider so hard he nearly fell over, he soon woke up to the situation and considering how he'd performed earlier in the day, he left me for dead in the dust he shook from his sprinting feet. If it hadn't been so scary it would have been funny, it was like a scene from Benny Hill as more and more Asians joined in the chase and I swear by the end the pursuing hoard was that great in number you couldn't count them. We jumped over fences gates and ran through gardens followed by a sea of hatred fuelled brown faces. Spider began to slow up he was out of breath and I couldn't believe it when he stopped a few yards in front of me and threw his hands up in surrender. Where did he think he was? It wasn't Queensbury rules and if he'd been waving a white flag, they would have only used it to wrap his lifeless body in when they'd finished with him.

"Get going you twat," I screamed at him as I got closer. He didn't move, he just bent over double and tried to inflate

350

his gasping lungs. "Run, run," I screamed louder but he just shook his head in defeat. I glanced over my shoulder just in time to see a pair of hands and a leg appear as one of our assailants scaled the fence behind us in hot pursuit. "Run, fucking run," I screamed in desperation, "They're nearly on us." I grabbed Spider by the jumper and with all my strength I pulled him behind me, but he stumbled and lost his footing. I hauled him back up and threw him over a fence at the side of us, "Hide just fucking hide, I'll meet you at Euston train station tonight," I shouted as I let him go and he fell out of sight on the other side of the fence. The lead I'd had was now lost and as I turned to look behind me an Asian kid was about to hit me with a lump of wood. I raised my arm and took its full force on my elbow, it hurt like hell, but I ignored it and hit him with a right uppercut on the chin and without waiting to see the result, I vaulted a different fence leading the gang away from Spider. Once I was safely back on the street, I had no trouble getting away. I was still very fit and although they chased me relentlessly, I would occasionally have to stop and wait for them to catch up before setting off again. I wasn't being cocky I wanted them away from where I'd left Spider as I knew if they saw him, he wouldn't be lucky enough to escape a second time.

When the gang had finally given up, I was completely lost. I'd run in so many different directions that I had absolutely no idea where I was. I didn't want to try to retrace my steps as I would only increase my chances of running back into trouble, and I was in enough already. The streets of London are an unforgiving and unfriendly place, and if I stopped anyone to ask directions they would size me up as though I was going to do them harm or had some ulterior motive for my seemingly innocent question. The odd few who did offer assistance were mostly bastards and would intentionally send me in the wrong direction, so you got to a stage where you didn't know whether to believe anyone or not. I completely gave up by around nine o clock that night and as I sat on a grass verge at the side of a main road, I wished I was anywhere but where I was. I wondered about Spider and if he was okay and more than anything I wondered where Euston station was. I didn't even know London, how the hell was I to get to Euston station? I'd only said it because it was the first station that came to mind and that was only because I'd played Monopoly with our Steve when I was younger.

I decided that sitting and feeling sorry for myself was not going to do me any good and besides, at least if I set off walking I might find a road sign or something that would help me work out where I was. I took the first main road I came across and walked what must have been six miles before I came into another built up area. It was a small hamlet with a high street and rows of expensive shops that seemed to sell anything that the average man in the street could not afford. I didn't like this place at all as I got more attention than I had anywhere I'd been previously. It was dark by now and as people got out of their expensive cars all dolled up to the nines they would look at me all strangely with questioning eyes. I quickened my step and was glad when I emerged at the end of the high street. I was feeling the cold by now and I pulled my hands inside the sleeves of my jumper and hunched my neck further into the collar in an effort to stay warm. I had given up on ever meeting Spider at Euston it was close to midnight by now and I thought that even if he had made it, he would probably have assumed I wasn't coming and moved on. Just as I thought that at least things couldn't get any worse, they did. The rain came down without warning and in a matter of seconds, I looked like a drowned rat. I ducked into a doorway and racked my brain for an answer to my predicament. It was hopeless and as I huddled in a corner watching the cars drive by, throwing waves of water on to the pavement, I kept them in sight until the rear lights disappeared in the spray they'd created, as they sped away.

My attention was drawn to a white building about a hundred yards down the street. It was lit up and every ten minutes large groups of people would scurry out holding bags, umbrellas or newspapers above their heads, as they ran for cover from the torrential rain. "You stupid, stupid, bastard," I said out loud realising what I was watching, it was the underground!

It wasn't difficult to get to the platform of the tube there wasn't anyone about and as I made my way down the four flights of stairs the place was silent apart from the distant rumbling of a passing tube train as it hurtled along the track towards the next station. The hardest thing now would be finding which tube to get on and as I walked from platform to platform through the many arches, I was more than a little confused. The maps on the walls had different coloured lines on them, blue, yellow, brown, green and red. I wondered what these meant and the longer I looked at them the more perplexed I became.

"You look lost," said a voice from behind me. It made me jump. I'd been that engrossed in trying to work out the map. I hadn't heard anyone approaching. I turned to see a middle-aged man wearing a large overcoat and a big smile. "Em, yes, you can't tell me which tube goes to Euston can you?" I asked in the most cheerful manner I could muster.

The man smiled and said, "I can do better than that young man, that's where I'm going, I'll show you," and with that he led the way and I followed on behind him. There wasn't much in the way of conversation between us both as we stood on the platform. The middle-aged guy tried his hand at small talk on a couple of occasions and I just gave one word replies that made it clear I wasn't the talkative kind. I wasn't being rude or disrespectful, but I couldn't get the thought out of my head that he might have been some kind of weirdo, so I didn't see any need to encourage him. It was at that point that I realised why everyone in London seemed to be on a heightened state of alert? They were frightened, of what I don't think they knew, but it was the way they were raised, to take no chances and watch your back. I vowed at that moment that I would never live in London. I could

353

never live in a place where people viewed everyone with suspicion and would see a kindly act as some kind of trick or way of wrong footing them.

The tube arrived and as the old gent said, "This is ours," I smiled at him and moved nearer to the platform in order to be first on. The train was just about empty and as I took a seat I felt excited. I was going to Euston and just maybe I'd meet up with Spider again. The journey was over in the blink of an eye or maybe it just seemed that way. I thought how amazing it was speeding along under the city of London with all that life going on, the bright lights and the noise that was far above us.

"Next stop Euston station, all change for Kings Cross and Piccadilly," the internal speaker crackled as the train began to slow. Once we'd ground to a halt, I wasted no time and ran out of the tube station as fast as my legs could carry me. I wasn't afraid of being stopped and asked for a tube ticket I just wanted to get away from the old gent who'd given me directions. I'd already convinced myself he was a potential mad axe man or something similar. When I was sure I'd lost him, I stopped at the station exit and caught my breath before moving out into the night air. The rain had subsided, and the roads were shining like a new penny as the street lights reflected off them. Considering the lateness of the hour, the place was alive with buses and taxis sounding their horns at each other as they hustled their way through standing traffic and pedestrians who ran out in front of them. It didn't take me long to find the main rail station and after following the signposted directions, I found myself standing outside the front door. I prayed silently before going inside, "Please God, let Spider be there." My prayers were answered and as I walked across the main hall, I spotted him. He was seated on a wooden bench smoking a fag and drinking a cup of coffee like he hadn't a care in the world. He looked up as I walked towards him. The expression of relief on his face told me he was as glad to see me as I was to see him and casting the coffee cup aside, he ran over, and we hugged each other like two star crossed lovers. A little embarrassed by our declaration of affection we both pushed each other away and as I punched him warmly in the chest I said, "And where the fuck, have you been?"

"Me, you want to know where I've been? I've been here over four hours. I thought you weren't coming," he laughed punching me back. When the initial jubilation of our meeting had subsided, we sat at a far end of the station and decided what we were going to do next. Spider said we had to get to Kings Cross station if wanted to jump a train that went to Peterborough and then we were home free. I was happy to go along with any plan he had, after all, I didn't have one of my own, so after Spider had bought me a cup of coffee from the money he'd begged whilst waiting for me, we set off back towards the tube.

Kings Cross was a scary place in the early hours of the morning. It was rife with prostitutes and muggers that vied for position in the darkened doorways of shops that had long since closed for business. We watched as over made-up tarts in short skirts ducked their heads to look in car windows as the drivers crawled by. Every now and then the driver must have liked what he saw and as the car stopped suddenly the prostitute would jump in shut the door and seconds later it headed into the night.

"Cor, look at the state of her, she'd have to fucking pay me," sniggered Spider as he elbowed me in the ribs.

"Yeah, they aren't exactly cat walk material around here are they?" I replied whilst looking at the woman he'd pointed out. She was around twenty-years old and her weight in stone was pretty close to her age, she had on a mini skirt with black stockings and suspenders and as she stooped to look in the cars you could see the cheeks of her spotty arse, she was a real minger. We soon got fed up with people watching and made our way into the train station. It was now around two in the morning and the only people around were tramps, hookers, druggies and pimps it was a pitiful sight. So many people selling themselves or somebody else, no conscience, no guilt and no hope.

Spider and I stuck to each other like shit to a blanket. I don't know if he was as scared as I was but like me, he didn't show it. We found an empty bench at the far end of the entrance hall just before the unmanned ticket barrier and sat down. "I'll go look and see when the first train leaves for Peterborough, wait here I won't be long," said Spider as he stood up and made his way to the large information board across the hall. I watched as he studied the timetable, his hands in his pockets and a fag in his mouth, he had a confident, carefree manner that was born of ignorance and because of this he drew little attention. I smiled to myself, I was glad we'd met up again I hadn't liked being on my own.

"Here, there's a train at seven in the morning from platform five, piece of piss," said Spider as he walked up to me. "We've just gotta get on the platform before the guard comes on duty and hide on the train," he finished, as he plonked himself down at the side of me. I turned to look at him his face was full of expectation like a child on Christmas eve. I just hoped that the journey didn't turn out to be better than the actual arrival.

"Good work mate, we've done it," I smiled trying to hide my concern.

"Hey want a drink? I've got a quid left, it might buy us a couple of coffees," announced Spider and without waiting for my reply he set off towards a coffee shop at the other side of the station. I'd only been on my own for a couple of minutes when I was approached. I had my eye on him as he surveyed the seating areas and when he didn't see what he wanted he quickly moved on his coat collar pulled up around his neck and his rat like features hidden under a flat cap.

"You alone kid?" he asked softly as he sat next to me, his leg was pressed up against mine and I pulled it away in disgust. He wasn't put off and put his hand on my knee as he lent closer. "You need somewhere to sleep? I know a good place clean and free and no questions asked."

I could smell his foul breath and subconsciously pulled a face as I moved my head away. He was a persistent bastard, either that or just plain fucking dense, he reached out and grabbed my face with his filthy hand holding me by the jaw.

"I just want to help; don't you want old Peter to help?" he continued his tone more than a little sinister. I pushed his arm away from my face and moved further along the bench.

"I'm fine, me mate will be back in a minute, no thanks," I stuttered.

"Oh no problem lad, yer mate will be welcome too, there's room fer everyone at old Pete's," he said shuffling his bum on the seat to close the distance between us. I remained rigid my legs refused to work, I wanted to get up, to run away but I didn't want to cause a scene, I didn't want to draw attention and I certainly didn't want someone to call the police.

"What do yer say lad? Come back with Pete, I'll give yer a meal and after you've had a sleep you can set off in the morning no harm done, what do yer say?" the vile man pleaded.

I don't really know where it came from, but I was as surprised as him. I leant close to him, almost nose to nose and gave him some advice he didn't see coming. "Listen you piece of shit. Leave me alone or I promise I'll tear your fucking ugly face off. Now move it!" I snarled as I pushed him backwards the palm of my right hand in his face. He stumbled backwards tumbling off the bench and fell onto the floor his hands trying to find a hold. I could see the shock in his slitty eyes and as he scrambled to his feet he didn't even look back he just scuttled away to wherever he'd come from.

"Alright mate, two sugars?" said Spider as he returned and handed me a cup of coffee with one of those plastic lids. I removed the lid and threw it on the floor and as I blew on the steaming contents, I fixed my stare on old Pete who had by now moved on to a young girl sitting in the station doorway.

357

"What yer thinking?" asked Spider.

"Oh nothing mate, just dreaming, like you do," I replied and taking a slurp of coffee I said, "Give us a fag then."

We had to beat a hasty retreat later on as two coppers entered the station doing their nightly patrol, they were prodding at people sleeping on benches and moving them on. "This way," I said as I nudged Spider and ran to take cover in the toilets.

"Cor, it fucking stinks in here," said Spider pinching his nose with his fingers. He had a point it smelt like people had ignored the toilet and just pissed directly onto the floor.

"Yeah let's get out of here and onto the platform, at least the coppers won't go that far into the station," I suggested.

"Well lets go, I can't stay in here any longer. I'm gonna puke," giggled Spider, his hand still over his nose and mouth.

Getting onto the platform was a breeze, we just walked through the unmanned gate and meandered along like we were going for an evening stroll. If we heard voices or footsteps we just ducked out of the way until they'd passed. The train was already on the platform when we got there, it was in darkness except for two end carriages where the mail was being loaded on by two men with a small electric cart. We hid behind a steel column and watched as they went about their business.

"Wait til they've finished, and we'll make a run for it and once on the train we're safe, okay?" I whispered to Spider.

Spider gave me the thumbs up and we fell silent both of us watching and willing the two workers to leave. At one stage when the cart was empty one of the workers left with the cart but the other stayed behind sitting on the edge of the carriage and puffing away on a pipe.

"Go on fuck off, you old twat," said Spider trying to will him to leave, but he didn't. A moment later the cart returned fully laden and we watched in despair as they leisurely lifted one sack at a time between them. "Fucking hell they'll be here all night at that rate, I've a good mind to give 'um a hand," said Spider who was knelt at my feet looking round the steel column.

"Shhhh," I whispered narrowing my eyes to show I was serious as Spider looked up at me.

The two workers eventually finished loading the mail and as I helped Spider to his feet he groaned, "Me fucking legs have gone to sleep, give us a minute." My gaze followed the two workers as they strode away chatting to each other until they disappeared from view.

"You ready?" I asked Spider as he was rubbing his knees trying to get the blood flowing back into them.

"Yeah let's go," he replied and without waiting for me he ran the short distance to the first carriage pulled open the door and disappeared out of sight.

"Wait for me," I half shouted, half whispered and as I did so Spider poked his head out of the window and waved me over frantically with his arm. I took a last look around to make sure it was still clear, once satisfied I sprinted towards the carriage and as I ran across the platform Spider opened the door wide allowing me to jump straight in without stopping. My feet landed on the soft carpet as Spider pulled the door shut behind me. "We're in, we're on our way."

Spider hugged me excitedly.

"We're not home free yet mate, we better find somewhere to hide, come on," I whispered as I opened the internal door into the next carriage. It was a large carriage about thirty feet in length with the seats back to back and a table in between each.

"This don't look promising. I said it's like trying to play hide and seek in a cardboard box."

"Why don't we hide in the crapper? They won't find us in there," suggested Spider. He was only trying to help, bless him, but he was such a dim bastard at times.

"Don't be a wally, they'll check the bogs first when the guard gets on with the driver. I know we can hide in there," I said pointing to a gap between the seat backs where the luggage for each passenger could be stored. The space was not exactly what you could describe as roomy, but it would serve our purpose. Spider got under the opposite chair across the aisle from me and our heads were facing each other only the width of the aisle separating us. It was a good spot, if any guard walked through the carriage, he wouldn't see us unless he bent down and looked into each luggage space. The only problem I could see was that once passengers started to board and took their seats, we'd be visible to anyone who sat on a seat close to us as their view was lower down.

"Ere Spider," I whispered. He turned his head to look at me through the darkness, when the passengers start getting on we will have to get out and sit in a seat, we can then move along the train if we see the guard coming, okay?"

Spider nodded that he understood and with that I said, "Get some sleep, we'll hear when the engine starts up." I don't remember falling asleep but when the lights in the carriages suddenly lit up and I heard the diesel engine shudder as it turned over, I awoke with a start. My eyes were like lead and struggling to open them I reached my hand out and tapped the top of Spiders head, he looked as knackered as me and forcing a smile he nodded that he was awake. We remained under the seats for what seemed an age, my legs had gone numb and screamed at me to be straightened out.

When I thought it was safe, I carefully crawled out on my knees and bobbed my head up to look out of the window on Spider's side. It was quiet. No signs of movement. All of a sudden, I heard voices and startled I turned my head a hundred and eighty degrees to look behind me and to my horror there were three guards standing outside, one leaning against the window, his back to the glass. I dropped to the floor my heart pounding and my mouth dry, I was awake now.

"What's it?" asked Spider as I hit the floor. I didn't answer. I put my fingers to my lips to indicate silence would be a good idea and pointed up towards the window

360

mimicking a talking action with my other hand.

"How many?" Spider hissed poking me with his outstretched hand to get my attention.

"What the fuck does that matter? You gonna take them on?" I said shaking my head in disbelief at his pointless question, "Be fucking quiet shhhhh," I finished and tucked my head back under the seat hoping, if Spider couldn't see my face, he might keep his gob shut. It wasn't long until we heard the carriage doors all the way along the train being flung open. At first, I thought they were on to us, but I quickly realised they were getting ready for the passengers to board.

"Out, get out, but stay low," I barked at Spider and simultaneously we crawled out into the carpeted aisle on our hands and knees. The guards had moved off and I gingerly rose to my knees and once sure it was definitely safe, I stood up. It felt good to extend my legs, but I didn't have time to enjoy it.

"This way. Get as far down as we can so any guards on the platform don't see us," I beckoned to Spider as I made my way through the connecting door and into the next carriage. I chose the seat at the other end of the carriage and as we sat side by side in it, we slouched low so anyone walking by would not see us. "When the passengers start getting on, just sit up and make like we've just got on before them, and we'll be okay," I instructed Spider.

"No probs mate," he replied, giving me one of his cheeky grins. The first passengers in our carriage paid no attention to us at all, they were too busy pushing their bags under the seats and getting out their newspapers or drinking lukewarm coffee they'd bought in the station café. The platform became a sea of bodies running, speed walking, pushing and shoving as they all tried to climb on board at once. I looked at Spider he was staring out of his window

"You alright mate?" I asked.

"Yeah just thinking about me mam. Its ages since I've seen her," he replied as he turned to face me.

361

"It'll be alright mate, don't worry," I said softly and patted his arm. He forced a smile and pushed his thoughts to the back of his mind.

"Yeah man, why won't it? Yer right," he replied and then went back to staring out of the window. The moment the train began to pull away from the station was the best feeling I'd had in a long time and both Spider and I glowed with excitement, we were on our way and there was no stopping us now. The heater in each carriage spread its warmth through the whole train and as we rumbled along to the rhythmic chugger, chugger, chugger, of the wheels on the track it became hypnotic and both Spider and I fell silent retreating into our own little worlds.

I don't know exactly how long we'd been asleep, but it was too bloody long. We'd been well and truly caught with our pants down. I felt a hand shaking my shoulder and as I opened my eyes, blinking to adjust them to the glare of the carriage lights, I made out the distinct uniform of Her Majesty's Constabulary.

Chapter 26

Who's sorry now?

Our return to Feltham was that speedy, I sat in the block and began to wonder if it had actually happened or had I just dreamt the whole thing. I wasn't unhappy about being re-captured it was inevitable at some point anyway. I was more pissed off at the way we'd been caught, we should not have both fallen asleep and what added insult to injury was that we'd even missed our stop and slept on all the way to Newark.

The governor did his usual, "I'm disappointed," speech and I did my, "I'm very sorry, won't happen again," speech and the board of governors gave their "Six weeks loss of remission," speech and everyone was happy. Just for good measure I was also put on the block for a further twenty-one days and lost a month's wages.

The loss of wages was a none starter anyway. I couldn't earn any wages whilst on the block so by the time they sent me back to the unit, I'd only be able to lose one week's wages. I kept this to myself. I didn't see any point in giving the board of visitors another stick to beat me with. My time in solitary wasn't a problem. I didn't mind my own company and used each day as part of a keep fit regime. I was filling out becoming a man, my shoulders and arms had begun to develop and as I pumped out press up after press up after two weeks, I was cut like a body builder. I didn't have the size, but my muscular definition was something most lads my age would have killed for.

"Your gonna do yourself an injury," laughed the screw who opened the hatch in the door with my breakfast one morning. I was standing on my hands, feet up on the wall, doing sets of inverted press-ups. I needed to use more of my body weight by now as I could do normal press ups for hours without breaking sweat. "Come on then your breakfast is going cold," said the screw, getting impatient.

"Just six more Sir, hang on," I said between gritted teeth, as I heaved my full body weight up straightening my arms and then quickening my rhythm. I knocked out the other five and stood up.

"I don't know where you kids get yer energy," the screw smiled as he handed me the tray and shaking his head he shut the hatch and was gone. My exercise regime became so intense that by the time my three weeks in solitary was up I was exercising for nearly eight hours a day. I had no time to get bored and as the lights went off at night, I would be asleep in seconds, my weary body submitting to rest. I was a little disappointed when the screw opened the cell door and announced that I was going back to the unit after breakfast one morning. All I could think about was that I hadn't done my squats or leg raises yet, and when would I find the time to do them. I was hooked I think, it must have been all that testosterone coursing through my adolescent veins. I'd found a way to harness it and I didn't want to let it go.

I hadn't seen Spider since we were brought back to the borstal in a police car over three weeks before, so it was a nice surprise to see his smiling tattooed face as I stepped out of my cell on the punishment block. "You alright mate?" I asked as we walked down the corridor towards South House escorted by a screw from the block.

Spider gave me his famous grin. "Alright mate he said, I'm fucking champion, champion," he repeated as if to drive the point home. Entering the steel gate into South House was like going home. I know that might sound crazy, but you crave anything that's familiar when you're inside, anything that has routine, no hidden surprises because you know where you are.

"Two on," shouted the block screw as we walked through the gates and he locked them behind us.

Seconds later Mr Mulligan walked out into the passageway to meet us. "Oh your back then?" he said his disappointment in our behaviour quite distinguishable.

364

"Yeah, sorry Sir," I replied unable to look him in the face.

"Well let's hope this time you've learned your lesson, now let's get you sorted. I'll talk to you later Marriot, now come on," he motioned as he walked away, and both Spider and I followed in silence. We were both put into the cubicles. I wasn't surprised that we'd forfeited the privilege of a comfy bed in the dorm and besides, that was where we'd broken out from and we were now a security risk.

"Right you two, stow yer kit and get yourselves down to the washrooms and have a shower, you stink!" said Mr Mulligan turning up his pointy nose.

"Okay Sir, two secs," I replied more politely than usual. I had bridges to build. I didn't bother waiting for Spider I just shouted "See ya down there mate," as I strode past his cubicle my towel draped over my shoulder and whistling loudly.

Life on the unit had changed. I didn't know what it was. It was something I just couldn't put my finger on, but as I watched the other lads return from work that first day back, something was very wrong. Although everybody was going about their business in the usual manner there was an unmistakable tension, an atmosphere that reeked of fear and apprehension. I didn't have long to wait before the facts were revealed to me, it was Mike who ran up to me in the corridor outside the cubicles a look of concern on his face.

"Jack, Jack, hey man it's good to see ya, how's it going?" he smiled as he offered his hand.

I shook it firmly and resting my left hand on his shoulder, I leant close to him and whispered in his ear, "What's going on mate? Is there something I should know?"

Mike looked nervous and dropped his gaze towards the floor. "Yeah man I was gonna tell ya, I was just waiting for the right moment. Don't be pissed wiv me man."

I interrupted him. "Why would I be pissed with you? Just tell me, the fucking suspense is killing me."

Mike looked around as though he was about to tell me something top secret and as he opened his mouth to say

365

something, he stopped short.

"Well?" I asked pushing him to spill the beans. He still didn't answer, he just made a kind of nodding motion with his head and widened his eyes. "What's the fucking matter with you?" I said angrily. I wasn't renowned for my patience but still he said nothing his head now nodding like it was going to fall off.

"You Marriot?" asked a gruff voice from over my left shoulder, and then the penny dropped. I turned to face the mystery voice my feet automatically finding a good centre of balance as I spun on my heels, my arms stiffened ready to deflect any blow that might be thrown as I turned.

"Yeah I'm, Marriot do you want something?" I said firmly as I looked into the new kid's eyes. He was a big lad about six foot two and his mother must have weaned him on fertiliser because he was built like a brick shithouse, but that didn't worry me.

"Well what do yer want? I ain't got all fucking day," I said my voice rising. The new kid looked stunned nobody had obviously talked to him like that before. I guess he was used to people kissing his arse because he was so freakishly big.

He found his voice eventually although he had lost some of his earlier confidence. "Yeah I'm Shadwell and me and me bruvver is the new chaps of South House so you best git used to it," he declared loudly, like he was making a presidential election speech. You could have heard a pin drop in the corridor as every kid on the unit held their breath waiting for me to hit him. I wasn't going to unless I couldn't avoid it and besides, I'd already sighted his brother hanging off his right shoulder and he was even bigger than the fucker in front of me.

"So you're the new chaps of South House, are you? Congratulations, I hope you're both very happy," I said sarcastically stepping back out of his range in case he decided to have a poke.

"Yeah we's the chaps," the big donut repeated throwing a

quick grin at his brother as if to say, "That's told him."

I hadn't finished yet. "Look, you two dimwits can do what the fuck you want but just leave me out of it and we'll all be fine, now fuck off!" I said and turned my back on them both. It was a calculated risk. I knew if they jumped me, I'd probably lose but something told me they didn't have the guts and anyway they would have lost even more face doing me together with so many witnesses.

"Fuck, that was close man," said Mike as the two Shadwells walked away heads together, planning their next move.

"Close, naw, their full of shit," I grinned and patted him heavily on the back. Mike turned and grabbing both my shoulder's he held me tight and looked straight into my eyes.

"Look man, you don't know the shit those two are up to, their fucking evil, be careful," he urged. I didn't reply but motioned Mike into my cubicle and after he'd made himself comfortable on the end of my bed, I sat on a chair facing him and said, "Right, tell me all about it and don't leave nothing out!"

Mike's story of the brothers grim surprised even me. I was used to violence and wasn't shocked easily but as the story of their rise to the top of the pecking order unfolded in all its grisly detail, I began to wonder if he was right, and I should be careful with these two psychopaths. The elder brother by ten months and the one who fronted me up was called Stuart and as I already knew, he was the mouthpiece and apparently the brain of the outfit. His brother Simon was, by all accounts, so thick that he would have had to study for a blood test, but together they formed a formidable team with Simon acting as the muscle. The brothers were convicted of street robbery, mugging old ladies and anybody else who was foolish enough to wander into their company. Stuart would demand the cash and Simon would batter them senseless even after they'd handed their cash over and begged not to be hurt. They were predators and had no guilt

367

over their crimes and would openly brag to anyone who'd listen about the old lady they'd dragged along the street clinging to her handbag that contained the paltry sum of five pounds twenty. They said she let go after Simon kicked her in the face and stamped on her frail body until she lay unconscious on the rain-soaked streets of Peckham.

I felt physically sick as Mike relayed this awful event to me word for word. "But they were laughing, fucking laughing, man, theys fucking evil, evil, man," said Mike his black face contorted in disgust.

He went on to describe how the two brothers arrived three days after my ill-fated escape and that they'd started as they meant to go on by battering Paul Macky senseless in the toilets after only being on the unit twenty minutes. They'd sought Paul out because, unfortunately for him, he was considered to be the hardest lad in the unit with me out of the picture (poor bastard) and they needed to take out the chap, to establish themselves as a force to be reckoned with. Paul was hospitalised, and nobody was brought to book for his appalling injuries which included a broken jaw and fractured skull as, true to form, nobody saw anything, and Paul was not about to become a grass. Just another clumsy slip in the toilets that's what the report would read, and nobody would lose any sleep over it except poor Paul that is! Mike continued to describe one event after another I began to realise that I was in a whole heap of shit and I would have to keep my wits about me if I was not going to end up another statistic in the accident book. The age-old tradition of taxing had raised its ugly head once more and the brother's grim had taken full advantage, relieving all the unit's inmates of their weekly wages, tobacco and anything else they saw fit to demand.

I didn't blame the others for giving in so easily, you had to see the size of these two freaks to believe it and the way they looked was nothing short of sinister. They both had thick set features and bushy eyebrows with a mop of straight brown wiry hair that hung over their eyes. The oddest thing was the matching scars they both had on their upper lips caused by an operation for a cleft palate and added together it made them look like they were spawned from some scientific experiment that went horribly wrong.

"What yer gonna do then?" asked Mike as he finished his gory tale and slumped backwards on my bed his back resting against the wall. I looked at his face all expectant and pleading. I knew that the whole of the unit was waiting for me to settle the score like some kind of hired gun. I fell silent for a few seconds contemplating my limited options, and once I'd made my mind up, I stood up and headed for the door without looking back. Mike shot out of my cubicle and called after me as I walked down the corridor.

"What yer gonna do?" he called after me, but I ignored him until I'd reached the door to the stairwell and then looking back over my shoulder, I shouted, "Fuck all Mike, like I said, they leave me alone and I'll leave them alone," and with that I headed down to the dining hall. I wasn't scared I was just sick of it all and it had begun to dawn on me that if I didn't screw my head, I was going to be in borstal forever.

Spider patted the seat at the side of him as I entered the dining room and pushed it back from the table to allow me to sit down. I got my meal from the servery and made my way over.

"Have you seen the two brothers yet?" he said excitedly, before my arse had even hit the seat, it was the last straw and I was going to tell them once and for all.

"Not fucking you as well, fuck me, what do you want from me? Can't you lot sort out your own crap without involving me, just fucking leave me alone, I shouted loud enough for everyone else in the dining room to hear, but just to be sure I looked around and said, "Do you fucking hear me." I picked up my food tray and pushing the chair back under the table I walked to an empty table and sat down on my own. I shot a glance across the packed room and as I met anyone's gaze I scowled until they quickly turned away like

369

they'd been stabbed in the eye with a hot poker. I bent over my tray and as I shovelled what passed as food into my mouth, I cursed the whole world and every bastard in it!

Chapter 27

Doing my bird

The next three weeks passed slower than any of the previous months I'd already served, the brother's grim saw to that. The days were no longer just something that you waited to pass they were now something you prayed to end. Every day was fraught with danger and expectation and I'd spent that long with my stomach tied in knots, it almost began to feel normal. Every corner I turned the Shadwell's were waiting whispering and plotting, they didn't outwardly challenge me but there was a general sense of unease whenever our paths crossed. I knew they were just waiting for the right time they wanted me on my own, off-guard like a lamb to the slaughter. The one thing that kept me going was that I knew I was smarter than the both of them and that they were scared of me. They'd heard the rumours and testament to my reputation before they'd even set eyes on me, and this worried them. I was an unknown quantity to them and like a lion stalking large prey there would have to be a period of assessment before moving in for the kill. At the end of each nerve shattering day, I breathed a sigh of relief as the screw would lock my cubicle door and I could at last drop my guard and rest easy. The other inmates on the unit made me feel like Judas and would plead with their tortured eyes as one or both of the brothers bullied or taunted them. It was painful for me to watch, but it was time to do something for myself and I wasn't going to be pushed or cajoled into something that would only add more time to my sentence, I just wanted to do my time, my bird and get the hell out of that dump.

I was given my old job back and as I mopped the piss-soaked floors of the toilets, I would allow myself to dream of freedom when this living nightmare would only be a distant memory. I imagined my life on the outside and what it

371

would hold for me, what kind of job I'd end up doing and the more I dwelled on it the more I craved to walk the streets unescorted, free to go where the fancy took me. Those times I spent reflecting and yearning for my release made me more and more determined that no matter what, I was going to stay out of trouble and if that meant giving the brothers a wide berth, then I could handle that.

Bad luck, bad luck always followed me around like a stray dog and I don't know why I thought it might be different, this time but it wasn't. The Shadwell's had intensified their stranglehold on the unit and the atmosphere was like that of a concentration camp, kids were crying into their pillows at night and during the day they would flinch like an abused child as the brother's waltzed by all cocky and arrogant. To cap it all I was moved back into the dormitory to make way for a new arrival. This was bad news as now I had to sleep with one eye open as the brother's grim slumbered only yards away from me. It was hard to suppress the urge as I watched them bully and hound anyone they chose to, the urge to jump up and shout, "Bollocks to this, come on then you fucking wankers," but suppress it I did, and it left me feeling guilty uncaring and callous, but still I held back and after a couple of months or so I despised myself so much I found it hard to even look at myself in the mirror.

My second monthly review after my return was excellent and much to my surprise, I was given a better job. Mr Beard said he was impressed with the way I'd kept out of trouble and worked hard, and he felt this should be rewarded. My reward was a job in the officer's mess. I couldn't believe it. It was the best job in the whole borstal and would mean I would be given a red band that allowed me to roam outside the borstal grounds without supervision. I thought are you mad, I've only been back for two months after escaping and now, you're going to open the main gates each morning and wave goodbye as I head off into the distance, but mad or not that's exactly what they did!

372

I loved working in the officer's mess and I would happily have stayed there twenty-four hours a day if they'd allowed me to. The regime was tiring but the work was so enjoyable. I didn't care. I would be woken by a screw at four-thirty each morning and after a quick wash, I would throw on my works clothes, slip on my red arm band and be let out of the unit to make my own way to the main gate. Once at the main gate I would wave and smile at the screw in the gatehouse and he would whip open the gates and I'd be on my way. The mess was situated about a kilometre from the borstal in a housing estate that was used for the prison officers and their families. That walk outside the borstal each morning was heaven. I was free and as I sucked in the cool morning air and looked through the fence at the main borstal building all its lights off, I'd smile to myself as I thought of all the other lads still asleep in their pits. I worked with three other inmates and whilst they would all meet up at the gate and walk to the mess together, I always preferred to walk on my own. It was not unlike the days when Dad would wake me up before daybreak and I'd pound the pavements for mile after mile not another soul in sight. I often thought of Dad as I walked along the outer fence line, just a shadowy figure in the darkness. I'd talk to him and gazing up at the stars I'd whisper, "Where are you? Can you see me?" and hoped more than anything he could.

Mr Cullen was in charge of the officer's mess, he was a civilian worker not a screw and because of this, we exploited his weaknesses to our own advantage. He was a real softy and saw the good in everyone and because of this I liked him immensely, but I didn't allow this to stand in the way, if I thought I could pull a fast one. I remember talking him into letting us cook our own lunch one day instead of eating off the screws' dinner menu. It was a decision he would live to regret and as we waved him off to the cash and carry the lads were already rooting around in the freezer.

"That's the baby for me," smiled Garbutt, one of the other mess lads as he held aloft the biggest Aberdeen Angus steak

373

I'd ever seen. Not wanting to be outdone we all helped ourselves to the choicest cuts of meat we could find, and after defrosting and grilling them to perfection we settled down at a table in the deserted mess and ate a meal fit for a king. It took two weeks before Mr Cullen realised his meat quota was a little low, but as he stood with the freezer door open scratching his baldy head, a puzzled look on his face, not once did it cross his mind, we'd turned him over. "Erm must have forgotten to check the delivery last time, I guess I'll have to watch those delivery guys, the buggers," he smiled, and it was never mentioned again.

The routine in the mess was a breeze and each of us had designated jobs, mine was the grill and water boiler. Garbutt was on the fryer, Michaels worked the servery and lastly Hutton worked the stove and oven. We would do the washing up and cleaning between us all and if there was a lull you would wash a few plates or the odd pan just to keep the peace. All in all, it worked well, and the mess ran like clockwork allowing us plenty of time to mess about and have a giggle. I formed a tighter bond with Hutton than the others, he was from West House and closer to my own age. He just had one of those faces you instantly liked, and his sense of humour was wicked. Garbutt and Michaels were from North House and as they already knew each other from their unit they naturally gravitated towards each other, but in truth we were all mates and filled any quiet periods by winding each other up or throwing food at each other when Mr Cullen's back was turned. I never ate on the unit again as we all ate in the mess, it was fantastic to be able to eat more or less anything you wanted and because it was food that was to be served to the screws, it was of a much superior quality than the burnt offerings that weaved their way down the borstal corridors to the units on a stainless steel trolley from the prison kitchens. I even began to gain weight and after several weeks I made a conscious decision to stop eating the full English each morning and leave the sugar out of my tea. I wasn't getting fat my metabolism was quite high and although my waist didn't expand my chest and shoulders did and I was beginning to look like I was taking steroids.

After we'd finished serving lunch each day which ended at One o'clock, we would clean down the kitchen and by Two o'clock we'd be lazing in a hot bath on our respective units whilst the other inmates were out at work. That was my time; time when I could soak in the deep cast-iron bath until my skin began to wrinkle and because I was now on a good wage I would lather myself vigorously with bar of Lux soap that only the wealthiest of inmates could consider buying. With my body sufficiently perfumed and smelling like a tarts handbag I would then make my way to my bed in the dorm and after dressing I would prostrate myself on top of the covers and as that warm contented feeling overcame me, I would drift gently off to sleep.

My job in the mess kept me out of trouble and there was one main reason for this, I was never on the unit! It hadn't escaped my notice that this was probably the screws plan and perhaps exasperated by my continual run-ins with the governor and board of visitors, they decided it was easier to keep me out of harm's way. I was aware I was being tested and I have little doubt that all the screws on my unit held their breath on that first day when they opened the main gates and I headed off towards the officer's mess. It was tempting to do another runner, of course it was, but it was a fleeting thought that I quickly dismissed and after that I never considered it again. The brothers grim had used my absence to maximum advantage and whilst the screws knew what was going on, they had no proof, so until either of the Shadwells fucked up, they were free to continue their reign of terror. They left me alone during the brief times we spent in any close proximity and as time passed, I think their attitude was just to let sleeping dogs lie. They had no reason to piss me off. I was no longer a threat and whilst they could assault batter and bully without my interference, they would continue to let me be.

"Come on sleepy head," smiled Mr Staton as he woke me from my afternoon nap. It was four thirty in the afternoon and I had to be back in the mess by five.

"Coming Sir," I said yawning and rubbing my eyes. Mr Staton smiled down at me as I sat up and slipped my feet into my shoes that I'd left at the side of the bed.

"You're really coming good, aren't you Jack?" he said and as I looked up at him, he cuffed my head playfully and turning to walk away he paused in the doorway and added, "You keep it up, now shift yer arse or you'll be late," he said jokingly.

When I arrived at the mess the other lads were already there. Garbutt was bent down trying to light the fryer with a piece of screwed up newspaper. Michaels was wiping down the servery top and Hutton was standing out back, puffing away on a cigarette. Mr Cullen was setting tables in the dining room, a tea towel slung over his arm like a silver service waiter as he placed knives and forks in perfect symmetry around the rectangular tables. He would stop occasionally, hold aloft a knife or fork shake his head in frustration before polishing it to a deep shine with the tea towel and after casting a beady eye over it once more he'd place it on the white linen table cloth smile to himself and move on to the next place setting.

"Hi Mr Cullen, what's to do?" I called across the servery from the kitchen. Mr Cullen looked up and totally engrossed in what he was doing he just waved his hand as if to say don't bother me. I pulled a face as he got back to polishing the cutlery and made my way over to the grill flicking the two switches that turned it on. I then twisted the dial to set the temperature to medium, reached into my pocket, took out my tobacco and headed for the kitchen door.

Hutton was by now back at the stove having finished his unscheduled fag break and I could hear him cussing loudly. "Fuck, fuck, fuck." I looked across at him. He was prodding a wooden spoon at some emulsified mess in a large saucepan.

"What the fuck is that?" I said, peering over his shoulder at a grey looking liquid with a spattering of black spots floating around it.

"Cheese Fucking sauce," he smirked as he lifted the wooden spoon and let the disgusting gooey gunk fall back into the pan.

"No mate," I laughed, what you mean is it's meant to be cheese sauce, it's more like engine oil and what the fuck are those dark bits?" I said jabbing a finger towards the sauce.

"Ooooh, looks like you've coughed your guts up in that, it's fucking gross," declared Garbutt who had joined us. "Eh, John look, you've gotta see this," Garbutt called over to Michaels who was busying himself pouring a large tin of baked beans into a dish on the hotplate. So there we all stood peering into Hutton's burnt offering and laughing hysterically while Hutton got redder and redder.

"Alright, you set of bastards, it weren't my fault, you was supposed to watch it and now look what am I gonna do with that?" he protested stabbing at the sauce one more time and glowering at Garbutt.

I cleared my throat, "Er, well do you know any pig farmers or perhaps you've invented a new kind of super glue?" I teased and even Hutton seeing the humour of his predicament joined in as we all fell about laughing.

The evening service soon got under way and after Hutton had redeemed himself with a new batch of sauce that even Egon Ronay would have been proud of, we settled down to business.

The evening shift always ran like clockwork as we only served meals to screws who had booked them earlier in the day. I suppose that this was aimed at officers who were on late shift and wanted to eat before going home, it was a good idea in theory but in reality we could find ourselves with a full complement of staff just to serve four meals throughout the entire evening.

The two months I spent working in the officer's mess kept me out of trouble, it wasn't that I made a conscious effort to behave it was purely a matter of circumstance. Unfortunately, this turned out to be a double-edged sword and whilst I would happily have served out the remainder of my sentence at the mess, keeping my head down whilst waiting for my release, the establishment however had other ideas.

I was aware that my monthly review was going to be favourable, it was hard to miss what with all the pats on the back and knowing smiles I got as I passed Mr Mulligan or Mr Beard in the afternoons when I was alone on the unit. But I was blissfully unaware of exactly what they had in mind.

"Come," boomed Mr Beard's dulcet tones as I knocked gently on the office door. I opened it and stepped inside. It was much the same as any other review. Mr Beard sat behind his desk, a cigarette burning away in the ashtray and Mr Mulligan was seated in a chair behind the door.

"Ah young Marriot," exclaimed Mr Beard as though it was a surprise that it should be me. I thought this a little odd as only ten minutes earlier he'd asked me to go to his office himself.

"Yes Sir," I smiled as I positioned myself in front of his desk.

"Oh, take a seat lad," he said pointing to a chair by the side of Mr Mulligan. I did as he requested and as I sat, I nodded respectfully to Mr Mulligan in acknowledgement of his presence and in turn he smiled and patted my leg with his hand.

"Right, Marriot," said Mr Beard wringing his hands, "How do you think you've been this month?"

It was a leading question and not wanting to sound over confident, I played it down, "Alright, I suppose," I replied, trying to look anywhere but into his bearded face.

"Alright? Alright? Well I think you've done a little better than that. What do you think Mr Mulligan?" he asked as he placed his hands behind his head. Mr Mulligan stood up and turned to face me I blushed and quickly dropped my gaze toward the floor.

"Well I think this young man has turned a corner, not only has he kept out of bother, but he's proved worthy of our trust whilst working in the mess, all in all a very good month, well done, Jack, well done," he finished as he sat back in his chair.

"So, Jack, we have a bit of a dilemma," said Mr Beard who had risen from his seat and walked around to the front of his desk and after clearing a space for his ample behind, perched himself on the edge of it, staring into my face. "You see," he continued, "We feel that good behaviour must be rewarded but you already have the best job in the borstal so what are we to do with you? Have you got any idea Mr Mulligan?" he asked in a mocking tone that left me in no doubt that they had already decided what they were going to do but wanted to tease me a little first.

"Oh well, I suppose we could give him some remission back, but we were going to do that anyway. Oh, wait a minute, why don't we let him out of the borstal every day and tell him he can come back at teatime," said Mr Mulligan trying to keep a straight face.

I was still trying to work out what he was getting at when Mr Beard chipped in, "Yes, yes, what a good idea, would you like that Jack?"

I pulled a face and nodded I didn't like games, people usually played them at my expense.

Mr Mulligan must have sensed my impatience and turning in his seat he smiled. "You're going out on community service as from Monday. Now what do you think to that?" he announced as though he'd just completed a feat of magic.

Community service was always reserved for the most trusted inmates and anyone nearing release and any other inmate would have gladly cut off an arm to be in my position. It would mean I would leave the borstal each day and get on a bus into the town where I would find my own way to my work place and my own way back, no screws no supervision, no nothing, it was the nearest thing to freedom

379

that an inmate could get and what did I think to that? I was fucking delighted!

"Thank you, thank you," I said as I jumped to my feet and shook Mr Mulligan's and Mr Beard's hands in turn my eyes wide and full of expectation. Mr Beard chuckled and threw a sideways glance at Mr Mulligan who was smiling warmly as he looked on at my obvious joy, these were two good men who genuinely wanted each boy in their charge to do well and, unlike other screws I'd met, they took pleasure from other people's happiness, if only the world was made up of more like them. Once my jubilation had subsided Mr Beard patted my shoulder and strolled back around the desk where he took his seat and reached for a file marked Marriot, J.

"Right then, that just leaves us with the matter of remission," he said as he leafed through a few pages and found what he was looking for. "Ah yes, your due for release in three-months-time Jack but based on your good behaviour, I'm going to bring that forward by one month." He stopped and looking up, his face now serious, he added, "You're nearly there, don't let us down."

Chapter 28

Light at the end of the tunnel

My community service was not exactly what I'd expected. I imagined I'd be digging flower beds, collecting litter or scrubbing graffiti from council estate walls until my fingers bled. To be truthful none of the aforementioned would have bothered me. I loved the outdoors and if I'd been made to pick up dog shit in the local park with my bare hands, I'd have gladly done it. The time I'd spent incarcerated had given me a thirst for open spaces, the wind in my face and the feel of soft rain on my skin, but as usual I was disappointed.

After breakfast on the Monday morning Mr Pope gave me a letter as I left the dining room. "Now, here's yer instructions of where to go and who to report to, oh and you'll find a bus pass inside too," he paused as he held out the envelope and as he slapped it into my hand he smiled. "Oh, and don't bloody lose it!"

"I won't Sir," I grinned turning away and eagerly ripping open the letter, it read:

```
Marriot

You are to report no later than 09.00
hrs each day Monday to Friday to Ms Learner
the supervising social worker at the
address below

Park Hill Community Centre Hill street
Feltham Middlesex

A bus pass has been provided and will be
renewed on a weekly basis. You can catch
the number 26 bus directly outside the
borstal gates at 08.15hrs. This goes to
Hill Street arriving at 08.50hrs. The
return journey leaves Hill street at
```

16.00hrs and arrives back at the borstal gates at **16.35hrs**. You must be back in the borstal by no later than **17.00hrs**. Any late returns could jeopardise your work placement. If for any reason whatsoever you are to be late returning to the borstal, you must ring the phone number below.

H.M.P Feltham Tel 0800-636999

The bus ride on that first day was as exciting as a ride on a big dipper. I couldn't remember the last time I'd taken a bus and as I took my seat on the upper deck I couldn't help grinning insanely as I looked out of the rear window, watching the borstal grow smaller and smaller in the distance. I soon got bored with the view from the back of the bus and as the upper deck was deserted, I made my way to the front where I put my feet up, rolled a fag and watched the rush hour traffic as we trundled towards the town. When we neared the centre, the bus began to fill up with other passengers and the upper deck became just a misty haze of exhaled cigarette smoke and chilly breath. I didn't pay much attention to anyone else and they reciprocated by ignoring me. I wondered briefly if they knew I was from the borstal and had banded together in order to send me to Coventry. I quickly dismissed my foolish thoughts, after all, I wasn't wearing a placard that read Borstal Boy and experience had taught me that the general public wouldn't recognise a prison uniform unless it had arrows on it. The journey soon came to an end and as promised the kindly driver shouted up the stairs to tell me we were on Hill Street. I hurried down the steps and nodded my thanks to the driver before jumping off, the doors swished shut behind me and as it pulled away, I put my hands in my pockets and began walking along the street. I had no idea on which end of the road the Community Centre was, but the law of averages gave me a fifty-fifty chance of getting it right.

The Community Centre was an old Victorian building

382

with three floors and was not in the best state of repair. I made my way from the pavement up the four concrete steps that led to the entrance avoiding a pile of puke that some kind soul had seen fit to deposit on the first step and pushed open the door. The first thing I noticed was the smell it was a kind of cross between vomit, disinfectant and digestive biscuits. I slowed my breathing to allow myself to acclimatise to it. I was still standing in the hallway when an elderly woman came out of another room. She looked at me, paused, took another look as though she thought she was seeing things and scuttled off without a word. I drew a breath and quietly walked to the end of the entrance hall until I could see several people gathered in a room to the left. They were drinking tea and gossiping about the previous night's television. A large woman of around fifty was holding centre stage, her personality as big as the orange floral dress she was wearing and as she burst into laughter her whole body reverberated from head to toe like some kind of monstrous orange jelly.

I cleared my throat as I walked through the doorway. "Er, excuse me," I said rather meekly but the women kept on chatting. "Er, excuse ME," I said rather more loudly than I'd intended and as if I'd fired a couple of shots into the ceiling, I was suddenly met with silence as every head in the room turned to stare at me. I gulped hard composed myself and asked, "Is one of you ladies Ms Learner? I'm Jack Marriot."

The room still remained silent and I was about to repeat myself when the large lady in the floral number spoke. "Ooh 'ain't he a little cutie girls? It looks like our lucky day," she smiled seductively as she preened her auburn hair with a sweep of her hand and moved towards me. My whole life flashed before my eyes and for a brief moment, I thought I'd been teleported into a cheesy seventies porno film. 'Say something, anything,' I thought but no words came out.

"Ooh, he is a bit of a love 'ain't he violet?" offered another lady with grey hair and the most horrendous knitted cardigan I'd ever seen.

383

"Ooh, I'll say he could scrub my back anytime and my Arfur could wait is turn," laughed another lady sporting a blue rinse as she pinched my face between her arthritic fingers. It was too much for the others and the whole room erupted into hysterical laughter as my complexion grew redder and redder. I wanted to run but I remained rooted to the spot frozen with fear.

"Eh look, he's embarrassed, the poor mite. Don't be embarrassed love, come to yer auntie Glady's," offered a middle-aged lady with her hair up in a bun as she walked towards me. I was bloody terrified and began to back out of the room my eyes never leaving the slobbering wenches in case they made a dash for me.

It was at this point I heard someone call my name. "Jack, you must be Jack?" I turned to my left where a woman of around thirty was standing. She was pretty with brown shoulder length hair, blue eyes and a slim figure.

"Er, yes miss," I stammered.

"Are these lot winding you up?" she smiled showing her immaculately white teeth. She didn't wait for my reply but turned to the other women and laughed

"You set of buggers. I bet you frightened the poor sod half to death, now leave him alone."

There was a unanimous groan but Glady's still wanted the last word. "Oooooh, you always get the new boys. Can't we have this one, just this once?" she begged.

The young woman ignored her and looking into my eyes she smiled and offered her hand. "Miss Learner, but you can call me Ingrid."

"Ooh, call me Ingrid," mimicked a voice from behind us.

"Ignore them they're always like that, come on," smiled Ingrid as she led me further down the corridor and into a large dining room.

The size of the dining room took me by surprise. The building was deceptive, and the rear of the community centre was enormous, a fact that most passers-by would be unaware of from the front elevation of the building.

"Do take a seat" Ingrid smiled flashing her pearly whites at me. I opened my donkey jacket, pulled out a chair and flopped in it. "Tea?" Ingrid smiled as she pulled out two mugs from under a counter and began filling them from an old-fashioned water boiler. I nodded my approval. "Sugar?" she asked holding up a sugar bowl. Again I nodded as she heaped a large spoon into the cup.

I let my eyes wander around the room taking in the surroundings. The layout was not unlike the dining room in the borstal just a little larger. The chairs and tables were old, and no two tables or chairs were a match, a fact that was neatly disguised with revolting PVC table cloths patterned with different kinds of fruit. The counter that Ingrid was standing behind was wooden, with a white Formica surface and directly behind her stood two large gas stoves in white enamel with a hint of rust showing through.

"Ah, get that down you," said the ever-smiling Ingrid as she pulled out a chair opposite me and after arranging her flowing skirt she sat down. I could smell her perfume and the shampoo in her freshly washed hair. It had been a long time since I'd been in the close proximity of a woman, any woman and I'd forgotten how pleasant they smelled. I looked up after taking a sip of my tea to find Ingrid studying me closely. I blushed afraid she had read my thoughts and as if to put me at ease she smiled, a girlie smile not provocative but a smile that said she was fun. I smiled back and quickly hid my face behind the mug I was holding.

"So Jack, I suppose you're wondering what on earth you will be doing here for the next month or so," said Ingrid as she cupped her tea in both hands and blew on it.

"Er, yes miss," I replied rather awkwardly.

"Ingrid please," said Ingrid. "We're all friends here. You can leave all that, 'yes Sir, no Sir,' business behind you when you come here, we're just one big happy family," she continued, her big blue eyes drawing my face towards her as I began to relax.

"Right then, let's get you up to speed with things and

385

then I'll introduce you properly to the rabble you met earlier." The look on my face must have given me away and she laughed out loud, her head tilting backwards and her brown hair gently falling from her shoulders. After she'd composed herself, she leant forward and rested her hand on my arm squeezing it gently. "Oh don't be worried about that lot, they were just teasing they always do that, they're harmless really."

I placed my cup on the centre of the table and grinned cheekily. "I hope your bloody right, they scared the crap out of me."

Ingrid laughed and as she got to her feet, she patted my shoulder and said, "Come on then, no time like the present." She hesitated, as though she was going to say something else but didn't, "Come on then," she urged, and I got to my feet and followed after her.

The ladies took it easy with me for the rest of the first day although Glady's did pinch my arse at every given opportunity. Christine the lady with the blue rinse continued to let me know bath night was Thursdays and I could pop round anytime and lather her up, she said her old man was past his prime and only managed to get excited about horse racing on a Saturday. Beryl the lady in the orange floral dress said perhaps Christine should dress up as a jockey and offer him a tumble in the stables or better still show him her arse and say it was good to firm. I never got the last joke, but the rest of the ladies did and laughed until they nearly wet themselves. All in all my first day on Community service was a success and the more I got to know the older ladies the more they made me smile.

My duties whilst on placement were to assist in the serving of meals to the homeless and the elderly, a job which the ladies did voluntarily. They were amazing and to watch them at work in that small kitchen churning out endless pies, roast potatoes, sandwiches and other home-cooked delights literally blew me away. They made it look so easy and even though they seemed to spend all morning chatting and taking the piss out of anyone they chose to, everything ran like clockwork. Gladys's even baked me a cake to welcome me into the clan and as they brought it out of the kitchen, they each in turn hugged me and planted a big wet kiss on my face. I had misjudged them and as we sat around drinking tea and devouring enormous helpings of Victoria sponge, I almost forgot I was a prisoner, they'd made me feel human again accepted me into their company and shown real kindness. I was going to enjoy my time working with them and as I left for my bus that afternoon I couldn't wait for the next day!

My second week on community service was overshadowed by Mike's release. I was happy for him, of course I was, but it saddened me to think I would probably never see him again. Like thousands of prisoners before us we talked of meeting up on the outside, sharing a beer and laughing over old times but we both knew it was just talk and once out of those gates, our friendship would evaporate quicker than a piss on a fire grate. I didn't mind and at least it helped while away what would be Mike's longest night since he'd been sentenced. Mike was so excited, he had such great plans for his future, alas none of them legal but I didn't give that a second thought, after all I was his mate not his probation officer.

"Come on, lads keep the noise down," begged Mr Linton as he patrolled through the dorm in the early hours of the morning. He should have saved his breath, we were on a high. Mike, because of his imminent departure and me? Well, I don't know why I was so excited, I suppose it had brought home the fact that in less than two months I'd be lying on my bed praying for morning to come. So I fed on Mike's mood, bathed myself in it until I had to actually stop myself believing it was me being released the following morning after breakfast. It was nearly five o clock in the morning before I finally gave in and fell asleep. Mike had no chance and like a kid the night before a family holiday, he tossed and turned cursed and mumbled as he tried to fall headlong into the darkness that signalled sleep, then and only then would the clock begin to move again bringing him nearer to the freedom he'd dreamt of.

I've always hated goodbyes, the hugging and pleasantries that go with it. I would rather just shout "see ya," and be gone leaving people wondering whether I'd actually been there at all. I never understood the need for people to thank each other for their visit and say how pleased they'd been to see them. I kind of figured if they weren't really pleased to see each other then surely at some point one or other of them might just pick up on it and have the good grace to piss off. But then again, I never have been a person who could be arsed with all that mutual appreciation, society bullshit. Surely my actions were enough to let anyone know if I liked them and it was a pretty good indicator that if you'd spent a long time in my company and I'd not thumped you or told you to fuck off, then you could be pretty certain I liked you.

It was for that reason that I left the dorm that morning without looking back, quickly grabbing my wash kit and heading for the washrooms where I splashed cold water on my face and pushed Mike to the back of my mind.

It was Jimmy who came to find me all breathless and red faced. "Er Mike, Mike is looking for you he wanted to say goodbye, he sent me to look for you, are you coming?" he asked when I just nodded and carried on brushing my teeth. I spat into the sink and as I wiped my mouth on my towel. I replied, "Just tell him to take care and to stay out of bother."

"Is that it? You're not coming?" said Jimmy confused by my answer.

"Jimmy, for once in your life take the hint," I snapped harshly, just say I wish him all the best, Okay?"

Jimmy's face dropped. "Okay, okay, I'll tell him," and with that he softly padded away. I had never washed myself as thoroughly as I did that day. I wanted to make sure there was no chance of Mike being around when I got back to the dorm, so I procrastinated until I was the only one left in the washrooms, the sound of water running down the plughole echoing eerily around the tiled walls. I got my wish and as I entered the dorm, I found myself alone, the other lads had already made their way down for breakfast. I glanced at Mike's bed it was stripped of bedding and just the foam mattress remained. His locker door was half open, the shelves bare, he was gone and to all intents and purposes he may have never been there, perhaps it was all just a dream and Mike was just a figment of my over active imagination. I got dressed quickly throwing myself into my clothes and as I ran towards the door I paused, looked back at Mike's empty bed smiled and said out loud, "Good luck mate."

I was like a fart in a trance all that day at the community centre, I just couldn't shake off the mood that had wrapped itself around me and even though the ladies tried to snap me out of it they were unsuccessful. I wasn't unhappy that Mike had gone. I wasn't even jealous it was one of those moods that just came from nowhere and had no explanation. We've all had them, you know the ones where people keep asking you why you're miserable, but you can't tell them because you really don't know yourself.

It was just after we'd finished serving dinner that Ingrid called me into her office. She peered around the door into the dining room and smiling sweetly called, "Jack can I have a quick word with you?"

I looked up from the table. I was busy wiping and threw the dishcloth in the centre, dried my hands on my jeans and followed after her.

"Jack, please take a seat," said Ingrid as I entered her office pointing to a swivel chair in front of her desk. I did as she asked and expected her to walk around and take her seat opposite, but she didn't.

"Now then young man," she began as she sat on her desk in front of me, "what is the matter with you today? You've been quiet all day and everybody has noticed." I didn't really hear what she'd said. I'd been drawn to her shapely smooth legs that were exposed from two inches above her knee and level with my face.

"Er, sorry, Ingrid," I blushed as I tore my eyes away and made an effort to keep them trained above her shoulders.

"Jack, you know if you're experiencing any problems, I'm always here for you to talk to, you just have to ask," she said as she pushed her hair behind her ears and leant closer to me.

Her big blue eyes bore right into me and I shifted awkwardly in my seat "I'm fine Ingrid, just one of those days, you know? I'm sure I'll be better tomorrow. I'm sorry," I replied.

Ingrid smiled and climbing off the desk reached out and stroked my hair. "You don't have to apologise Jack, you're not in trouble, we were all just concerned for you that's all." She smiled again and slid her hand off my head until it rested on my shoulder. "Just remember my door is always open, now go on cheer up, we miss that cheeky face of yours," she finished as she walked over to the door and held it open.

"Thanks, I'll be fine Ingrid, I promise!" I grinned as I pulled the door closed behind me. I had shaken my grumpiness off by the time I got on the bus that afternoon, and as the borstal came into sight, I comforted myself with the fact that it was a journey I would not have to make for very much longer.

"Hi Sir," I called cheerily as I saw Mr Staton heading towards the front gate to commence his shift.

"Oh hi Jack, you had a good day out?" Mr Staton replied as he fell into step beside me.

"Oh yeah, how could it not be great? You haven't seen Ingrid the social worker who I work with, have you?" I beamed. I had got Mr Staton's attention the merest hint of a bit of totty and he was all ears.

"Is she nice?" he asked, trying be all nonchalant but tidying his hair with his hand as though we were about to meet her.

"Naw, she 'ain't nice Sir, she's fucking gorgeous," I laughed as I punched him in the arm playfully and ran towards the gate. The gate screw opened up and after making me empty my pockets and patting me down, he opened the inner gate allowing me into the borstal grounds. I was just walking along the road that led to the security gate for South House when a breathless Mr Staton caught me up, although the smell of his aftershave reached me first.

"Ere, tell me more about this social worker Jack, is she really fit?" he pleaded.

"Oh well Sir, that's for me to know and you to find out," I giggled.

"Oh go on, tell me, tell me," he begged his face lit up with anticipation. We were now at the security gate to South House and I nodded my head towards the locked door to indicate Mr Staton should open it. He put the key in the lock and as it clunked open and I went to walk through he pushed it shut to prevent me getting in. "Go on tell me what's she like?" he persisted. I grabbed the door and pulled just hard enough for it to open wide enough for me to slide through and as I did I laughed loudly over my shoulder, "A gentleman never tells, not never," and I ran as fast as I could along the corridor.

I could still hear his voice, "Jack, wait, wait, go on tell me." I was out of breath and still smirking to myself when I ran into the dorm.

"What you fucking laughing at?" spat Stuart Shadwell as we nearly collided in the doorway.

"Get out of my way dimwit," I said pushing him backwards as I stepped past.

"Eh, don't push me, I'll fucking do yer," Stuart said grabbing a hold of my arm. He seemed to have found some backbone and I couldn't understand why he seemed so determined to antagonise me. He'd usually only go so far and would back off before we actually came to blows, but today he was different, and I was mystified by his sudden change in character.

"Get off moron," I snarled, pulling my arm free, sorely tempted to give him a smack in the mouth but a little voice

391

in my head reminded me of Mr Beard's last words, "You're nearly there, nearly there." I let out a sigh and stepping back I looked into Stuarts face, there wasn't much to like, what with his hair-lip, deep sunken eyes and bulbous features but I had to give it a try.

"Listen Stuart, we don't have to keep doing this. I don't like you, you don't like me, that's fine let's just agree to stay out of each other's way and everyone will be happy," I reasoned, my voice now lowered.

Stuart took my change in demeanour exactly the way I expected. "What's the matter you scared?" he glowered as he stepped closer his foul breath reaching my nostrils.

I was trying really hard to be reasonable, but I could feel my temper beginning to rise and the temptation to kick the crap out of him was just too much. "Right you fucking arsehole you just don't know when to quit do you? I shouted, "Come on then, let's fucking settle it now."

Stuart's eyes widened, and I watched the colour drain from his face. I'd called his bluff and now he was the one who had to make a move. "Uh you'll fucking wait," he said, "You'll fucking wait," and with that he walked out of the dorm although he tried his best to do a cocky swagger, but his exit was tempered with an urgency that betrayed his cowardice and spurred me on.

"You tossers, I'll be ready any time," I shouted after him, "Just make yer move."

Chapter 29

Into Temptation

I knew that spending more time on the unit was going to mean more run-ins with the brothers grim but there was no way out of it and it was just another hassle that I had to deal with. The weekends were the worst, a whole two day's watching them bully and ridicule one inmate after another. Saturday mornings got to me more than any other time and I would purposely find a quiet corner, read a book and shut out what was going on with the other inmates. You see Saturday was canteen day, the time when everybody got to go to the prison shop and spend their hard-earned wages. It was a time when the Shadwells pulled out all the stops in order to maximise their taxing potential. I knew how it worked, I'd seen it so many times before and it never differed from one establishment to another. Firstly the person or persons doing the taxing drew up a shopping list and would decide which lucky inmate was to buy what, the said inmate would then go along to the canteen make the purchase that he'd been ordered to buy and on his return to the wing, hand it over to his laughing tormentors. If an inmate was foolish enough to refuse to carry out his instructions or kept his booty for himself, retribution would be swift, and he would quickly find his name alongside an entry in the accident book. The Shadwell's were pretty thorough and out of fifty-two inmates on our unit only a few were spared their unwanted attention on Saturday mornings. The lucky few were myself, Jimmy, Spider and last but not least Paul Macky. Spider and Jimmy were considered untouchable because of their association with me and although the Shadwell's were not that bright they were well aware any bullying of my friends could just be the last straw, so they left them alone. Paul Macky on the other hand had paid a heavy price for his immunity. The beating he took from both brothers when they first arrived was that brutal he could easily have died, but as far as the brothers were concerned it was not personal just a necessary evil that established their position at the top. Paul was now untouchable for two reasons, he'd kept his head down and not grassed them up and secondly by all accounts he'd put up such a brave fight they wouldn't want to risk a repeat performance. So every Saturday was the same with me, Spider, Jimmy and Paul sitting quietly in some corner our pockets bulging with tobacco and sweets whilst the rest of the unit went without.

It was one such Saturday as I was seated in a comfy chair under the window in the recreation room, that events took a rather surprising turn. I was engrossed in a Harold Robbins book, sucking noisily on a boiled sweet, when I heard someone clearing their throat in order to attract my attention. It was Mr Pope and to be truthful I was more than a little surprised as we'd never really talked unless I was in trouble. Generally, he just monitored me from a safe distance and cast a critical eye in my direction if I stepped out of line.

"Can I help you?" I said lowering my book and looking in his direction.

"You enjoying your book?" he smiled trying to put me at ease. It didn't work. I knew he was up to something but thought I'd play along anyway.

"Yes it's pretty good," I replied casually, "I like Harold Robbins."

"I don't get much time for reading," continued Mr Pope as he leant against the wall in a relaxed manner, "But I do love the way two people can read the same book and picture the main characters in such a contrasting way, don't you think that's amazing?" he asked as his eyes studied my face.

I lowered my book further until it was in my lap. "Is there something you want, Sir?" I asked in a way that told him I was on to him.

Mr Pope blushed like a child caught with his hand in the

biscuit jar, he shuffled his feet and clearing his throat once more, he bent close to my ear and whispered, "We've got to talk."

I was intrigued; did he have some big secret he wanted to let me in on? Perhaps he was just the resident paedophile, but intrigued as I was, I couldn't ignore him. "Okay let's talk," I smiled sarcastically.

Mr Pope straightened up looked quickly around the room and once satisfied we were not being observed he crouched down, his back against the wall and began. "Look I know about the Shadwell's, I know what they are up to. I know everything."

My face dropped, you could have knocked me down with a bloody feather, the old fart was pretty switched on. I just thought he walked around in a permanent trance, but it appeared I was wrong. "I don't know what you're on about," I smiled cockily. I wasn't a grass and if he thought I was going to be his snout or something, he was in for a bloody shock.

Mr Pope grabbed my elbow and shook me, his face now only an inch from mine. "Just shut up and listen Jack and you might just get a pleasant surprise," he urged.

I flopped back in my seat and let out a long deep breath "Okay, I'm all ears, go on."

The conversation that took place blew my mind. Mr Pope told me how he was due to retire the following month but wanted to leave on a high. He said how he was sick of watching as inmate after inmate was battered and beaten at the hands of the Shadwells and thought somebody should settle the score. I knew immediately that that someone was me. I could see my release date getting further and further away and didn't need time to think over his proposition.

"No fucking way, I'm out in a less than six weeks and the Shadwells will no longer be my problem, you want me to risk all that, no fucking way, now piss off," I snarled as I pushed him away and lifted my book to my face and pretended to read.

Mr Pope tutted to himself, rose to his feet and just as he was about to walk away he said softly, "If you change your mind?" I watched him as he ambled towards Mr Mulligan who was supervising a couple of lads playing table tennis. Mr Pope said something into Mr Mulligan's ear. No sooner had it been said, than Mr Mulligan shot a look in my direction, but turned quickly away when he realised, I was watching. I sought refuge with Harold Robbins, but my concentration had been broken and no matter how hard I tried I couldn't pretend that what had happened hadn't. I read the words and got through a dozen pages before I finally gave up and threw the book on the floor. I took out my tobacco and made a roll up and as I tried to hide behind the white cloud that enveloped me, I couldn't take my eyes off the Shadwell brothers. I hated them. I hated everything they stood for, but I couldn't, no wouldn't risk everything, just for once I was going to do something for me.

I managed to get through the next week without much hassle although I had to deal with the disapproving looks of Mr Pope whenever we happened to be in the same room. My job was a bloody Godsend and the ever-lovely Ingrid kept my mind focused on other things during the working day. The ladies were always on top form and Glady's in particular, would wind me up with her sexist remarks and the points out of ten system she used to determine a blokes shagability. I was flattered that she gave me an eight out of ten, the only one who was marked higher was the meat man who came on a Monday morning, but I thought that was fair enough, as he always gave Glady's a prime cut of beef for her Sunday dinner. I really became a team player at the community centre and after a while I just got on with whatever job needed doing. I had even managed to overcome my initial revulsion to some of the homeless people who would arrive in the early afternoon seeking warmth and a hot meal. It was not that they were homeless that I had a problem with, it was simply their lack of personal hygiene, sometimes the smell was so bad, it was difficult not to gag or hold your nose as some old reprobate held out his cup for a refill of stewed tea. The ladies seemed to be oblivious to the pungent aroma that preceded many of the vagrants and I put that down to the fact that each one of them wore such enormous amounts of perfume that it overpowered their own sense of smell. I preferred the elderly who would arrive in four mini-buses. They had their lunch between twelve and one in the afternoon allowing the homeless to arrive at one-thirty for a second sitting. The old folk were hilarious and not many a day would pass without something to brighten our otherwise dull existence. I would listen in as they insulted the cooking complained about the cutlery, the crockery, the veg of the day and just about anything else they thought of. It always made me wonder how they had the cheek to utter a word as the whole thing was free gratis and if it was that bad why did they keep coming back.

The couple who always had us in fits of laughter were Elsie and Alfred and in order to explain their antics I will first tell you a little about each of them. Elsie was around ninety years old, a frail little thing with pure white hair and two national health hearing aids that continually whistled and annoyed the shit out of Alfred. Elsie was also a little senile but would have intermittent moments of complete clarity when she would leave you gob smacked with her revelations from her younger days. There was not much Elsie hadn't done, a fact she hid well from the razor-sharp Alfred who was always out of earshot when Elsie took a trip down memory lane. Elsie once recalled how she would sleep with young American airmen during the war, so she could get black market food to feed her children, she giggled and said she didn't mind as some of them weren't bad looking and she was the only lady in her street with four pairs of silk stockings.

Alfred was a different kettle of fish he was a big man, over six feet tall with a full head of shocking white hair and the bluest eyes I'd ever seen. I could tell that he must have

397

been a ladies' man in his younger years, a fact he never denied when we were alone. Albert had been posted to France during the war and was a member of an elite commando unit, he'd worked with the resistance and his adventures kept me captivated for hours. It was during one of our chats that Alfred revealed his love for a member of the resistance who went by the name of Monique. Alfred and Monique became friends and after a few months, lovers. Alfred said he never stopped loving Elsie, but it was war time and sometimes it was hard to believe it would ever end so people sought comfort wherever they found it. I never had the heart to tell him Elsie would have probably agreed with him, but I'm a great believer in letting sleeping dogs lie.

Lunch time with Elsie and Alfred had to be seen to be believed. You see, Alfred had a hatred of all things vegetable, he said he was a red bloodied male and meat, meat and more meat was what kept the blood flowing through his veins, an opinion that in times past, Elsie had disagreed with. So during the middle years of their marriage Elsie would dish up the meat and two veg that were the building blocks of a strong and healthy life. Alfred in turn would smile sweetly and wait until Elsie wasn't looking before feeding them to their dog who he insisted sat under the table as they ate. This strategy worked for several years until unfortunately, his canine friend passed away and was replaced by a new dog whose philosophy was, unfortunately for Alfred, the same as his, meat, meat and more meat. This left Alfred with a dilemma and he devised an alternative method to rid himself of his troublesome greens. Alfred suggested a change round of the dining-room furniture and cleverly arranged himself near a large pot plant that flourished on its daily compost provided by the emaciated Alfred. This proved a winning method for the next ten years or so until they moved to a bungalow because the, by now frail Elsie, could no longer cope with the stairs. This compounded Alfred's problem because they no longer had a dining room and ate on their laps in front of the television.

398

Alfred wasn't a commando for nothing and concocted a ploy that even I was impressed with. He told me how he spent two weeks secretly training their little Yorkshire terrier to scratch at the back door whenever they sat down to eat, he did this when Elsie went to her mid-afternoon sessions of bingo with two of her friends. So once again the status quo was reached and as the gullible Elsie would moan, "That bloody dogs at it again," and go to let him out. Alfred would quickly put his veg on Elsie's plate and pretend he'd eaten his. All was well with this plan until alas poor Chalky went to that municipal park in the sky and Alfred was back where he started. The saving grace by now, was poor Elsie's state of mind, she was slipping in and out of senility and Alfred found it easy to distract her whilst he loaded her plate with whatever he didn't want.

Their meal times at the community centre followed the same path that had been established over the years but with a slight twist. By now Alfred was bloody blatant and would slip his food across to Elsie without so much checking if she was watching. Elsie either pretended she hadn't noticed or genuinely didn't and this only encouraged Alfred to push his luck and now, not only did he rid himself of his veg, he helped himself to whatever he fancied on Elsie's plate. We would be in hysterics as we watched that cunning old devil smiling to himself as he was convinced, he'd pulled one over on her.

Glady's was good with them both and would remark, "Oh Elsie you've eaten all your meat. Would you like a little more, and quickly replace what her light-fingered husband had pinched. One afternoon when I was clearing Elsie's table, she looked up at me and smiled.

"Did you enjoy your lunch, Elsie?" I enquired and in what must have been one of Elsie's moments of clarity she answered, "Oh yes it was lovely, but I wish that old bugger would eat his own veg cos all that fibre is giving me the shit's!"

Back at the borstal things had not improved and I was

counting the days until my release. I'd already been to see the probation officer who had informed me that upon my release I would be given a place in a probation hostel until I could be found somewhere more permanent to live. This didn't exactly fill me with joy, but I suppose I would at least be allowed to come and go as I pleased, although where I would come and go from, I had no fucking idea.

The Shadwell's began pushing and pushing, the closer my release date got, they knew I had too much to lose and were confident that I would not chance being back dated by losing anymore remission. They were right, I'd had enough, enough of borstal, enough of authority but most of all enough of them.

It was during association one fateful Tuesday evening that I was forced to reconsider my passive stance. I had just nipped to the toilet in the corridor and upon exiting the recreation room, I saw Simon and Stuart kicking the crap out of a new kid outside the washrooms. Stuart had head butted him full in the face and as he dropped to the floor, they were both kicking him and laughing as he begged them not to hurt him. I'd be a liar if I said I wasn't tempted to walk away. I was, in fact I got as far as the door to the rec room before my conscience kicked in.

"Eh you two fuckers get the fuck off him," I shouted from the top of the corridor. The Shadwell's immediately stopped looked in my direction and after grinning at each other launched a last drop kick into the poor kids face.

"We've fucking finished anyway," they laughed as they swaggered past me and disappeared into the toilets.

My whole body was screaming at me, "Kill them, Kill them, Kill them," and unable to quieten the voice inside, I rolled up my sleeves and went to walk into the toilets. It was at that point a hand grasped my arm and as I turned to see who it was, I looked directly into the disapproving face of Mr Pope.

"Want to talk yet?" he said cocking his head sarcastically. I pulled his arm away with my free hand my temper now taking hold.

"The time for fucking talking is over," I said and stepped into the toilets. The brothers were still laughing as I entered but stopped short the moment, they saw me. They could see the venom in my eyes and if they were in any doubt I meant business, I soon dispelled that. "Right, come on then, you want to know what hard is, I'll fucking show you," I snarled my face twisted with rage, a rage I was ready to release upon them. I surged forward my body taught like a drum every muscle and sinew yearning to lash out, to hurt to maim to kill I didn't care. It was Simon who stepped forward to meet me head on and as I pulled back my arm, I knew I was going to hit him harder than I'd ever hit anyone before. I was less than a second away from releasing my fury upon Simon when Mr Pope launched himself at me from behind and gripping me by the waist spun me around and began dragging me backwards out of the toilets.

"Enough, you lot, you two get back in to the recreation room, Now!" he shouted at the brother's as he struggled with me as I fought to shake him off. The Shadwell's squeezed past smirking at me as Mr Pope heaved me to one side and held me against the wall his grasp tightening.

Once the Shadwell's were out of sight Mr Pope eased his grip and spoke softly in order to calm me down. "Okay lad, okay, not yet, not yet, you'll come off worse, use yer head."

I stopped wriggling and hung my head as tears of frustration began to roll off my face and under my breath I mumbled, "I can't help it, they've gotta pay, they've gotta pay."

Mr Pope hugged me, his hand resting on the back of my head and whispered, "They will lad, they will."

The stage had been set and now it was not a matter of, if I fought the brother's, but just a case of when. It went against all my instincts to trust a screw no matter how plausible he might be, but it looked like this time I had no choice. Mr Pope kept me waiting until he was ready and no matter how much I pleaded with him to divulge his plan, he simply told

401

me to be patient and that he had the matter in hand. It was probably the longest three days of my life trying to avoid the inevitable clash with the Shadwells, but I did as I was told and although there was a lot of verbal obscenities and threatening looks swapped between both parties, I waited pacifying myself with the thought that vengeance was just around the corner.

It was on the Wednesday evening, after I had returned from Community service that Mr Pope caught up with me as I walked along the main corridor towards South House. "Glad I've seen you, we have something to discuss," said an out-of-breath Mr Pope from behind me.

I stopped walking and turned to face him. "Yeah, about time too," I said, a hint of excitement in my voice.

"Over here," continued Mr Pope pulling me into the doorway to North House that we were passing. "Just listen and don't say a word I've only got five minutes, alright?" he asked. I shook my head obediently and after Mr Pope took a quick look up and down the corridor, he began to divulge his plan. "Right listen up, I'm on night duty tonight here's the plan. After supper I will as usual ask for two volunteers to clear the tables in the dining room and I will make sure that Stuart Shadwell is one of them, as you know they will remain behind whilst everybody else makes their way to the dorms and cubicles, that is everybody but you who I will not see double back down the stairs or indeed returning to your bed afterwards, do you understand?" He finished shaking me as if to help the information sink in.

I smiled and said, "Don't worry I won't screw it up," and with that he leant close and whispered, "I know nothing about this and you tell no one or I promise you the Shadwells will be the least of your worries."

I could tell he meant business, but he had nothing to worry about, I wasn't a grass and if it went tits up, then I'd carry the can, a fact I think he already knew and for that reason alone he had decided to stick his neck out. The plan was good. I liked it apart from one thing. Mr Pope had not

402

considered the other brother, Simon would also have to be dealt with, a fact I had omitted to tell him. It didn't matter I had another plan of my own and was going to take maximum advantage of the situation. The daft old fucker would never see it coming and what's more, even though he'd know what I'd done, he would be in a position where he could do or say nothing. I was definitely two steps ahead of the game.

The whole of that evening was spent running the order of events through my mind. After tea whilst the other lads watched television, played snooker or exchanged pointless chit chat, I sat myself in a corner and pictured the whole scenario as I expected it to run. Once supper had ended, I would climb the stairs to the dorm with everybody else, when I was sure nobody was paying attention, I would slip downstairs and take Stuart out. Once he'd been dealt with, I would quickly run back upstairs and administer the same treatment to Simon and then go to the toilets clean myself up and act all surprised when I came out, it was fool proof and the more I replayed it in my mind the easier it seemed. I had not considered for one moment that I might lose to either brother, or that in order for everything to work out how I wanted, I would have to beat both brothers within an inch of their lives, so they were unable to gang up on me afterwards. I also had to avoid any serious injury as this could immediately put me in the frame, a broken nose two black eyes or anything that might draw attention to me was not an option.

"What you looking so smug about?" asked Spider dragging me away from my thoughts as he pulled up a chair and sat beside me.

"Smug, me? I don't know what yer on about," I replied as I stood up in order to take my tobacco tin out of my pocket.

Spider wasn't convinced. "Fuck off your planning somert, I know you," he smiled nudging me with his elbow as I sat back down.

"No, you're fucking imagining it, you daft twat now give

403

us a light," I said, putting a roll-up in my mouth.

Spider pulled one of his sulky faces. "Oh well, don't tell me then, I didn't really want to know anyway, here," he mumbled as he held out a lit match, the flame dancing on the end of my cigarette. I pulled away blowing smoke straight into his face.

"You're such a wanker," I joked. "Now, are we gonna talk bollocks all night or play snooker?"

Spider's eyes lit up. "Snooker it is then, I'll set em up," he smiled already half way to the table.

"I'll be there in a minute, just let me finish this fag," I called after him as I stared across the room at the Shadwell's who were huddled together by the TV. They were laughing about something, it made me even more determined to go through with it and I silently vowed that I'd make them laugh on the other side of their ugly faces when supper was over. I took one last look at them puffed heavily on my roll-up and threw it on the floor stamping on it as I rose to my feet. "Right Spider get ready for an arse whooping, I'm gonna beat you like a Ginger step child," I chuckled as I approached the snooker table.

As promised after supper Mr Pope asked for volunteers to clear the tables. "Oh very kind of you, Stuart," he shouted across the dining room much to the amazement of Stuart who was busy throwing pieces of broken biscuit at a kid on another table.

"Oh, eh, Sir," he moaned but was cut short by Mr Pope.

"Stop whingeing and get on with it, everybody else upstairs," he shouted as fifty odd chairs scraped noisily across the floor followed by the pitter patter of a hundred feet as they filed out of the dining room and up to the dorms. I climbed each stair as though I had lead in my shoes. I was waiting for Simon to leave the dining room, but he was lagging behind and helping his brother clear up. I had an awful feeling that things were not going to go as planned.

But just as I was about to despair, I heard Mr Popes sweet voice, God bless him. "Simon get up the stairs or are you two joined at the fucking hip? Go on git, he'll be up in a minute," he said his voice tinged with a note of annoyance . I quickened my pace and just made it safely to my bed in the dorm before Simon came in. He didn't even look my way he went straight to his bed sat down and with his back to me began to remove his shoes. The rest of the dorm were going about their nightly rituals, undressing, flicking each other with towels and generally fucking about. My eyes raced around the room, nobody was looking, now was my chance and making the best of it I slipped quietly out onto the landing. I could hear my own heartbeat and the noise from the other inmates began to fade into the background until the only sound I could hear was the rhythmic thud, thud, thud of blood pumping through my arteries. Stuart was in big trouble, he didn't know it yet, but I was like a runaway train racing down the track on a direct collision course with him. I couldn't have stopped myself even if I'd wanted to, which of course I didn't. I stood for a few seconds at the top of the stairwell took three deep breaths and hurtled down the steps like my arse was on fire. I didn't give myself time to think, I was ready and with each step my anger repulsion and pure hatred for Stuart Shadwell filled my head until I thought it might explode. Once I was at the bottom of the stairs I ran as fast as I could into the dining room, I could hear Stuart's voice and it drew me to him like a moth to a flame. He was standing to the left of the door and as I entered our eyes met and as soon as they had his expression changed. He knew I was there for him and this time there would be no reprieve. I didn't speak I just strutted towards him, a man on a mission, our eyes locked together in anticipation of what was about to take place. He was scared his face was aghast with terror instantly turning to shock and surprise as my right hand hit him full in the mouth and a left hook caught him in the right temple. Stumbling backwards Stuart let go of the cups he was holding, and they clattered along the floor bouncing and spinning as they fell. I moved onto him and hit him again and again and again. I

405

didn't give him time to recover and with each blow I rained upon him I drove him further across the floor until he was at the rear of the dining room, his face now a bleeding battered mess. He raised his arms in a pathetic attempt to protect his face, but I simply punched through the middle, parting his arms with the ferocity of each punch. The fight was all but over but to Stuart's credit, he tried to throw a punch out of pure desperation, it was a long round sweeping right hand and as I stepped into him, I took the force of the blow on my left ear. I could easily have side stepped or parried it, but I wanted to get inside. I drove an uppercut straight into his bottom jaw, it shattered with a loud cracking noise followed by a thud as Stuart collapsed unconscious to the floor his eyes half open. A pool of blood began to emanate from his mouth which hung open and was pushed to one side like the mechanism of a typewriter. I leaned over him watching his crimson offering gradually encompassing his entire head.

"You fucking wanker, not so fucking tough now are you?" I screamed down at his lifeless body, still full of rage I kicked him as hard as I could in the bollocks but even that failed to stir the comatose Stuart. "Cunt," I snarled as I spat on him in disgust before turning my attention to Paul Jennings who was backed into the furthest corner of the dining room his complexion a deathly white colour, as if reading my mind he spluttered, "I didn't see nuffin, I won't say nuffin Jack, you know that."

"Good lad," I smiled. "Good lad," and with that I ran out of the dining room and headed back upstairs. I was out of breath and my limbs felt heavy, but I pushed on, I had to get to Simon. Once at the top of the stairs I took a quick peek down the corridor where the cubicles were, and as expected Mr Pope was right at the far end, a cup of tea in one hand a fag in the other and leaning against the wall like he was waiting for a bus, not a care in the world. I wasted no time and was in the dormitory and halfway towards Simon's bed before I was stopped short by the event I was witnessing, I couldn't believe what I was seeing. Simon was cowering beside his locker, his knees pulled up to his chest, rocking backwards and forwards like a nutcase. There were splashes of blood stretching from the toilet in the middle of the dorm to where he now sat whimpering, blood and snot hanging from his nose.

"I'm sorry, sorry," he wailed like a five-year-old child only pausing to gasp deeply or suck up the two long snot trails hanging off his chin. I turned to look at Spider who was lying on his bed staring at the ceiling and blowing smoke rings.

"What the fucks happened to him?" I said in astonishment.

Spider lowered his eyes from the flaking paintwork on the ceiling and flashing me a toothy grin he declared, "Didn't see a fing mate, must have been them tiled floors in the crapper, they does get slippy ya know."

I was about to question Spider further when the tell-tale footsteps of Mr Pope's brogues warned me of his imminent approach. I ducked quickly into the toilet I needed to wash the blood away that had invaded every crevice of my hands, it was beginning to dry and as I clenched and unclenched my hands it cracked and flaked as though I had some kind of hideous skin condition. "Oh bollocks," I mouthed as I noticed the broken ceramic washbasin, it was smashed in half and the remaining portion that hung on the wall contained several teeth and at least half a pint of congealing blood. It was like a scene from an X-rated horror movie. I took a long lingering look at the scene my mind racing as I tried desperately to make sense of what I was seeing. It didn't add up, who had beaten up Simon? How had they done it? And why was everyone in the dorm acting like they'd seen nothing? I pulled myself together and after flushing the toilet, I washed my hands in the clean water before flushing the toilet once again and watching the tell-tale reddened water being sucked away. I dried my hands on the roller towel hanging on the wall and looked myself up and down, amazingly there was no blood on my clothes

407

and as I turned my hands over to inspect them there were no lumps bruises or cuts that might single me out to any of the screws.

I smiled to myself and under my breath I whispered, "You're one lucky bastard, Jack." I took a deep breath and gingerly pushed open the toilet door before nonchalantly walking out into the dormitory. I tried not to look in the direction of Simon's bed, but I was drawn to him like a rubber necker staring at an accident. Simon was still howling and babbling like he'd lost his favourite teddy. Mr Pope was bending down and trying to coax him up and for one second, I nearly laughed out loud. It reminded me of someone trying to beckon a puppy out from under the sofa, all Mr Pope needed was a biscuit. The toilet door clicked as it closed behind me and instinctively, Mr Pope turned to investigate the sound, our eyes met briefly but it was as though I wasn't there, he just looked right through me, no expression at all. I shrugged my shoulders and crossed the dorm to my bed before throwing my arms behind my head and flopping noisily onto my pillow.

"Those toilets certainly are slippy, it's a wonder nobody's been killed on those floor tiles, they're fucking lethal," I said sarcastically to nobody in particular.

"Yeah, yeah, those bogs 'ain't safe, man," Spider offered and all of a sudden everybody in the dorm chorused, "Yeah those bogs is lethal."

It wasn't long before Mr Pope was joined by the hospital nurse who he'd called up on his radio. Together they hauled the still bawling Simon to his feet and began to lead him from the dorm. It was at this stage that Stuart Shadwell fell through the doorway and landed at their feet the ground shaking like we were about to experience an earthquake.

"What on earth has been going on? Who the fuck is that?" asked the prison nurse as he struggled under the weight of his shared burden.

Mr Pope was taken aback; his face went white and his eyes bulged as though on stalks. It seemed like an age before

408

he spoke, "Er, that's his brother," he replied nodding his head from one Shadwell to the other.

"Hang on to this one," ordered the nurse slipping Simon's arm from his shoulder and leaving him dangling like a battered scarecrow as Mr Pope tried to hold his entire bulk. "This one's in a bad way too," said the nurse as he lifted Stuart's head and looked into his eyes. "Quick call for assistance, now!" screamed the nurse as Mr Pope hesitated.

"One nine, one nine assistance required South House dorm, medical emergency, over," Mr Pope called as he held his radio to his mouth, he let the button go and held it beside his ear awaiting a reply.

"One nine message received, on way, out," crackled the radio and with that Mr Pope let out a large deep breath and let Simon fall to the floor his enormous frame too much to cope with on his own.

"Steady on," snapped the nurse annoyed that Mr Pope had let Simon fall.

Mr Pope calmly placed his radio back on his belt and shaking his head he replied calmly, "Oh do shut up, you're really not fucking helping." The nurse reddened and pretending he hadn't heard, he busied himself checking Stuart's vital signs whilst Mr Pope just crossed his arms and tapped his foot impatiently on the ground. The pounding of heavy leather footwear and jangling key chains on the stairs signalled the arrival of the long-awaited assistance. Talk about overkill, there were eight screws at least five of them carrying first aid boxes and all jostling each other for a piece of the action.

"I've got him," declared one trying to pull Stuart to his feet.

"No I've got him, let go," argued another. The whole thing descended into a farce and from my vantage position lying on my bed, I sat spellbound by their antics.

It was Mr Pope who eventually managed to restore order. "Look, can we just get these two out of here and down to the hospital wing, it doesn't matter who bloody carries who,

409

let's just get them gone." A few moments later I sat on my bed wondering whether I had fallen asleep and dreamt the whole thing. The dorm was deathly silent and as I looked at the other inmates frozen to their beds their eyes locked on the spot where seconds early the group of screws had been flapping around like headless chickens, I knew I hadn't imagined it. It was strange it was as though everybody was afraid to be the first to speak, so we just sat deep in our own thoughts like a spell had been cast and we had been turned to stone. My main worry was that I might have gone a little too far. I knew Mr Pope wouldn't grass me up, but I wasn't retarded enough to think if Stuart died, I wouldn't be found out. He wouldn't die, would he? What if he did what would happen to me? I thought. My thoughts were invaded as one by one different kids summoned up the courage to speak and what began as hushed whispers quickly rose to excited chatter.

"Fucking hell, I think that the Shadwells are gonna think twice before fucking with us again," announced one kid with relish.

"Yeah the fucking tossers, they got what was coming," offered another.

"Did you see the state of Simon, we did him good," crowed another.

"Will you lot shut up or do you all want to get done for this, now keep it down," shouted Paul Macky as he stood up from his bed at the far end of the dorm. I turned towards his voice and studied him closely. He had blood spatter all over his hairy legs that protruded from his shorts. The fucker it was him, he did Simon! but how? And more to the point was it just a coincidence that he chose the same time I was administering justice to Stuart, I thought not.

"Hey Paul, over here," I whispered just loud enough for him to hear. "Right do you wanna tell me what the fuck is going on here, because to be honest I 'ain't got a fucking clue," I said as he ambled over and stood at the foot of my bed. Paul knew better than to piss me off and he lowered his gaze to hide his guilty expression. "Well I'm fucking waiting, cough," I demanded. Paul shifted his feet awkwardly.

"Can I?" he asked indicating he wanted to sit on my bed.

I nodded, and he plonked his heavy frame beside me leaning close until our faces were nose to nose.

"It was Mr Pope," he began. I screwed up my face and raised one eyebrow to show my disbelief.

"Go on," I nodded. Paul shifted his position and thought for several seconds before he continued to speak. I sat in silence just nodding occasionally until he had finished. I was that shocked and surprised that words failed me and as Paul waited for me to talk you could see he was getting more and more uncomfortable.

I found my voice. "You fucking serious?" I enquired.

"Yeah, Jack, for real, it's true, everything I swear honest," he stuttered. I stared intently into his eyes I could tell he was being sincere. "Go on, get out of here before the screws come back, oh and wash that shit off yer legs before someone sees it," I finished as I pointed to his lower legs.

Paul looked down and realising what I was talking about, he blushed, thanked me and ran straight into the toilets. I lay back on my bed my hands behind my head and began to digest the conversation I had just had. Spider reached across from his bed and shook my arm indicating he wanted to talk. I didn't, so I gave him one of my 'not now' looks and he went back to staring across the dorm, whatever he wanted would wait. My mind was racing, and I just couldn't believe how wrong I had been about Mr Pope, he was a more cunning old fart than I'd given him credit for and as for me being ahead of the game, I wasn't even in his league. I ran the events of the evening through my mind in slow motion, it was a work of art the way he had orchestrated events. One thing for sure he was not the kind of guy you would want to piss off without seriously considering it first. You see old Pope had played everyone off against each other, he'd been quietly whispering in Paul Macky's ear that he should get his revenge on the brothers for the good hiding they'd given him when they arrived. Paul wasn't a pussy and I have no doubt he'd already considered it even before Mr Pope intervened and gave him a little push, but none the less it was Mr Pope who loaded the gun. What amused me the most was the fact that whilst Mr Pope was cultivating Paul Macky, he was doing the same with me, none of us the wiser about the other. I slowly but methodically pieced together the chain of events that happened that evening and to the best of my belief this is how it unfolded.

Operation Vigilante

20.30hrs. All inmates are called into the dining room for supper.

21.00hrs. Supper ends, and Stuart is volunteered to clear up the dining room by Mr Pope, Paul Jennings stays to assist.

At this point Paul Macky has been told by Mr Pope that he will separate the brothers allowing Paul the opportunity to gain his revenge on Simon without worrying about them both. Unbeknown to Paul, I would be doing the same to Simon's brother in the dining room. It was pure genius, I thought I was the only one who had considered that both brothers needed to be dealt with at the same time, but boy I was never more wrong.

21.10hrs. I enter the dining room and deal with Stuart

21.10hrs. Paul Macky follows Simon into the toilets in the dorm and a fight ensues.

So far everything is going like clockwork but just in case Mr Pope had a back-up plan. He would have known that if Simon and Paul were still scrapping when I came back, I would obviously jump in and finish off Simon. (Nice to know he had confidence in my ability)

21.10hrs and ten seconds. Paul Macky and Simon are going at it hammer and tongs in the dorm toilets when the rest of the dorm decide to lend a hand. Paul gains the upper hand and together with four or five other inmates they continually pound his ugly fat face into the washbasin until after losing half his teeth and a good quantity of blood he is dragged into the dorm and kicked from one end of it to the other. At this stage the remainder of the dorm decide to join in until no less than the entire dorm is tearing gouging and kicking for all they are worth. Simon had no chance and after trying to scramble under his bed and being repeatedly dragged back out he found himself trapped between his locker where he remained frightened babbling and incoherent.

21.14hrs. Jack Marriot returns to the dormitory where he finds all the other inmates lounging on their respective beds and Simon huddled where they'd left him, by now bleeding profusely and sobbing like a four-year-old child.

Chapter 30

The Fallout

The following day each and every inmate from the dorm was summoned in turn to Mr Beard's office and given the third degree. I sat patiently in the dining room after breakfast until my name was called.

"Marriot your up," called Mr Mulligan as he popped his head around the door and motioned me to follow him. I was worried but tried my best to hide it.

"If this is about last night Sir, I don't know anything, I didn't see anything either, I was asleep, honest," I declared pretty unconvincingly.

Mr Mulligan ignored my pleas until we reached the office door he then spun around to face me, his brown eyes looking deep into my lying face. "If that's your story Jack then I suggest you stick to it, and don't worry I have a feeling things might just go your way on this one," he winked as he gently turned the handle and pushed the door slowly open. I'd only been in the office a few minutes when I realised, I was worried about nothing. The whole atmosphere was jovial, it was the most half-hearted interrogation I'd ever been involved in.

Mr Beard asked what I'd seen. I said nothing, and he just smiled and said, "Okay get yourself off, your late for work already."

I was that stunned to be let off the hook so easily, I just stood there not quite believing that was it.

"Off you go then, or do you have something else you want to say?" said Mr Beard waving his arm towards the door.

"No Sir, sorry Sir," I grinned and shot out of his office as fast as my little legs could carry me.

The screws never did get to the truth, but they were not really looking for it anyway, they made all the right noises, but they were simply going through the motions. The Shadwells had grown too big for their boots, they'd got careless and cocky and I have a strong suspicion that the screws were as relieved as the inmates when they finally got what was coming to them. Luckily the brothers' injuries had appeared worse than they actually were, and after a few stitches, a visit to the borstal dentist and a certain person having his jaw wired shut the case was closed. It didn't come as a shock to me that the Shadwells kept their mouths shut, (no pun intended) they couldn't grass, they would have been marked men for the rest of their sentence and after the beating they'd both just had it wouldn't have been a chance they would have wanted to take. I never saw either of them again after that. Stuart was kept in the hospital wing on a diet of soup in order to allow his jaw to heal and Simon was transferred to West House upon his own request, his wounds would probably not heal in a lifetime and reports from inmates on West House indicated a very different Simon Shadwell than the one we'd grown to know and hate. Simon was by all accounts a changed man, he was polite helpful but most of all afraid, afraid of each breaking day any sudden noise or indeed any raised voice. Simon was afraid of everything. I didn't feel any sympathy for him I hadn't forgotten that old lady he'd kicked half to death on the pavement for a few measly quid, and as the saying goes what goes round comes round!

Life returned to what passed as normal on the unit and even the initial wave of euphoria that had affected everyone after the Shadwells were dispatched, subsided after a few days. I couldn't help laughing to myself that Saturday, as the other inmates returned from the prison shop. I watched as kid after kid devoured never ending mouthfuls of sweets and chocolate, they were like puppies frightened a treat might be taken away at any given moment. Some of the younger kids who had suppressed their natural character began to come out of their shells and although this only showed itself as play fighting, giving cheek to the screws or

415

just generally being insolent, the screws had their work cut out keeping them all in line.

"Jenkins, stop that, put him down. Olsen don't throw that. Wilson get down off there. Stop that Mitchell," poor Mr Staton was struggling to maintain order.

"What the fuck has got into this lot?" he moaned to Mr Mulligan as he walked over to the window where he stood.

"Beats me, but at least their only sodding about and not killing each other. I suppose we ought to be thankful for that," reasoned Mr Mulligan.

"Yeah you've got a point, I don't want to be mopping up blood all afternoon, besides I'm wearing my best strides," replied Mr Staton as he stepped back and pointed at his trousers as if to emphasise his point.

Mr Mulligan looked him up and down. "You must tell me where you bought them, and I'll make sure I don't go there," he teased.

I was disappointed when the weekend was over. I couldn't remember laughing so much in ages, but I was in for a surprise that Monday morning and by the end of that day my whole world would be turned upside down. I had just finished my breakfast and was putting on my coat ready to leave for community service when Mr Mulligan called out across the dining room.

"Marriot, you stay behind when the others leave, you're having your assessment today."

I was puzzled my assessment? I wasn't due another assessment I was due for release in just over four weeks. I began to panic what if they'd found out it was me who beat up Stuart? What if they were going to take some remission off me?

"But Sir, I'll be late for work, I'll miss me bus," I pleaded.

"Marriot just do as I ask, don't worry about work, now get outside Mr Beards office and wait for me," he said dismissively.

"Ooh looks like you're in the shit," giggled Spider as he walked behind me and continued on out of the dining room.

416

"Eh, Spider," I called after him and as he looked back, I stuck my two fingers up at him. "Fuck you," I smiled sarcastically.

Mr Mulligan waited until the rest of the unit had departed for work, before he joined me in the passageway outside Mr Beard's office.

"Come on lad, let's get it over with," he said, opening the office door, his face totally expressionless.

"Take a seat, Mr Beard will be along shortly," he ordered, without turning to look at me. I could feel my whole future slipping away and as I sat down, I became more and more convinced that whatever was about to take place was going to be bad.

The clock ticking on the wall above Mr Beard's desk seemed to get louder and louder until I couldn't hear myself think, tick, tick, tick, tick, tick, tick. Mr Mulligan was seated opposite me and casually flicking through my file. I cleared my throat in order to attract his attention, I wanted him to say something, anything, but he didn't.

"Ahhh, your here already, well let's get started," smiled Mr Beard as he trundled through the door and made his way behind his desk. Mr Mulligan had risen to his feet and handed my file to Mr Beard as he sat down.

"Marriot, you've been a bit of a problem for us," he said opening the file he'd just been given. Oh here we go, I thought this is where I get sent down the block with another six weeks on my sentence. "You see Marriot, you've been a good lad for the last couple of months and we wanted to reward you, but we were unable to because we couldn't release you until a place was available in the probation hostel you're going to." Mr Beard stopped and looked at me to ensure he had my full attention, he didn't have to worry he couldn't have got any more of my attention if he'd run around the office butt naked with a rose between his teeth. "You see, he continued, as he exchanged a knowing glance with Mr Mulligan, the probation hostel has now indicated that a place is available for you and because of this we can

417

now look at offering you some more remission based on your good behaviour."

Bugger me, this was getting better and better all the time I thought, as my eyes burnt deep into Mr Beards face. Mr Beard paused and as he broke into a huge smile, he looked again at Mr Mulligan who seemed to nod his agreement and then he said it, **"You're going home tomorrow."**

I remained on the unit for the rest of the day and was given cleaning duties. It didn't matter I just ambled about mop and bucket in hand smiling like a kid with special needs. The screws would call me from time to time and I would fill in this form or that form.

"This is where you report tomorrow, and this will be given to you in the morning," they would say, and I would smile stupidly and reply, "Yes Sir, no problem Sir," all the time trying to stop myself laughing out loud like a lunatic.

After lunch I was instructed to take myself off to reception where I would be given my own clothes to try on, the authorities didn't want me walking out of those gates looking shabby, they wanted to at least give me a fighting chance of fitting in with normal society.

"Oh dear, looks like we have a bit of a problem here Sir," called the reception orderly as he looked me up and down, as I stood in my own immaculately washed, starched and ironed clothes. The borstal laundry had done their best, and to be truthful, they were spotlessly clean and would have looked a treat if I could have lost three inches in height and around two stone.

"Fuck me lad, what you been eating?" laughed the reception screw as he stood in front of me his eyes working their way up and down my attire. My feet had grown and were only halfway into my cheap leather shoes, my heels flattening the backs of them, my waist band was open like the pages of a tatty old book revealing my now skin-tight underpants and just to finish the whole outfit off, my trouser legs were only six inches below my knees.

"Yeah Sir, I don't think it'll work if we let the turn ups down, do you?" giggled the reception orderly and together we all burst into fits of laughter.

"Right lad, get yourself out of those. I think there's a can opener in the drawer over there," the screw chuckled at his own joke, "I'll be back in a few minutes," he finished as he sauntered off still laughing to himself.

"You've gotta admit you do look a right twat," smiled the orderly as I stuck two fingers up behind the screws back as he disappeared out of sight. I waited in reception for nearly an hour and passed the time taking the piss out of any other inmates who were due for release and trying on their own street garb. It was strange how until you saw people in their own clothes you had no real sense of who they were, or who they'd been. It's kind of like school uniforms, they blend each and every kid into anonymity, their identity hidden, they could be poor they could be rich, they might be dedicated followers of fashion or complete nerds, but you would never know until the moment they stood before you in clothes they'd bought themselves. I saw it all in that hour, lizard skin shoes, smart leather jackets, designer shirts bought with ill-gotten gains and at the other end of the spectrum nylon trousers, cheap training shoes and flowery shirts that looked like they had been run up from an old pair of curtains. Some of the kids took on a whole personality change as they slipped into their own gear, strutting like peacocks, pushing their chests out and walking back and forth with a distinct swagger in their step. The poorer kids looked themselves up and down in disgust. They were being reminded of what they were, what they would once again be, and their pain was apparent to anyone who cared to look. They didn't hang around parading and smiling they simply threw on their clothes declaring quietly, "Yeah their fine," and hurriedly tore them off like some stage artiste in the middle of a quick-change routine before throwing them back into the box and quickly closing the lid on their shameful secret.

I knew how they felt. The ones who had nothing, the ones who could never hope to fit in, they couldn't be part of the in-crowd, street cred could not be bought on the local market for the price of a three quid pair of jeans, or a rip-off copy of some designer label your Dad bought in the pub for a tenth of its actual price. I was lucky nobody taunted me about my cast-off clothes, my last year's fashions, my steel toe-cap boots or my home mutilated hair-cut, they could try but as sure as God made little green apples, they would never do it again. You see we are what life makes us, we're not born bad, we don't enter this world with the sole purpose of creating anarchy or an uncontrollable impulse to dish out violent retribution on those who cross us. We become what we are, affected by those around us, their values or lack of them, their beliefs, their kindness, their compassion or their loathing. Long story short, subject a child to ridicule and hatred and he learns how to fight, give a kid love understanding and value and you give him a fighting chance in a world that is just waiting for him to screw up!

I was seated on the wooden bench in reception biting my nails in order to relieve the boredom that had by now set in, when the reception screw returned.

"Marriot, over here lad," he hollered. He was standing next to a half-open door just the other side of the main reception desk.

"Yes, Sir," I beamed as I rushed towards him.

"In yer go, you've ten minutes to pick something," he said pushing me through the doorway without another word and closing the door behind me. I found myself in a twenty-foot square room filled with clothes racks and on each hung sets of brand-new clothes, jumpers, trousers, shirts, jackets, coats. It was like a mini-department store and as I scrutinised each rail in turn, I was totally overawed. I had never chosen my own clothes before. I either got our Steve's cast-offs or Marie would buy me whatever cheap crap she managed to get hold of. It didn't seem that important back then I was young, and full of appreciation for whatever I was given. Things were

420

different now, I'd changed, grown up, I was a young adult. I was aware that the clock was ticking, and I would have to make a decision, before the screw came back in, but there was so much to choose from. I just kept drifting from rail to rail, fingering jumpers, holding up shirts to my chest to see how they looked and talking to myself. 'Naw, looks a bit girlie,' I laughed as I put a shirt back on its hanger. 'Oh no, not you, too fussy,' I continued as I moved up and down my pace quickening as time grew short. "A-ha," I said out loud plucking a pair of blue jeans from a rail, they were perfect not designer or anything but adequate. I held them to my side, the length was just right. I had no idea what waist measurement I was, so I threw off my prison issue pants and jumped into them, they were perfect.

"Now a nice shirt," I said as I perused another rail. I settled on a white tee-shirt can't go wrong with that I thought. Next a pair of white training shoes, some underwear and finally a black bomber jacket with a woollen collar. After putting on the entire ensemble, I stood behind the door gazing into a full-length mirror that adorned the back of it. "You dapper fucker," I smiled as I admired myself. I couldn't remember when I'd last looked at myself properly in a mirror and was pleasantly surprised by what I saw. Gone were the puny arms and legs I'd arrived with, they'd been replaced with muscular forearms, shapely toned legs and a chest a navvy would have been envious of. "You sure aren't a bad-looking fucker," I whispered at my reflection and began to chuckle as I turned this way and that way flexing my arms and admiring myself. I was that caught up in the moment that the door nearly knocked me over as the screw opened it and poked his head round. My face flushed red as though I'd been caught in the middle of a dreadful act. Of course, I hadn't been. The screw hadn't seen anything, but my face refused to co-operate and grew redder and redder as I tried to compose myself.

Chapter 31

Sweet liberty

It was the night of a hundred hours, the night before I was released. Each second seemed like an hour and each hour like an eternity, as my freedom grew ever nearer. Spider did his duty and, as was the custom, stayed awake all night, in order to keep me company. I was going to miss him he was badly misunderstood, a kid from the wrong side of the tracks who'd slipped through the system and whose future held little hope. I promised to keep in touch to write and let him know how I was doing, but in those early hours, even as I made those promises, I knew I would never see him again. I had to move on, I didn't know what my future held but I was not going to hang on to the past, dragging around my guilt and wishing for a brighter future.

I thought of Dad several times that night as I sprawled on my bed, smoking cig after cig. He used to have a saying, "God didn't put you on earth to be happy, he just put you here. Happiness is your own business," and never had it seemed more appropriate than in those twilight hours, as I contemplated my future.

When morning eventually arrived, I had already packed everything I owned into my pillowcase and as Spider had finally given way to the weariness that he had fought off for the best part of that long night, I decided to let him sleep.

I quietly ducked out of the dorm as the night screw turned on the lights and shouted, "Let's have you then you lazy lot, time to get up."

I wasted no time and no sooner had the screw opened the unit gate than I was gone making my way towards the reception area as fast as my little legs could carry me. When I arrived the reception door was still locked but several other kids were stood outside clutching their pillowcases there, excited chatter echoing the length of the corridor.

"Come on, come on," said one lad kicking the bottom of the gate in exasperation. "What's keeping them? We's got places to go, people to see," offered another kid.

I quietly joined the back of the queue just as the familiar sound of key in lock alerted everyone that the door was about to swing open. It was like a stampede and the poor screw was pinned against the wall as each eager kid barged and pushed through the doorway.

"Steady lads, bloody hell you won't get out any quicker," he shouted after them as they tore into the reception area like a band of looters, oblivious to his pleas. They wasted no time and as each kid spotted his clothes-box they threw off their prison garb and jumped into their clothes like someone had just shouted fire. When everyone was fully attired, a kitchen orderly handed out our breakfast from a stainless-steel trolley and after taking our places along the wooden bench, we tucked in like we'd never seen food before.

"Well lads, this is the last breakfast we'll ever eat in this dump," smiled a dark-haired kid as he rammed spoonsful of runny porridge into the gaping hole under his nose.

"Yeah thank fuck for that, can't wait fer some proper grub," laughed a spotty ginger kid as he dropped porridge all down the front of his shirt. He wasn't at all perturbed and wiped it away as though he was playing a banjo, smearing it downwards towards his trousers.

"You messy twat," laughed another lad as he shook his head and raised his eyes.

"You not hungry?" asked the spotty kid as he noticed I wasn't eating my porridge.

I hated porridge. "Naw, you have it," I said, passing my tray over to him and without a word he threw his own empty tray to one side and eagerly tucked in.

After breakfast we were each called in turn, given a one-way train ticket to our destination and a week's unemployment money together with instructions of the time and place we were to attend our respective probation offices. A few moments later, we moved en-mass to the holding area

423

inside the front gates where after a final check of our release papers, the gates swung open and we strode out of them like a football team emerging from the player's tunnel.

A handful of kids were met by parents, brothers, sisters or friends and after the mandatory hugging and kissing, they each roared out of the car park on their way to a new life, the sound of their car engines carrying on the morning mist as they disappeared into the distance. I turned and looked back at the borstal. Spider would be just getting ready for work and the dining hall emptying after breakfast, everything and everybody I knew was behind those gates and I was going to miss that.

"Eh, Marriot, you coming or what?" shouted the screw who was standing by the minibus waiting for me to board. I spun round.

"That's Jack or Mr Marriot to you," I smiled as I ran towards him leapt into the back and took my seat.

The drop off at the train station took place without much ceremony and as soon as the wheels of the minibus had stopped turning the screw in the front jumped out, pulled open the sliding door and nonchalantly uttered, "Off yer go," as though he was releasing a basket of homing pigeons.

I didn't look round and as my feet hit the pavement, I fixed my eyes on the station entrance and headed directly for it.

I could hear the other kids behind me giggling excitedly. "Shall we get some proper fags from the newsagent" "Should we go fer a coffee in the station caff?" "Which way should we go?" I smiled as I got closer to the entrance their voices trailing off somewhere behind me. They had just been released from borstal after being told when to eat, when to shit and when to sleep and the first time they have the chance to make a decision for themselves they were looking to others for suggestions, they were truly screwed but just didn't know it!

My train did not leave the station until nine thirty and having an hour to kill, I bought a newspaper and a can of coke and sat on the platform catching up on the news. It wasn't that we didn't get to read newspapers in borstal, but it was a refreshing change to read it first, rather than after sixty other kids had written on it, torn out the pictures of any half-naked women they could find or drawn enormous penis moustaches or tits on every photograph throughout it. I kept forgetting it hadn't been censored and was surprised with each turn of a page that no neat square had been cut out in order to protect my naïve innocence. The screws must have had a great old time snipping away in the office at any vaguely interesting bit of news and by the time you actually got their censored version if you wanted to know anything more than the date or the weather forecast, you were truly screwed.

From time to time, I saw the other kids who had got off the bus with me, they were walking around laughing loudly and looked like any bunch of teenagers with time on their hands. They hadn't gone unnoticed, and as I looked over the top of my paper, I could see a member of the transport police tracking their every move. He was trying to blend into the background but his attempts at covert surveillance were more than a little amateurish. The constant peeping around corners or from behind notice boards, where you could clearly see his uniform trousers and boots together with the bottom half of his reflective green jacket, made me chuckle so much that my copy of the Daily Mirror began shaking so violently, it must have looked like I was suffering from a bad case of Parkinson's disease. I eventually grew tired of the floor show and after ordering a coffee from the station café, I settled in a seat staring out of the window as I clasped the cheap mug in both hands and felt its warmth begin to thaw out my numb fingers. I hadn't realised how cold I was. I guess I had been distracted by other things, but as I blew on the frothy contents, I smiled to myself.

I had just finished my coffee when the station address system crackled to life. "The train now standing at platform three is the nine thirty to Kings Cross. All passengers wishing to board, should go to the platform at once, thank you."

My arrival back in my home town of Leeds unnerved me. I was apprehensive, excited and worried all at the same time and as I made my way from the platform to the station exit, I had butterflies in my stomach. I don't quite know why. I don't know exactly what I was expecting, perhaps it just felt good to be in a place that was familiar or perhaps I had some idiotic notion that I might bump into someone who was actually glad to see me. I didn't and as I mingled with the other passengers, as we snaked our way out towards the street, I went unnoticed.

The city hadn't changed at all but even if it had, I didn't have the time to take in the scenery. It was three thirty in the afternoon and I was already late for my appointment with the probation officer, but I'd been held up in Kings Cross and there was nothing I could do about it. I picked up my feet and hurried the short distance to King Edward Street where the offices of the probation service were situated.

The probation office building was pretty unimposing, a dirty grey colour with equally dirty windows caused by the heavy city centre traffic. The entrance was a narrow wooden door that slotted in neatly next to the printer's shop that was carrying on its business on the ground floor. A small engraved notice read (Department of Probationary Services.) I glanced at it and reassured that I was in the right place, I pushed open the door and headed up the flight of stairs in front of me.

Once on the first floor, a large stencilled arrow on the wall pointed me towards reception where a fat middle-aged woman was slumped across a desk flicking through a copy of Woman's Weekly. She didn't look up, even as I approached her, and I found myself clearing my throat in order to attract her attention.

"Oh sorry, miles away," she smiled as she tore herself away from the problem page. "And you are?" she said still

426

smiling cocking her head slightly like an obedient spaniel.

"Marriot, er, I have an appointment with Mr Spiro," I offered politely.

"Your late Mr Marriot," she said sternly as her finger found my appointment time in her diary. I wasn't going to offer her any excuses besides my lateness was none of her bloody business and if I was going to apologise, I was only going to do it once and that would be to Mr Spiro.

"Well? she persisted not wanting to let the matter drop, I'm still waiting," she finished as she fixed me with her best steely stare. She'd picked on the wrong person that day. I couldn't help myself. It was her challenging manner; her arrogance and self-importance and I was having none of it. I leant over the top of her desk until our noses were almost touching.

"Look, I'm late already as you have already pointed out, so be a good secretary and let Mr Spiro know I'm here, then you can get back to reading Marjorie Proops or whatever it is you are supposed to do around here, got me?" I whispered in the best sinister tone I could muster.

Her mouth fell open and you could see her brain working overtime as her expression changed from outrage to defeat as she realised, she'd bitten off more than she could chew.

She sat back in her seat, "Well I never," she stuttered.

"Yeah that I believe," I smiled as I reached across and picked up the phone from in front of her. I held it out and smiled.

"There's a good girl," she tutted loudly and took it from me like I'd handed her a turd. She dialled a three-digit number and announced my arrival before throwing the handset back in its cradle and snatching up her magazine opening it and holding it directly in front of her craggy old face.

I found myself a comfy chair by a small coffee table to the left of the reception area picked up a two-month-old copy of Readers Digest and began to flick through it.

I was only seated a couple of minutes when a more

friendly voice called to me, "Jack, nice to see you lad, how does it feel to be a free man? How was the journey?"

I didn't know which question to answer first so I didn't bother. I just shook Mr Spiro's hand as he held it out to me.

"Come on Jack, this way lad, we've got a lot to get through," he said as he led the way through a doorway down a corridor and into his office.

"Come in come in grab a pew. Drink? Tea? Coffee?" he enquired as I parked my weary arse in the seat in front of his desk. "No, no, thanks," I replied as I looked out into the street through his grubby window. I wanted to get this over with, get myself sorted and then I had plans of my own.

"Right then Jack, we better get you sorted at the hostel; I suppose you're keen to see where you'll be staying?" Mr Spiro smiled as though reading my thoughts.

"Er yeah, that'd be good," I smiled back, turning away from the window to look at him. He was still standing and rummaging through several files that littered his desk top.

"It's here, somewhere, bear with me a sec, Jack," he muttered without looking up. He was your typical Probation Officer/Social Worker. They all ate from the same trough and by the look of his clothes, all shopped at the same retail outlet. I imagined it to be called, 'Corduroy's R Us' and as I looked him up and down from his brown Hush Puppy shoes, his Jumbo cord slacks and finally a heavily knitted cardigan, I instinctively knew that any battle of wills between us would see me the victor.

Mr Spiro was a fully paid-up member of the bleeding-heart brigade, children weren't bad just misunderstood and he saw himself as some kind of shepherd in the darkness, leading lost children towards the light. He was a bloody fool like those that came before him and those that would follow, we were never lost, in fact we knew more about the world that we lived in than they did. We had seen and experienced life's realities and because of this were hardened cunning and manipulative, tools we would use to tie do-gooders like him into very tight knots!

"Ah, ha, here it is, so sorry about that, can't find a bloody thing in here. I really should get myself a little more organised," Mr Spiro apologised as he flopped into his leather swivel chair and threw his feet over the corner of his desk showing four inches of Lilly white flesh and an abundance of leg hair as his trouser legs rode up.

"Right, you will be staying at the Hostel on Becketts Street, Jack," he paused and looked thoughtful for a couple of seconds. "Er, it's a bit rough and ready but we will find you something better as soon as we can," he paused again and looked at me, waiting for a reaction but realising he wasn't going to get one he continued. "Now I understand that you don't have much in the way of clothes or belongings, so I've arranged an emergency payment from the DSS which should be enough to get you sorted out until we can find you a job," he stopped and looked at me again, and I remember thinking, I really wish he'd stop doing that, if he had a question why didn't he just bloody come out with it. Once again as though reading my thoughts, he added, "And what kind of job would you like to do? Have you had time to think about it?"

I couldn't help grinning, had I had time to think about it? Time was something up until this morning I'd had an abundance of and in answer to his question I hadn't wasted any of it wondering what job I could do to become a pillar of society.

"Er not really, I'll do owt," I lied knowing that's what he wanted to hear.

"Good, good," Mr Spiro beamed as though he'd won his first victory, bloody fool would they never learn?

I hated the hostel the first time I set eyes on it. It was hardly a place that inspired hope, although it must be said that the only way to go from there was up. It was an old pre-war building that even the Luftwaffe avoided bombing, obviously working on the principle that we would suffer far more by being subjected to its ugliness than if they did us a favour and blew it apart. It was a place of broken dreams not a place where great adventures began but where you ended up when they went wrong. The stone steps to the front of the building were stained with dried vomit, empty cider and beer bottles lay in the street where they'd landed after being slung from some drunken resident's bedroom on one of the upper floors and just to top it off, every dog in the neighbourhood had deposited a turd on the pavement for a hundred yards either side of the front entrance. Perhaps they were trying to tell us something?

My first memory of that awful place was the sense of despair that enveloped me as Mr Spiro pushed open the front door and we stepped inside. The hallway was adorned with instructions and lists of rules of which there were many. No drinking, no fighting, no swearing, no eating in the bedrooms, no drugs and one huge sign in bold black letters **All residents to vacate building by no later than 09.00hrs each morning - return forbidden until after 17.00hrs!** It must have been some meeting that came up with that winning formula. I could just imagine a pack of corduroy and striped jumper wearing, do-gooders, sat around brainstorming, "I say anybody got any ideas on what rules we should have in one's hostel?"

"I know, let's throw them out on the streets each day where with time on their hands and questionable morals they will probably all end up in trouble."

"Oh, I say, splendid idea, that way they'll be back in prison and off our hands in no time, all those in favour?"

After a brief introduction with a woman that Mr Spiro called matron, a stern-faced battle-axe with her hair tied back in a bun and weighing in at a good two hundred and twenty pounds, I was given a key and told my room was on the first floor. With that, she turned on her heels like a member of the Gestapo and goose-stepped off into an office slamming the door behind her.

Mr Spiro looked at me and pulled an apologetic face, his embarrassment plain to see.

"Come on then, let's get you sorted," he smiled nervously and led the way up the winding tiled stairs to the first floor. We emerged into a long corridor with rooms along the entire left side. On the right were shower rooms and toilets the doors were half open, and the smell of neat bleach permeated the hallway but beneath its pungent aroma you could still detect the sweet acrid smell of puke. I pulled a face as I caught Mr Spiros eye and not knowing quite what to say he smiled sadly, "Come on, I bet your rooms not so bad, which one is it? Ah, here," he said answering his own question and trying his best to be cheerful.

The room wasn't any better but we both pretended it was.

"Oh yes, that's more like it, you'll soon have this place looking nice," said Mr Spiro optimistically.

I played along with him, I don't know why but I didn't want to hurt his feelings. I walked over to the window and looked out on to the shit ridden pavement, directly below my window was a pile of puke where the previous occupant had obviously hung out of the window and deposited his entire stomach contents down the wall before its final resting place on the pavement where it formed a circle at least a metre wide.

"Yeah it'll be fine, your right, I'll soon have it looking nice," I lied as I raised my eyes heavenward still staring out of the window.

Mr Spiro couldn't wait to leave so we made polite conversation. He told me when our next appointment was and beat a hasty retreat. I watched him from my bedroom window as he unlocked his car. I couldn't help but wonder which cosy suburban street he would retire to that evening. It was as though he sensed me and pausing briefly, he threw me a half wave and with a sad smile climbed inside and drove off. It didn't take me very long to become acquainted with my new surroundings after all my room was hardly over furnished. There was a single wardrobe with a creaky hinge that on closer inspection contained three coat hangers that hung forlornly on the steel rail inside. There was a bedside table containing a single drawer that had been used as an ashtray, a small side table and a plastic moulded chair with a wonky leg. I thought it best not to investigate the single bed too thoroughly, working on the principle that, what the eye don't see, the heart don't grieve. So I contented myself with the fact that the bedding was clean and whatever tell-tale stains lurked on the mattress beneath should forever remain one of life's great mysteries.

Chapter 32

Land of hope and glory

I didn't sleep very well that first night, the constant comings and goings and raised voices would wake me the moment I nodded off. It was in the early hours of the morning that I was startled most and sat bolt upright in bed. An ear-splitting high-pitched scream had echoed down the corridor outside, followed by the slurred ramblings of several drunks. I shouted several times for them to shut up, but they took no notice. In the end I pulled my duvet up until only my eyes and forehead were showing and wrapping my pillow around my ears tried to drown out the noise. I don't know what time it all became quiet, but I suddenly found myself listening to the chirping of early morning larks as they prepared for daybreak.

Morning in the hostel didn't arrive with the finesse of a peck on the cheek by a loved one, it booted you out of bed and stomped on you until it was sure you were awake. The sound of gut-wrenching coughing, the kind that fills your imagination with lumps of green thick phlegm carried through my wall from the neighbouring occupant. Footsteps outside in the corridor followed by incessant farting and belching convinced me that there was probably enough methane floating around that one spark would be enough to send us all to hell and back, perhaps that was the reason for the no smoking rule? I didn't dare leave my room until quiet had once again descended and not wishing to hang around, I threw on my clothes and after locking my door shot down the stairs and headed for the street.

I'd nearly made it when the matron from hell shouted after me, "You should have left ten minutes ago, it's after nine." I ignored her tore open the front door and ran as fast as I could along the pavement playing hop scotch with the piles of dog shit as I went. I quickly settled into a gentle walk as I made my way to the nearest bus stop. I even allowed myself to feel a little smug after all I had over a hundred pounds in my pocket, more money than I'd ever had (well legally anyway). I chuckled to myself as I remembered Mr Spiro's words as he handed me it.

"This is a one-off emergency payment from the DHSS to buy clothes, make sure you do!" I wonder how many drunks he'd said that to who even as they were agreeing with him, were calculating how many days, that could get them drunk for. That was the problem with do-gooders, they were only too willing to see the best in everyone, at the cost of everything else. He'd fallen lucky with me, clothes it was for and clothes I was going to buy but not before I'd taken care of something else that was far more important to me.

I waited over an hour for the bus and by the time it arrived I had to stop myself demanding where the fucking hell he'd been. It wasn't that it was unusual to wait for a bus, God knows anyone who has ever used public transport knows that, it was purely that I couldn't wait to get where I was going. I bit my lip and smiled politely as I paid the driver, and by the time I'd taken my seat, my anger had evaporated. I was on my way and my optimism was at an all-time high. The bus was warm, and I felt contented as I eaves-dropped on other people's conversations. I was free I could go where I wanted, when I wanted, and it felt great.

"Can I?" asked an elderly lady as she squeezed her ample buttocks into the empty seat beside me. I smiled and shuffled over before staring out of the window.

"You going anywhere nice?" asked the old lady adjusting the shopping bag she'd deposited between her legs. She had a kindly face and kind green sparkling eyes and I warmed to her immediately.

"Just to meet someone I've not seen in a while," I replied.

"Ooh I love meeting friends, that's where I'm going today. I always meet my friend Elsie in town on a Saturday for a coffee and a bit of cake and a walk around the shops," she said her eyes never leaving mine. By the time I'd reached my stop, I knew the old lady's entire life story and to be truthful I'd enjoyed every minute of our little chat, it had been a long time since I'd just exchanged pleasantries with anyone, no hidden agenda no angle just polite friendliness. I waved at the old lady as the bus pulled away and in turn she waved back and smiled, it was just at that moment that a strange notion crossed my mind. What if there was no Elsie? What if the old lady was just using her free bus-pass to travel around chatting to strangers because she was lonely, and had nothing better to do? No, no, I was just using my over-active imagination, of course she was going to meet her friend, a nice old lady like that, I bet she has loads of friends, I thought, God I hope so!

I hadn't realised how hungry I was until I passed a bakery and no sooner had the aroma of freshly baked bread and confectionary found its way to my nostrils than the hungers pangs started. I hadn't eaten since breakfast at the borstal the morning before so a few moments later was devouring the biggest pork pie the baker had to offer as I ambled along the high street. It was better than any pork pie I'd ever eaten and to this day I've never had one that tasted better. My next port of call was a coffee shop where I bought a large coffee in one of those polystyrene containers, the type that get so hot you have to switch them from hand to hand, in order to avoid first-degree burns. It tasted good and as I sipped at the steamy contents, I allowed myself to think that life wasn't so bad and there were people far worse off than me. I found my way to my destination in no time and as the tall masts and swaying flags came into view my heart pounded excitedly. It wouldn't be long now, I wouldn't be alone I'd have someone, he'd take care of me take me away from that hostel and help me sort myself out. I broke into a run and the nearer I got I swear I could hear those fluttering flags calling to me on the breeze.

I avoided the front door. I hadn't forgotten my run-in over a year earlier with that buffoon in the top hat and besides, I wanted the kitchens and this time I knew my way

435

there. I broke into a sprint only stopping when my palms slapped heavily into the outside of the kitchen door bringing me to a halt. I took a moment steadied my nerves and knocked loudly three times. I heard the sound of a heavy bolt being drawn back and then the door flew open nearly knocking me over as I jumped out of the way.

"Yeah?" said a spotty young lad, his glasses steamed up and sweat running down his brow.

"Er, yeah, can I speak to Steve Marriot please," I asked politely.

The young lad nodded his head and said, "Wait here," before disappearing back into the kitchen. My stomach somersaulted, and I could feel my mouth dry up, what if he didn't want to know me? What would I do? He was my only hope. Before I had time to torment myself anymore the door began to open, and an involuntary smile sprouted across my face.

I was about to say something stupid like, "Surprise," or something else more feeble if that were possible, when a middle-aged man wearing a tall chef's hat confronted me.

"Hi, I'm sorry but Steve doesn't work here anymore, and he didn't tell anyone where he was going. he just upped and left."

He must have seen the desperation in my face. "Sorry kid wish I could help. "What about his girlfriend, the one who worked on reception" I asked clutching at straws.

"Sorry kid she left with him, sorry," he sympathised and with that he shut the door leaving me standing rooted to the spot my illusions well and truly shattered. I didn't handle the news well and in a mixture of rage and frustration, I kicked several boxes across the yard scattering rubbish everywhere, tears filled my eyes and I cursed like never before. "Bastards fucking bastards, cunts I fucking hate you," I screamed at nobody in particular. I was still raging as I made my way back through the town, "Yeah what you fucking looking at?" I would challenge anyone who dared look at me. I wanted an excuse just one and I would have

436

unleashed such a ferocious beating on anyone who crossed my path. I would have been locked up for life, but God was keeping watch either over me or over them that day, I don't know which but thankfully nobody got hurt. I don't know how I ended up there but end up there I did and by that evening I found myself standing in my old street my eyes scanning each window of our house as the occupants moved from room to room switching lights on and off inside. I don't know how long I'd stood there before it began to rain but it didn't deter me, I really didn't give a damn if I died of hypothermia and I didn't think anyone else would either. I remained transfixed my mind playing tricks on me. I would see silhouettes pass by the window silhouettes of my Dad, of our Steve and I watched in a dream like state as a young boy returned from boxing, his bag over his shoulder, skipping up the stairs to the back door. "I'm home Dad," he called and from the room a voice would call out, "Come here son, let's have a look at you, did you win?"

I did a lot of crying over the next few weeks, but I saved it for when I was alone which was more often than not. The hardest thing was killing time and trying to convince myself I still had hope. I wouldn't have known where to start in order to find our Steve and made a conscious decision to remind myself that my destiny was in my own hands nobody else's.

I kept my appointments with Mr Spiro and made all the right noises to keep him off my back. He was a pushover and must have thought I was the most cheerful person he'd ever met. I was never going to tell a total stranger that I was hurting, that I'd considered slitting my own wrists. I wasn't made that way and to be honest I wasn't all that good at expressing my feelings especially to some do-gooder all corduroy and optimism. So, time being the great healer that it is, I played the waiting game, it was easy, each week I waited for my Giro cheque and after I'd spent it, I waited for another. I didn't have a lot of money, but I was given breakfast and tea at the hostel so didn't bother eating in the middle of the day. I always ate my meals in silence preferring a table on my own away from the other misfits and as if they knew, they respected my wishes and left me alone. It may also have been something to do with the fact that I kicked one drunken old bastard down two flights of stairs for stealing from my room. It was only a pack of cigarettes, but it was the principle. I would have gladly given them to him if he'd asked nicely.

I'd been at the hostel for around four months when boredom finally got the better of me. There was only so much walking around looking in shops and sitting in parks you could do. It was different for most of the other residents they spent all of their day in a drunken stupor, so time was not really an issue for them. So it was one sunny Monday morning that I set off in search of work. I had of course gone through the motions before but mainly to keep Mr Spiro off my back. I'd even had an interview but made it blatantly obvious I didn't want their crappy job and in turn they didn't give it to me, so everybody was happy. But that day felt different and as I strolled along with the sun warming my face, I knew that by that evening I was going to have a job, not just for the sake of it but because I really wanted it, like I'd never wanted anything before.

"Reach for the skies and you might just hit the treetops," Dad would say and whilst I agreed with him in theory, I was well aware that openings for chairman of the board at ICI were probably a little over ambitious for a sixteen-year-old with a criminal record. I would have to set my sights a little lower or lie through my teeth so lie I did, and by that evening I found myself being offered a position as an apprentice welder with an engineering firm. I was due to start the following Monday, so I used the time in between to study all the different welding methods that I could find at the local library. It was of no fucking use whatsoever and whilst I could reel off the theory verbatim, the practical was going to be a little tricky.

I had when I was younger, helped Dad weld some stuff

438

down in the cellar but to be honest, although he praised me and told me I was a natural, the welding finished up looking like a flock of seagulls had crapped all over it. My nerves nearly got the better of me and as that first Monday morning approached, I very nearly bottled out, but then I thought well what have I got to lose? They can only sack me and there are lots of things far worse than that.

I was awake with the larks that first Monday morning and although I was a bag of nerves, I constantly told myself I would be alright. I'd never had a proper job, not with real men and I wondered what it would be like. Would we be bossed around all day like being at school? Would the other workers think I was an easy touch because I was the new boy? Would I be able to last a full day without rising to the bait if someone overstepped the mark? Well one thing was for sure I was going to find out.

I hadn't really given much thought to what I would wear and in any event, I wasn't exactly spoilt for choice having only four changes of different clothes, the one hundred pounds I was given didn't quite go as far as I'd expected although I did buy my clothes from the market. Funny how we always resort to what we know, what we're used to. The good thing about being up and about early was that none of the other residents were, and when I went into the dining-room I had the place to myself.

"Look at you Jack, all ready for your first day at work, don't you look a picture," teased Sally who cooked breakfasts for us all each morning. I didn't answer I just stood holding out my plate which she dutifully loaded with the full English breakfast as she did every morning.

Sally was a nice woman and had on several occasions tried her hand at mothering me, but she was also wise enough to know when to back off and when I didn't reciprocate, she would let it drop until another time. I had a real mistrust of women and it would be many years before my opinion would change but she wasn't to know that and even if she had she was the type of woman who would have

439

persisted anyway. I took my seat at my usual table and tucked in greedily. I knew that I needed to fill myself up there and then as it would have to last me all day. I had only enough money for my bus fares, so any thoughts of dining out were only a pipe dream. Once I'd finished, I mopped my plate with a slice of bread and butter swallowed my tea and handed my plate across the counter to Sally.

I was nearly out of the door when I heard her, "I'll just put this straight back in the cupboard then," she chuckled to herself. I smiled and gently closed the door. I'd only gone twenty yards, when I heard a familiar voice, "Jack, Jack, wait up, I forgot something." I turned to see Sally her flowery pinafore blowing in the wind as she ran towards me. "Wait up lad, I've somert for you," she gasped a little out of breath. "Here then yer big lump take it, it's only a few sandwiches but they'll see ya on til tonight" she said pushing a carrier bag into my arms. I didn't know quite what to say such kindness was a rare thing, it was to me anyway, so I just stood there smiling at her as though I'd lost the power of speech. "Go on then, you'll be late, off with yer," she said in a stern voice as she crossed her arms, but as the soft morning breeze blew her greying hair from her face her eyes were smiling giving her away.

What I did next took me by surprise, and poor old Sally nearly fell over with shock. I reached out grabbed her by both shoulders and planted a big wet kiss on her cheek. "Thanks, thanks," I said as I winked at her and turning on my heels, I ran for the bus stop without looking back. I didn't have to, I knew I'd made her day and from that day onwards, Sally made sure she made me sandwiches each morning.

Sometimes she would sneak me something special. "I've dun yer a bit o cake," she'd say. It would have only gone to waste anyway."

I knew she was lying we didn't get such luxuries as cake at the hostel and I knew damn well she would go home and bake them just for me. On the rare occasions when she

440

hadn't had time, she'd look at me sadly and say, "Sorry, no cake today petal, but I found a couple of bars o chocolate in me handbag, and with a figure like mine, I can't afford to be putting any more weight on, you do me a favour and take em off old Sally's hands."

She was my saviour, the only person who showed me kindness when I most needed it and during my stay in the hostel, she was the only person who I would have called a friend. Sally died in 1981, the result of a heart attack. She was forty-eight-years old, the world became a sadder place on that day!

My luck seemed to take a turn for the better and not only did I get through my first week at work without getting fired, I also found I had a bit of a flare for welding. Maybe my father wasn't kidding after all. My job mainly consisted of site work and each morning after clocking in I would jump into the passenger seat of the flatbed wagon and head off with Albert to whom I was apprenticed. We'd weave our way through the rush hour traffic with Albert whistling away to the radio and me puffing on a fag, my arm hanging out of the half-open window and my feet on the dashboard. Once we'd arrived at site, Albert would stop the wagon pull out his thermos flask and pour us both a cup of hot sweet tea. Albert had an addiction to tea and if he didn't have a cup at least once an hour, he would get a little grumpy, this was all well and good but due to his large liquid intake he would spend a good part of the day looking for somewhere to take a piss.

After our morning cuppa, we'd get started. Firstly I'd unload the back of the flatbed. I'd do this on my own as Albert had a bad back, or so he told me. He hadn't fooled me, I knew that he was just a lazy old sod and putting one over on me, but I let it go, after all he made up for it in many other ways.

After the wagon was unloaded, I would carry the gear bit by bit to wherever we were working on the site that day.

Albert would take a supervisory role from his seat in the cab, barking instructions whilst slurping away on another cuppa. "Yeah, good lad Jack, take those cables up onto the second gantry and chuck em over so we can hook em up to the welder genny." "Get the welding rods and grinder, don't forget my flask," and so on. I loved to watch Albert work which was a good thing because that was mainly what I did apart from passing him a new welding rod or pouring his tea if he wanted one. He made welding into an art form and everything he did left me in awe of his ability. "Go on then, you can tack that up whilst I go for a piss," he would smile as he held out the welding tongs and I eagerly snatched them off him before he changed his mind.

I remember one time he left me alone for just a little too long and kids being kids my boredom led me into mischief. I'd tacked the two pipes in place as he'd shown me, leaving a three-and-a-half-millimetre gap, so he could put a root run in, but trying to run before I could walk, I decided I'd have a bash myself. The result wasn't good and no sooner had I burnt my first welding rod than I knew I'd made a big mistake. Realising what I'd done I tried to grind it out and ended up cutting half of the pipe away. Twenty minutes later, by then flapping like a headless chicken, I was all but ready for having it away on my toes before Albert returned. I needn't have worried, Albert laughed so much when he saw it, his whole face turned a reddish-purple colour and he had to steady himself on the scaffolding hand rail to prevent himself collapsing to the floor.

"I'm sorry, I was only trying to help," I pleaded as I looked down at him, but he just waved his hand in the air and laughed even more.

When he eventually composed himself, he took a closer look at my handy work whilst sucking his teeth and scratching his head in exasperation. "Eh tha's made a reet pig's ear o that, come on then pass me the grinder and I'll show you how to put it reet," he said cuffing me around the ear playfully. That's why I liked Albert he was like a kindly

442

old granddad with one of his grandchildren, his patience never ending. I learnt a lot from him not just about welding, but that life didn't always have to be serious, sometimes it could just be fun. "Come on lad lets sack it and go tut pub, we've dun enough to keep gaffers happy," he'd say in his broad Yorkshire accent.

I used to protest in the early days as I was afraid of being found out and finding myself back on the dole. "But what if we get caught? Won't we be in deep shit?"

I'd try to reason but Albert would just dismiss me with a wave of his hand and say, "What gaffers don't know won't hurt," and that was that, a few minutes later we'd both be nursing a pint in the local pub tap room and playing darts. Albert was a shit darts player. I nicknamed him blind Pugh and would laugh hysterically as he screwed up his eyes trying to focus on the dartboard. "Are you sure we should be this far away?" he'd protest as he tried to move nearer.

"Back behind the line, you dodgy old twat, I'm watching you," I'd giggle.

"Eh, you're cheating. I'm sure you was nearer," he'd tease in return.

Albert's dart playing became legendary and after calling in to the same pub three weeks in a row the landlord had got to know us both. "Ere they are dead-eyed-jack and his oppo," the landlord would laugh as we walked through the door.

"Less of your cheek and pull us two pints or we'll take our custom elsewhere," smiled Albert.

"Oh no! then what'll I do? Based on your spending I've ordered myself and the wife a couple of them new Mercedes sports cars," said the landlord sarcastically.

Albert wasn't finished yet, "Yeah, yeah, very funny now are you gonna pull those pints or do we have to come round there and pull em ourselves like we usually do when you're not looking?"

The landlord pretended he didn't hear. "Darts? I suppose you'll be wanting the darts? It's okay, I've moved my collection of antique whisky jugs to a safer place and the cats upstairs. It won't come down anymore, not since that dart ricocheted off the optic and stuck in its arse," laughed the landlord.

"Eh, that wernt my fault, the sun coming through't lounge window blinded me, and besides it's a pub in it, not a bloody pet shop?" reasoned Albert.

"Naw, your right there, it's more like Dodge fucking City when you two are playing darts. My staff have asked for danger money, either that or body armour," the landlord guffawed, and several regulars joined in.

"Bloody cheek of that man, anyone would think he don't want our custom," winked Albert as he took a large gulp of his beer and made his way to the dartboard.

Time went by pretty quickly and before I knew it five months had passed. I was still working with Albert but by now doing a little more other than watching, fetching or carrying. I'd even moved out of the hostel and into a small bedsit. The hostel was only meant to be a temporary measure anyway, so when Mr Spiro told me it was probably time for me to get a place of my own, I jumped at the chance. It was weird, suddenly being totally on my own and I could never quite get used to the fact that I could come and go as I pleased, although in truth, I never actually went anywhere, because I had nowhere to go. It was a dark time for me. I hated the seclusion the lack of companionship and every week as the weekend approached, I would dread it. It was just so hard trying to fill my time and by Saturday night I was always pissed off and miserable. I must have been the only person at our firm who looked forward to Monday mornings.

The other tenants in the house were pleasant enough and would smile and say hello if you met on the landing or on the way to the bathroom, but for the most part, everybody kept themselves to themselves, carrying on their own secret lives behind the doors of their pokey bedsits. I soon developed a routine. I liked routine. I suppose I'd got used to it in borstal, and besides, now I was totally responsible for myself, I had to make sure I kept on top of everything.

Friday night was always shopping night, this was purely because that is when I got paid. I didn't mind shopping, it was a bit of a novelty especially as I could buy what I wanted, although I had to be careful not to overdo it, as my meagre wage would not sustain even a small amount of reckless spending.

Saturday was washing day and I would pass the time in the local launderette watching my clothes go round and round in circles as I lived other people's lives, listening to their conversations and imagining they were talking to me.

I always treated myself on Saturday evening and would nip down to the local Indian takeaway where I'd buy a curry and a few chapattis. It was always at the same time each Saturday, and after a few weeks Mr Rajpaul would hold aloft my order, as I walked through the door. He was a friendly chap and would ask how I was and being polite, I in turn would ask how he was or if he was busy. The answers were always the same, he was very well, and business was steady. I think Mr Rajpaul was probably the only person I ever really spoke to at the weekend and although it was only briefly, I looked forward to seeing his smiling face.

It must have been after I'd been calling at the takeaway for a couple of months that I first noticed a change in Mr Rajpaul. He began to ask different questions, the kind you ask when you're genuinely interested in someone and not just the usual shit you ask when you really couldn't give a toss.

I never did tell him the whole truth but a version that was as close to it as I dare get. How could I tell him I had been in borstal? How could I tell him how it had happened? When I didn't know how it happened myself. I couldn't justify what I'd done, and I didn't see any point in trying. In the end Mr Rajpaul was satisfied with the story I gave him. I was just a young orphan boy who had come out of a children's home

445

and was trying to make his way in the world on his own. I didn't think my version of events was that far away from the truth and in order to ease my conscience I told myself it was none of his business anyway.

It mystifies me to this day how it happened, but Mr Rajpaul somehow managed to ease his way into my life until a couple of months later it was as though I'd always known him. "Just a few extra things in there for you, you're a growing boy you must eat, I do worry you're not eating enough," he said one Saturday evening as he passed me a takeaway bag that appeared bulkier than normal.

"Er, I can't take this Mr Rajpaul, I can't," I said trying to hide my embarrassment.

"Take. Take, Take, off with you now and enjoy," he replied as he walked from behind the counter and pushed me towards the door. I tried to turn round and protest, but his eyes pleaded with me and I knew he would be offended at my refusal, so I thanked him politely and left staggering the few hundred yards home laden down like a packhorse.

I ate well that night, Somosas, onion Bahji's, Naan bread, Pilau rice and a Special curry and all for the usual price of a paltry one pound twenty. My visits to Mr Rajpauls takeaway became more frequent and as the weeks passed by, I would often spend my evenings leaning on the counter chatting away to him as he went about his business. It was a constant battle trying to stop him feeding me and in the end, I had to tell him I was only calling in for a chat, and that I'd already eaten, or he would insist I sit at a table behind the counter whilst he cooked me something. Mr Rajpaul was an interesting man and when the phones went quiet, he would sit on the window-sill alongside me and in his softly spoken Indian accent tell me stories of his life in India.

He had been a tailor and before he came to England had amassed several shops specialising in suits and dresses for the English gentry. Tales of the distinguished people, Lords and Ladies, balls and ball gowns spirited me away to a land of intrigue and adventure and I would hang on his every

446

word. Mr Rajpaul always looked thoughtful after he'd finished, and I could tell that deep in his heart he yearned for his home and for those days gone by.

"Oh well, no point in living in the past," he would say dismissively as he jumped to his feet and set about wiping down the worktops he'd already cleaned. I'd sit and watch quietly for a few moments and when it seemed appropriate, I'd make my excuses and leave, sometimes you can tell when people need to be alone.

Before I knew it, my Seventeenth birthday had come and gone. I hadn't celebrated it in any way in fact I didn't bother to tell anyone, it was just another birthday and pretty unimportant. My weekly visits to the probation office had been altered and now I only reported once a fortnight which was good as I saved a little money on the bus fares. Mr Spiro considered me a reformed character and would often say he wished more of his boys were like me. I didn't press him as to what he actually meant. I didn't really care and as long as he was happy, he would stay off my back.

I'd even summoned up the will to start running again. It wasn't an attempt to keep fit but merely to relieve the boredom and pent up frustration that was always bubbling away just under the surface. Those misty cold mornings blew away the cobwebs, and sometimes, just for a few moments I imagined that Dad would be sat at the kitchen table watching the clock and waiting for me to return from my run.

It was on one of those early morning runs that I began to ask myself questions about where I was going. I was simply marking time in a dead-end job with crap pay and equally crap prospects. I wanted more, something else but at that time I didn't know what it was. I often spoke to God and to Dad as the miles fell away beneath my feet of course in my head. I never actually ran through the streets talking out loud, even I wasn't that insane.

"Oh Lord, there's gotta be somert better than this," I'd

ask. "Please give me just a little sign to show me the way." If he ever replied I never heard him, although they do say God works in mysterious ways and I would soon learn to my cost just how true that was!

It all happened one Saturday evening as I was walking to Mr Rajpauls to collect my takeaway. It was a cold miserable night and I pulled up the collar of my coat in order to hide from the driving wind. I was just about to turn a corner when all the hairs on my neck stood on end and a shiver ran the full length of my spine. It wasn't the first time this feeling had come over me and I knew better than to ignore it, something was wrong, but I didn't know what. I slowed practically to a stop and took the corner wide, just in case, but it was clear there was no one there.

I was just about to put it down to my imagination when I heard a high-pitched scream. I knew straight away it was Mr Rajpaul and within seconds I'd covered the twenty yards to his shop. When I arrived, I could still hear him screaming but there were also two other voices cursing and shouting.

"Give us it, you fucking Paki."

"Let fucking go, go on Mick, fucking hit him again."

The scene through those misted windows will haunt me for the rest of my life. My poor friend was being kicked about the face and body while his assailant tried to prise something out of his hand. The cash draw from the till was upturned on the floor and all the small change was scattered about like a giant game of checkers. The other male stood and shouted encouragement his eyes wide with excitement and bloodlust. I didn't think about what I was going to do. I couldn't the anger had taken over.

I gently pushed open the door and called out, "You touch him once more and I promise I'll tear your fucking heart out!"

The man kicking Mr Raj stopped in his tracks, his foot still hovering in mid-air, he looked in my direction and with an evil psychotic stare he brought the sole of his boot down squarely on Mr Raj's face. The first man didn't even see the

448

punch coming that knocked him unconscious, but it was delivered with such force he lay halfway over the counter with his feet dangling in mid-air. He wasn't important he was just in my way, in the way of the true object of my aggression and before the other man knew what was happening, I was on him. My first punch hit him in the chest with a strength I never knew I possessed, and as the wind rushed out of his body he was propelled backwards with the momentum. I didn't wait for a reaction I moved forward and hit him with a straight right that drove the back of his head into the wall and then unable to stop, I hit him again and again and again. I don't know how long I lost control for, but I suddenly found myself dragging the half-unconscious assailant into the back of the shop and threatening to put his head into the deep fat fryer.

"Please, please, don't, don't," he cried through the swollen bloody mess that was once his mouth. It was no use pleading to me he didn't show Mr Raj any mercy and I wasn't fucking gonna show him any either.

"Come here you fucker, I'm gonna give you something to fucking remember," I screamed at him my right hand holding a big clump of his curly hair as I pushed his face nearer and nearer to the red-hot oil.

Suddenly I felt a hand on my arm and heard a familiar voice. "Jack, he's had enough, you mustn't do this, you know it's not right, please for your own sake, let him go."

That's why I loved Mr Raj he was the kindest most forgiving man I'd ever known and even as he stood there, his clothes torn and bloodied one eye half-closed, he begged for the life of his attacker. I don't know if I would have done it, fried his face, I think not, but in any event Mr Raj's timing was beyond reproach.

I was the one who put in the call to the ambulance service and I knew that along with the ambulance the boys in blue would surely follow. I didn't hang around and within minutes I was back in my bedsit stuffing a few clothes and some cash into the only holdall I had. There was

449

no way I was going back to prison, borstal or any other place they chose to send me to. I'd had a belly full of that. I didn't stop to reason it was sheer blind panic and I thought that running was my only option. It never actually occurred to me that nothing might come of it, that just perhaps, the police would consider that they had it coming. I never thought of any of that I just ran.

Chapter 33

Nowhere to run

Leaving in a hurry had many disadvantages the primary one being the lack of planning. It wasn't until the early hours of the following morning, as I sat in the city bus station shivering that the realisation of my predicament really hit home.

"Stupid, stupid, stupid," I cursed loudly as I paced back and forwards across the deserted waiting-room, rubbing my arms and legs in order to fight off the bitter cold. I was fortunate that night, fortunate that the Police hadn't come into the bus station on patrol. They would have taken one look at me and known that there was something wrong. I wasn't thinking straight. My whole thought process was mixed up in differing emotions that clouded my judgement and to any passer-by, I would have looked like an escaped lunatic who'd thrown away his medication.

The first coach arrived at six thirty in the morning. The sound of its diesel engine as it reversed into its parking space waking me from the much-needed sleep that I had succumbed to. I vaguely remembered lying down on the bench and resting my head on my holdall and saying to myself, "Must stay awake" "Don't fall asleep." The image of me and Spider awaking on that train with the Police standing over us, still firmly etched in my mind.

I was cold before I went to sleep, but that was nothing to the cold I felt when I awoke. It had penetrated that deeply into my bones even my jaw ached. I was extremely close to hypothermia but even at that stage I still had some survival instinct and forced myself to move about in order to warm up. Once I'd got the feeling back in my extremities, I picked up my holdall and headed off in search of a hot drink. The shutters on the bus station café were still pulled firmly shut but inside I could see a member of staff moving about behind the counter in the half light.

Tap, tap, tap, I knocked on the glass until I'd caught her attention. "What time do you open?" I mouthed from outside the window holding up my forearm and pointing at my non-existent watch.

"Sorry love, another half hour," she mouthed apologetically. I smiled, nodded at her and walked away cursing under my breath. The pain in my jaw had now spread upwards and it felt as though my head was going to explode if I didn't warm up soon. I was tempted to go in search of somewhere else but even though I was in a shit state I realised that if I was seen walking the streets by a passing Police car it was highly likely they'd stop me and begin to ask questions. Best to stay where I was until at least other people were moving about. It would be far easier to blend anonymously into a crowd.

The sound of the shutters being lifted brought me back to my senses. I was in kind of a half-dream state as I sat bolt upright on a seat hugging my holdall to my chest with my face buried in it trying to find just a little warmth.

"Ttttttt tea ppppplease," I barely managed as I held out a handful of loose change. "Oh you poor luv, you look frozen to the bone. You take a seat and I'll bring it over," the assistant smiled as she counted out the correct money from my open hand.

I nodded and tried a half-smile, but my face hurt so much I nearly cried out, so without a word I made my way to a table in the far corner and sat down.

"There you are, get that inside you luv, and you'll soon 'av a bit of colour back in those cheeks," said the woman as she placed a steaming mug of tea on the table in front of me. I reached for it and wrapped my hands tightly around the hot ceramic. My fingers were that frozen it didn't even feel warm, and rather stupidly, I raised it to my mouth and took a big gulp. It was so hot it nearly blistered my tongue and I jumped involuntarily spilling it all over the table in front of me. I'd barely had time to look up before the assistant's blue and white striped pinny came into view, and her chubby hands waved a cloth over the table wiping away the spillage I'd just created.

I was about to apologise when the sound of the café door opening startled us both, and as I turned towards the door there stood two Police officers all bright eyed and bushy tailed.

"Morning gents the usual is it?" asked the assistant a girlish tone creeping into her voice.

"Oh yes please Linda, quick as you can, if you don't mind, luv, we're supposed to be somewhere else, you know how it is?" replied one of the coppers as he removed his hat and ran his fingers through his hair. Ordinarily I would have been a little amused at this rather clumsy mating ritual that was unfolding in front of me but at the time I had other more important matters that needed my attention.

I wanted out, out of there as quick as was humanly possible but there was one thing stopping me, the big fat copper standing right in the bloody doorway.

"So Linda you been up to owt this weekend?" enquired the copper standing at the counter as he rested his hat on top of a glass cabinet that contained the unsold sandwiches from the previous day.

"Ooh you must be joking Dave, me? I don't have a life outside work, it's purely work and nights in, in front of telly," chirped the assistant I now knew to be called Linda.

"That's a shame," grinned the copper turning to throw a sly grin at his fat mate who was still standing in the doorway and by now looking me up and down with a little more interest than I was happy with.

"Perhaps we could get together one weekend?" he said cockily as he twisted round to meet Linda's reply.

"You asking me out?" said Linda sheepishly without looking up from the two bacon sandwiches she was neatly cutting in half.

"For fucks sake Linda, just say yes, say, yes, and the fucker will leave," I muttered into my half-empty cup as I took a sip. Dave blushed a little and fingered at his collar, his confidence by now a little shaky.

"Er, yeah, if you like, we could go for a meal or whatever," he said as he tried to sound as though he wasn't particularly bothered. Linda smiled broadly, as their eyes met over the two bacon sandwiches, she handed over the counter neatly wrapped in two white paper bags.

"Alright, Dave, lets arrange something nearer the end of the week."

"Yeah, yeah, let's do that. I'll catch you later in the week then Linda," gushed Dave his enthusiasm getting the better of him. "See ya then," he said with a wave of his arm as he quickly left the shop pushing his fat mate out in front of him. I looked on as they walked past the window, the fat copper straining his neck to get a closer look at me. It wasn't his day though Dave was in love and was far too happy to be bothered about some young kid having a brew in the bus station café, so I breathed a sigh of relief as they eventually disappeared out of sight and out of my life.

I went back to finishing the remainder of my tea which was now just barely lukewarm. I drained it and placed it back on the table and as I bent down to pick up my holdall, I saw Linda's canvass shoes approaching me from across the room.

"Pair of fucking tossers," said Linda as she reached out and picked up my empty mug her other hand resting on the table's edge.

"He's been asking me out almost every day for the past two weeks, he sure is a persistent bastard, pity he's so fucking ugly. I'd rather roll in shit than spend a second longer than I had to, in that arseholes company," she laughed as she picked up my mug and waved it in the air.

"Another luv?" she asked as she flounced back behind the counter. I smiled to myself. "Go on then, you've twisted my arm."

I had three more cuppas with the rather comical Linda and it was just what I needed. By the time I'd left I'd almost

454

forgotten my troubles, almost but not quite. It was still bitterly cold, so I made my way back to the waiting room lit up a cig and collected my thoughts as I paced back and forth, the sound of my own footsteps my only distraction. I was in deep and I knew that but the harder I thought the more desperate I felt. I reached into my trouser pocket and took out the handful of notes I'd stuffed there the night before. One hundred and twenty quid not a fortune I thought but enough to get me away from here. I made my mind up to hell with it, I was going to buy a ticket for the first coach due out of the station and I'd consider my options again when I arrived wherever it ended up, not a great plan but a plan nevertheless and at that moment the best I had.

It was after ten thirty that morning that the next coach revved up its engine in preparation for departure and as soon as I heard it, I made my way out of the waiting room and stared out across the forecourt hoping it would be heading somewhere I might like. The destination panel above the driver was still showing Leeds so I stood tapping my foot on the cold concrete floor as I waited for the driver to change it.

"Come on you bastard, change," I said under my breath willing the sign to begin scrolling. My heart began to pound in anticipation, where was it going? Where would I find myself later that day? I watched as the driver reached up and began turning the handle above his head and slowly the destinations began to roll by. Birmingham, Bristol, Bath, Coventry, Corby, Darlington, Derby and so on, of all the places in Great Britain and where was it going?............... London.

Twenty minutes later I found myself seated at the back of the coach reading a newspaper as the white lines on the motorway shot by in a blur. The coach was hardly full. There were only a handful of other passengers on board as well as me. A couple of old ladies chatting away and sharing a home-made sandwich they'd lovingly wrapped in tin foil and a middle-aged gent studying the Sunday Times crossword and nearer to the front two young women who I could immediately tell were students. The students were giggling and pushing each other like small children on an outing. I tutted and went back to reading the paper, if these were our future doctors and scientists, the upper echelons of our education system, we were all well and truly up shit creek without a paddle. It didn't take me long to begin enjoying the journey. My body had at last fully thawed out and as I nibbled on a cheese and tomato sandwich, I'd bought from Linda earlier that morning, I began to feel a whole lot more optimistic about my current situation. It's really strange how being warm and fed can lead you into a false sense of security.

The first stop was at Sheffield where a dozen or so other passengers climbed aboard as the driver threw their bags and cases into the hold under the side of the bus. I did my usual trick and put on my best menacing look in order to discourage anyone from plonking their fat arse in my personal space. It nearly always worked and many a tattooed skinhead had changed his mind at the last second and sat somewhere else. Old ladies now, they were another kettle of fish, they were oblivious to killer stares, gritted teeth or deep frowns they just simply sat beside you smiled and would say, "Alright dear, don't look so sad, it spoils your lovely young face," and then offer you a sweet. Why do old ladies go everywhere with the entire contents of the local confectionary outlet in their handbags? And why do they always buy fucking boiled sweets? And lastly why do they always sit next to me?

"You going far young man?" asked the blue-rinsed old Doris who'd managed to nearly sit on my knee despite there being at least another forty seats she could have sat in.

I forced a smile. "London," I replied hoping my one-word reply may be a strong indicator that I wasn't really interested in forming a long and lasting relationship with this bubbly pensioner. "Sweet?" she asked as she waved a paper bag under my nose.

I managed to stifle the laugh that my brain was trying to force up my throat and out of my mouth. "Naw, you're alright love, got a sandwich," I replied as I nodded towards the half-eaten offering nestling on my lap.

"Yes, big lad like you shouldn't eat sweets, bad for your teeth. At my age it doesn't matter, there all false anyway," she said widening her lips to give me a good look at her off-white dentures. I shook my head smiled awkwardly and lifted my paper in front of my face in a vain attempt to isolate myself from further conversation. It didn't work and on the six-hour journey I only managed to read two pages of the newspaper that in the end only acted as a shield to fend off her idiotic questions. Considering how much I hated London I can honestly say that was the one time I was glad to see the place. The ear bending I'd been subjected to throughout the journey was bad enough but when the old dear did stop to draw breath I had to put up with the most horrendously annoying noise as she bounced a boiled sweet around her mouth and it ricocheted off her dentures like a bullet in a steel drum.

It had just gone five o clock in the evening when the coach pulled into Victoria coach station and I bid a polite goodbye to Beryl who in truth I could have cheerfully mown down with automatic gunfire and then slept soundly in my bed. London was always busy it didn't seem to matter if it was some ungodly hour in the morning there were always people meandering the streets each with their own story and very little time for each other. That was probably the one good thing about London. I wouldn't raise an eyebrow and the moment I stepped off that coach I disappeared into that fog of anonymity that we call population.

I have very little memory of that first night in the big smoke other than to say it was cold, lonely and long and when the dawn finally arrived, I was glad to see it. I still had not made any kind of life changing decision. I didn't know what my next move was going to be and any thoughts I had during the early hours were purely about not being found frozen stiff like a pack of fish fingers stuck to the pavement in some piss stained back alley, rather than what I would be doing a week later.

Inspiration can come when we least expect it and that is exactly what was to happen to me. I had just purchased a cup of coffee and was sheltering in a shop doorway from the early morning breeze that carried with it sub-zero temperatures, when my attention was drawn by a sign in a window across the road, it read: Army Soldier. Be the Best. I liked that it was catchy so picking up my holdall I made my way across the road and began to read the posters in the window. I was mesmerised by the photographs, photographs of happy smiling faces people rock climbing, parachuting, driving tanks but best of all people carrying guns! I had never had any aspirations to be a soldier. All that 'yes Sir, no Sir' bollocks had never really appealed to me but as I stood there, I began to think, after borstal how fucking hard could it be? It was only a brief moment of madness and I knew in my present position it could never happen, a criminal record and wanted by the Police I could just see it now. "Oh don't worry about that, Mr Marriot, can you fire a gun? You can, well fucking great, come in and meet the family."

I was just about to walk away when it hit me like a bolt of lightning, a criminal record, wanted by the Police, there was an army that just might take me or was it just a myth? I was determined to find out more after all I had time on my hands and nothing to lose. It took me nearly all day to find a library and I was just beginning to think the whole of London society must be illiterate when I happened upon the central library. It was not entirely good news I'd spent that long looking for it the bloody place was closed.

"I don't fucking believe it," I cursed as I pushed hard against the door and realised it was firmly locked. I quickly traced my finger down the opening times displayed on the inside of the glass Monday to Friday 9-5 PM. Saturday 10-4 PM. Closed Sundays. It was fast turning into one of those days when everything seemed to be stacked against me, but I'd come that far, and I was determined I would not be put off.

I remained close by that night, huddled across the road in a shop doorway and although it was bitterly cold, I never really felt it. I was miles away walking through sun parched deserts trekking in humid jungles and marching proudly in an immaculately clean and pressed uniform. The night could not pass quickly enough for me and as would usually happen it did exactly the opposite. At five in the morning, I couldn't stand it anymore and walked the streets counting each minute until I could charge through the library doors and put myself out of my misery.

"Yes, yes, I'm coming, hold yer 'orses," shouted a big plump lady as I rattled on the front door. It was one-minute past nine. I stepped back as I watched her bend down and unbolt the door at the bottom and then reach up and pull the bolt at the top. I tried the door again, it opened, and I deftly slipped inside squeezing past the fat lady and began to run down the short corridor that led into the main library.

"Where's the fire?" she shouted after me, but it fell on deaf ears. I had other fish to fry!

There were so many books, books on every possible thing you wanted to know, and I didn't have a clue where to start. I could say hand on my heart that I hadn't wasted any of my childhood on mundane things like swatting in libraries and as I ran up and down each aisle, I began to wish I had.

"Can I help you, young man?" the fat lady asked as though she'd just wiffed a steaming turd. Her eyes looked me up and down from my white trainers past my jeans and upwards to meet my face where her expression confirmed she hadn't liked what she'd seen.

"Er, yeah," I said not bothering with even a hint of nicety; after all it's a two-way street, you talk to me like shit and I'll gladly reciprocate.

"Yeah books on the military," I finished, stepping closer to her just to make her feel uncomfortable. I can be a bit of a

459

bugger at times.

"Yyyyes, over here," she stuttered walking away from me as she tried to distance herself. She didn't get away that easily and I matched her pace never putting more than a couple of inches between us. "Here," she said pointing at a bookcase and hurrying off as fast as her fat corned beef complexioned legs could carry her.

"Thank you so much for all your trouble," I called after her sarcastically. "You fucking fat witch," I added on the end quietly enough that she wouldn't hear.

"Uhm right, let me see," I whispered as I ran my fingers over each book on the middle bookshelf "First world war, no, Second world war, no, Vietnam war, no, One Hundred years war, no, whatever that is, Korean war, no, Combat soldier in the twentieth century, no, The battle of Britain, no, Submarines and their part in the war effort, er no. Come on, where the fuck are you?" I muttered and on and on I went until I was finally on the very top shelf and my hopes of finding what I was looking for were steadily dwindling.

"Ah ha, that's the baby," I nearly shouted as I read the title on the spine of a book last but one from the end, "Life in the French Foreign Legion."

I wasn't to know back then, as a young boy of seventeen, standing in that library on a cold winter morning, that my life was about to change forever. I could never have imagined that I would find myself in Beirut during the height of the troubles, that I would risk my life in covert operations, be wounded by South American drug smugglers and take the lives of others but most of all I wasn't to know how I'd live with my conscience when it was all over . But that's another story!....................